Farming in Prehistory

For Jan and Sam

Farming in Prehistory

From hunter-gatherer to food-producer

Barbara Bender

Illustrations by
Annabel Rowe and Jan Farquharson

John Baker · London

First published 1975
Reprinted 1977
John Baker (Publishers) Ltd
35 Bedford Row, London WC1R 4JH

ISBN 0 212 97003 8

Printed in Great Britain by offset lithography by
Billing & Sons Ltd, Guildford, London and Worcester

Contents

Illustrations

FIGURES

PHOTOGRAPHS

Preface

When I began this book I thought, in my innocence, that it might take eighteen months to write. It has taken five years. And in those years great quantities of words have appeared on various aspects of early food-production. The neglect of the subject, lamented by Roth in 1887 as the result of the 'general indifference, if not contempt, with which tillers of the soil are usually regarded' has been amply compensated. Sometimes my heart has sunk at yet more to read and more to digest and sometimes I began to wonder whether more words were really of any value.

My justification is that much of the information is still widely dispersed and does need to be drawn together. And as I worked over other people's material – for I readily admit that this book is mainly a synthesis – I have come to realise that much of the evidence is in need of a critical re-examination and that much of the specialist information has remained undigested by the archaeologist.

An understanding of the problems involved in the transition from hunting and gathering to food-production requires a great range of knowledge and no archaeologist can be competent in all the relevant fields. An interdisciplinary approach is essential and as many experts as possible must be brought in. But each expert exercises his knowledge within a limited field and it may well be that 'expertness in one science often leads to myopia in other directions; it is often easier to examine the trees than to attempt to comprehend the wood' (Harris 1967). The archaeologist cannot abdicate responsibility, nor should the experts' information be relegated to learned appendixes. I cannot agree with Masters' dictum in 1882 that, 'He who would devote himself to this branch of knowledge must be first and foremost a systematic botanist, and he must be versed in history, in archaeology, in geography, in ethnology and in various ancient and modern languages' (cited by Stearn 1965). It is not the concern of the botanist to understand the development of past societies, it is the concern of the archaeologist. And so it is he who must, in the end, understand and co-ordinate all the different types of evidence – 'Archaeology does not need climatic, zoological, geological or even ecological information in itself; its primary concern is with the impact of these factors, if any, on human behaviour, and here it is the archaeologist himself who has the only key forthcoming at the moment' (Jarman 1971). So I have tried to bring together a wide range of information and to look at it critically. I have looked at the theoretical frameworks within which the processes of change can best be understood, at technical evidence to clarify how plant or animal domestication can be recognised, at 'specialist' evidence of climatic change and of plant and animal distributions, and at archaeological evidence of cultural development in three different parts of the world, South-west Asia, Meso-America and Peru. Only when all these aspects are interwoven can one hope to begin to understand something of the process whereby man the hunter-fisher-gatherer became man the herder and cultivator and thereby radically altered his relationship with the physical environment.

BARBARA BENDER

London, 1973

Acknowledgements

I wish to thank the following for permission to reproduce the figures listed below:

Koninklijke Nederlandse Botanische Vereniging and W. van Zeist for figs. 2 and 4 from W. van Zeist and W. A. Casparie, 'Wild einkorn wheat and barley from tell Mureybit in northern Syria', *Acta Botanica Neerlandica* (1968); The Botanical Society of Edinburgh and the author for fig. 3 from D. Zohary, 'Origin of Southwest Asiatic cereals: wheats, barley, oats and rye', in P. H. Davis (ed.) *Plant Life of South-west Asia* (1971); Universa and the author for fig. 5 from W. van Zeist, 'Palaeobotanical results of the 1970 season at Cayönü, Turkey', *Helenium* (1972); Scientific American Inc. and the author for figs. 6 and 30 from Richard S. MacNeish, 'The Origins of New World Civilization', *Scientific American* (1964); Koninklijke Nederlandse Botanische Vereniging and W. van Zeist for fig. 9 from J. Niklewski and W. van Zeist, 'A late quaternary pollen diagram from northwestern Syria', *Acta Botanica Neerlandica* (1970); Gerald Duckworth and Co. and the author for figs. 10, 11, 12 and 13 from D. Zohary, 'The progenitors of wheat and barley in relation to domestication and agricultural dispersal in the Old World', in P. J. Ucko and G. W. Dimbleby (eds.) *The Domestication and Exploitation of Plants and Animals* (1969); Edinburgh University Press and the author for fig. 14 from S. Piggott, *Ancient Europe* (1965); the Palestine Exploration Fund and the author for figs. 21 and 22 from D. Kirkbride, 'Five seasons at the pre-pottery Neolithic village of Beidha in Jordan', *Palestine Exploration Quarterly* (1966); the Museum of Anthropology, University of Michigan and K. V. Flannery for figs. 24 and 25 from F. Hole, K. V. Flannery and J. A. Neely, *Prehistory and Human Ecology of the Deh Luran Plain* (1969); American Heritage Publishing Co. Inc. and the author for fig. 28 from Michael D. Coe, *America's First Civilization* (1968); University of Texas Press Ltd. and the author for fig. 29 from Richard S.

MacNeish, 'A summary of the subsistence', in D. S. Byers (ed.) *The Prehistory of the Tehuacán Valley*, Vol. I (1967); the author for photographs I and II from J. Perrot, 'Munhata', *Bible et Terre Sainte* (1967); Leonard Hill (Books) Ltd. and T. W. Whitaker for photograph III from T. W. Whitaker and G. N. Davis, *Cucurbits. Botany, Cultivation and Utilisation* (1962); W. Bray for photographs IV and V.

Some figures have been based on originals which appeared in other publications, and in such cases the authors concerned have kindly given permission for this to be done.

I cannot mention individually all the people who gave me information, advice and help. I would, however, particularly like to thank those who read and criticised sections of the book: Professor G. Dimbleby, Dr C. Vita-Finzi, Dr W. Bray and Dr I. Glover. And particularly Dr M. Rowlands.

My thanks also to Susan Frankenstein who read most of the book and typed large portions of it, to Annabel Rowe who translated my maps and figures into something more professional, to Louisa Browne who was a very sympathetic editor, and to Bobby Ullstein who took some of the grind out of the proof reading.

The librarians at the Institute of Archaeology, London, were unfailingly helpful; so too Terry Rackal in the photostating department of University College.

Finally, most thanks of all to Jan who impeded, bullied, edited and encouraged me through to the final deliverance.

I Towards an Understanding of the Transition to Food-Production

Food-production involves the domestication of plants and animals. Domestication implies that the plants or animals have been manipulated to such an extent that genetic changes have occurred resulting in new races or species. The manipulation can take many forms; right from the beginning there is evidence of agriculture, horticulture, mixed farming and herding.

These different systems represent subsistence adaptations. They are partly a response to environmental conditions, partly a reflection of cultural heritage.

There is no break between hunting and gathering and food-producing. Hunter-gatherers also manipulate plants and animals. Their subsistence strategies are just as varied as those of food-producers and are also a response to environmental and cultural conditions. To understand the emergence of food-producing societies we have to understand the hunter-gatherer background.

Food-production is a recent development. Tool-using hunter-gatherers have existed for four million years; food-producers for eleven thousand – a mere four hundred generations. In that short time the consequences of the shift from food procurement to food-production and the resultant control of food resources have profoundly affected all aspects of human culture.

Why did it take so long for food-production to begin? Was it fortuitous that it began at about the same time in widely dispersed parts of the world – in South-west Asia, Meso-America, Peru and South-east Asia? Were the reasons cultural? Was it linked to the development of more finely adapted hunting and gathering strategies? Or to the intellectual evolution and the emergence of *Homo sapiens*? Were environmental changes significant – in particular those associated with the retreat of the Pleistocene ice sheets *c.* 11,000 years ago?

Much of this book concentrates on assembling evidence that may help to answer some of these questions.

Meanwhile, this introductory chapter is concerned with three themes: the hunter-gatherer background and the problem of defining the transition to food-production; the effects of food-production; and the evidence of early domestication in places other than Southwest Asia, Meso-America and Peru.

THE DEFINITION OF FOOD-PRODUCTION

It is often difficult and rather artificial to differentiate between hunter-gatherers and food-producers. There were hunters that had so close a relationship with their quarry that it constituted a form of loose herding (Sturdy 1972). Some culled (selectively killed) the herd, thus operating a primitive form of selective breeding. Some 'gatherers' may have undertaken a little clearing or even planting. At what point are they to be labelled food-producers? It would surely be stretching the term to apply it to such present-day groups as the Siriona of Bolivia. They clear and plant small plots of maize and manioc, often in a number of places, then set off on their annual hunter-gatherer round and simply return when the crops have ripened (Holmberg 1950, 28). Or to apply it to the Owens valley Pauite who improve the wild plant yield by periodic ditching and damming of streams: 'Irrigation increased the natural yield of several wild seed plots in Owens valley. Tilling, planting and cultivation were unknown' (Steward 1933, 247). Or to the Auen Bushmen who burn the vegetation in order to increase the yield of tubers (Isaac 1970, 19). One could draw the line when a specific percentage of the total food supply is obtained from domesticated plants or animals. But what should this percentage be – 30%, 40%, 50%? It is perhaps better to try and define the point at which the process has become irreversible – when the environment has been so modified, by forest clearance, etc., that the hunter-gatherer way of life is no longer viable, or when the population has increased to such an extent that it can no longer be sustained by a hunter-gatherer economy.

THE HUNTER-GATHERER BACKGROUND

The transition from hunting and gathering to food-production was a gradual process. There was no sudden change from a miserable, shiftless existence to stability and secure food-supplies.

The hunter-gatherers that lived towards the end of the last Ice Age, the Pleistocene,[1] and in the millennia that followed were not a miserable half-starved bunch. And the early farmers were not a stable, leisured society. Flannery (1969), when comparing the early farming community at Ali Kosh in south-west Iran with the preceding hunter-gatherers, suggested that 'there is no reason to believe that the early "food-producers" were significantly better nourished than their "food-collecting" ancestors. Nor was their subsistence base necessarily more reliable.'

By Late Pleistocene, and even more by early Post-Pleistocene times, hunter-gatherers in many parts of the world were well adapted to their local environments. They had a detailed knowledge of the natural resources available and the technical competence necessary for their exploitation. There was a wide gamut of subsistence patterns. 'Then, as now, there may have been hunters, hunter/gatherers and those practising close man/animal, man/plant symbiotic relationships according to the environment' (Higgs and Jarman 1969).

It is probable that a high proportion of these societies depended primarily on plant-foods. Hunting – and the hunters – probably got the kudos but gathering – usually the women's job – was more reliable. A survey of modern hunter-gatherers throughout the world has shown that hunting only predominates in latitudes above 60°, fishing is important between 50° and 60°, and plant gathering makes up two-thirds of the diet in latitudes below 50°. It is the primary activity of 90% of the total sample (Lee 1968). Only at certain times of the year when plant resources are reduced, or at times of crisis, does hunting assume a greater importance. The operative lines of latitude would have been different in the Late Pleistocene and early Post-Pleistocene; colder conditions and hunting as a primary activity would have extended further south. Even so, it seems likely that over much of the world gathering was more important.

In some regions, for example South-west Asia, the increasing importance of plant foods in the Post-Pleistocene is underlined by the development of more complex processing paraphernalia including stone-inset sickles, querns and grinding stones, mortars and pestles, and storage pits.

Although plant gathering was often the most important activity,

1 Conventionally the retreat of the ice-sheets, *c.* 11,000 years ago, marks the end of the Pleistocene epoch and the beginning of the Holocene. But it may be that the Ice Age is not yet over and that we are living through an inter-glacial, in which case the Pleistocene epoch extends right up to the present (West 1968, 1).

many Late Pleistocene and Post-Pleistocene groups utilised game resources intensively. Sometimes a form of animal husbandry was practised. There might be stock culling, loose herding, possibly even taming. Carvings on rocks in the Sahara, tentatively dated to the eighth or seventh millennium b.c., show 'wild' bovines with collars around their necks or discs between their horns, indicating perhaps 'some closer association between the wild game and the hunting bands, such as might be brought about by initial attempts at taming' (Clark 1971). Such practices could be termed 'intensive conservation' (Higgs and Jarman 1972). At the other extreme, intensive exploitation could be extraordinarily wasteful. On the North American plains whole herds of mammoth and bison were driven to their deaths over the edge of bluffs or ravines. Far more were killed than were needed and this wholesale slaughter probably hastened the extinction of these species (Martin 1967; Hester 1967).

A frequent Late Pleistocene/early Post-Pleistocene adaptation involved an intensive exploitation of a great range of edible resources. In archaeological jargon this is a 'broad spectrum' economy. It might involve collecting seeds, nuts, fruits, roots and shell-fish, hunting and trapping large and small game and fishing. This type of exploitation has the great advantage of reducing the risk of famine; if one resource fails there are others to fall back on.

The way in which the broad spectrum economy functioned would largely depend on the natural distribution of resources. Where conditions were very favourable, with abundant and stable resources concentrated within a limited area, permanent or semi-permanent home-bases could be established. Such 'optimal environments' were often close to rivers, lakes or lagoons where the aquatic resources could be tapped. Where resources were relatively scattered, groups evolved seasonal patterns of exploitation and a scheduled round of activities.

Given this flexibility, hunter-gatherer groups would have been able to adapt to very marginal conditions. One such adaptation is illustrated by the present-day !Kung bushmen living in the Kalahari desert in Botswana. These hunter-gatherers, who have a level of technical competence inferior to many Late Pleistocene or Post-Pleistocene groups, were studied by Lee (1968) in the middle of a long drought. Not only were they surviving, but they were extremely selective in the exploitation of plant resources. They gathered only a third of the potentially edible plants and the highly-rated mongongo nut made up half the plant food diet. Not everyone was employed in the food-quest. 40% of each group, the young and the old, played little part. Even so, the rest of the group, mainly the women, spent only three hours a day, a mere twelve to nineteen hours a week, getting in food. That this is feasible in a marginal area, in the middle of a drought, for groups that utilise no complex equipment, suggests that the hunter-gatherer way of life need not have been the harsh struggle to exist that people so often assume.

Nor would the manipulation and domestication of plants and animals have had any immediate effect on the economy. No group would risk concentrating on a limited number of domesticated crops or animals, for failure might bring starvation. So, for millennia, cultivation and/or herding were carried out in conjunction with gathering and hunting. In America where virtually no suitable animal domesticates were present 'all the cultures . . . high and low alike depended on their hunters' skill for most of their animal produce' (MacNeish 1964a). In Northern Europe, after at least 3000 years of cultivation and herding, the stomach of the Iron Age man extracted from the Grauballe bog in Denmark contained 66 species of fruits and plants of which only 7 were cultigens (Helbaek 1969b).

So hunter-gatherers were not in dire straits. Manipulation and domestication did not instantly transform the way of life nor raise the standard of living. Why then did people initially undertake these new forms of subsistence? Some theoretical reasons are given in chapter 2, more practical evidence appears in chapters 6 and 7.

Meanwhile let us consider some of the consequences of food production.

THE CONSEQUENCES OF FOOD-PRODUCTION

(1) THE EFFECT ON THE CARRYING CAPACITY OF THE LAND

As man began to manipulate plants or animals he was able to move them out of their natural habitats and thereby enlarge their environmental range. He could also remove them from scattered ecological niches and so concentrate the edible resources in a limited area. He could remove certain pressures of natural selection so that deviants could survive. And, eventually, he could select for characteristics that were not necessarily beneficial under natural conditions (Flannery 1965). This combination of factors eventually increased the carrying capacity of the land: the same amount of land could support more people. Obviously in areas which had been optimal for hunting and gathering the carrying capacity was already high and early food-production might not have had much effect. The importance of food-production was that it extended the area in which a high carrying capacity was possible.

The trend of this argument is that innovation in the economic base allows increased population. It would therefore seem to be opposed to Boserup's thesis (1965) that it is population pressure that stimulates innovation. But the two ideas are not incompatible. It is undoubtedly a chicken and egg question. Population pressure may stimulate innovation (chapter 2, p. 32); innovation stimulates population growth. As Sanders (1972) says, in the context of agricultural innovation, 'If population pressure leads to an intensification of cultivation, doesn't intensification relieve population pressure and then stimulate and permit population growth?'

The increase in carrying capacity would have come about slowly. In regions of low rainfall cultivation would at first have been limited to areas with reasonable water-supplies. In South-west Asia early farming settlements were sited close to marshes or in zones of permanent high sub-surface water. In the upland valleys of Mexico early cultivation seems to have been limited to the river banks. Even in the tropics where water-supplies were not a problem, cultivation may at first have been limited to the more fertile river banks. Perhaps this early, limited, food-production, in both semi-arid and tropical regions, was confined to small garden plots: horticulture rather than agriculture. It would probably have been a polycultural system. Rather than discrete patches of wheat, or rows of maize and runner-beans, the variety of wild plants would simply have been replaced by a variety of tended plants, or sometimes mixed tended and wild. It is thus a replica of the broad spectrum economy and reduces the risk of crop failure (Harris 1969).[2] Only with improved crops and techniques would more land have been brought under cultivation.

The gradual increase in carrying capacity and in population is suggested by tentative estimates of population density in South-west Asia. The average Late Pleistocene hunter-gatherer carrying capacity was probably 0.1 person per square kilometre, the early dry farming carrying capacity 1 to 2 persons per square kilometre. With irrigation this increased six-fold (Flannery 1969).

In the long run, with the additional innovations and improvements that stem from cities and large-scale industry, the world

2 In South-west Asia and the Aegean food caches often contain a high percentage of emmer wheat mixed with – and therefore presumably cultivated with – einkorn wheat, barley, peas, beans and lentils (J. Renfrew 1973, 26).

carrying capacity has become some 100 times greater than was possible with a hunter-gatherer subsistence: 'It has been calculated that if man had never progressed beyond the hunting and food-gathering stage, the maximum population which the world's surface could sustain at any one time would be twenty to thirty million people. The present population is of the order of three thousand million: the difference between the two has been made possible by cultivation' (Dimbleby 1967, 76).

(2) THE DEVELOPMENT OF SEDENTARY SOCIETIES

In optimal environments not only was the hunter-gatherer carrying capacity high but, as mentioned earlier, permanent or semi-permanent settlement was sometimes possible. Since such optimal areas were limited, concepts of 'territory' and 'ownership' would have been important and would have further encouraged permanent settlement. Where there were storable resources such as wild seeds or nuts the creation of immobile facilities such as pits would again have favoured permanence.

Food production mimicked these optimal conditions and *extended* the potential for permanent settlement.

South-west Asia provides an example. Here there were sedentary hunter-gatherers in optimal areas, particularly where high-yielding winter grains were available. Plant cultivation and the transfer of these grains beyond their natural habitat enlarged the areas where sedentism was viable. Domestication permitted the artificial concentration of edible resources and thus decreased the need for seasonal mobility. There may still have been some seasonal movement, to get wild plants or to take animals to fresh pastures, but these could either have occurred from the home base or could have been carried out by part of the community moving to seasonal camps. Since primitive cultivation was limited to well-watered terrains there would again be a premium on 'territory' and 'ownership'. Immobile storage facilities would again tend to tie the population to specific places (Flannery 1971).

In contrast, in other areas such as the Mexican highlands the lack of concentrated resources prevented the development of sedentary hunter-gatherer groups and it was only after millennia of cultivation that the required concentration of high-yielding resources was achieved. This then led to permanent settlement.

Sedentism – whether based on a hunter-gatherer or a food-producing economy – has a direct bearing on population increase. In mobile societies births are widely spaced. In a recent paper

7

Lee (1972) has shown that the !Kung women travel 2400 kilometres in the course of their annual round and carry substantial loads for much of the time. They also carry their children until they reach the age of four. It is extremely difficult for the women to function efficiently if they have more than one child under four and in fact, as a result of natural adaptation and occasional artificial constraints,[3] births are usually spaced at three- to five-year intervals. This is a necessary adaptation to nomadic conditions and similar wide spacing has been noted in other mobile societies. Hayden (1972) has given a tentative run-down on the effectiveness of the various controls available to mobile hunter-gatherers: '. . . we might suspect that out of a maximum possible fertility of 20–30 living off-spring per female, this is reduced to 5–6 or fewer primarily by prolonged lactation, physiological controls, abstinence and abortion; that this is further reduced to 3–5 by infanticide, etc.; that a moderate natural infant and child mortality rate reduces this even further (perhaps 20–50%) and that 5% or more of the remaining adolescents or young adults are killed in fighting.' Sedentism, by reducing the need to have births widely spaced, may drastically modify the natural constraints. The effect of a more sedentary life-style may be bolstered by food production, in that it may provide a more assured and perhaps more nutritious food-supply and so reduce infant mortality (Smith and Young 1972). Agriculture may in some cases provide the 'milk and mush' missing from most hunter-gatherer diets and so allow earlier weaning (Lee 1972).

(3) Changes in the structure of society

Hunter-gatherer societies tend to be structured on a flexible kinship base and to exhibit strong fissionary tendencies. Whenever the !Kung bushmen congregate in any number they become more than usually quarrelsome, for a larger group entails more work – in terms of distance to the food resources – and there are few social mechanisms for controlling strife (Lee 1968).[4] Agricultural societies, on the other hand, tend to be organised on a more permanent corporate basis. This is necessary because there is a great need for long-

---

3 The child is breastfed until three or four years old and there is probably a correlation between the long lactation and the suppression of ovulation. Births are surrounded by some secrecy; possibly on occasion infanticide occurs.

4 There are occasional hunter-gatherer groups in areas with rich and concentrated wild resources who have a corporate structure; for example, the north-west coast Indians of North America (Sanders and Price 1968, 80).

term stability to permit co-operative land-clearance, defence, etc. Even in the early stages of food-production, mixed farming (with both herding and crop-growing) may require community organisation. For example, the animals may have to be moved to seasonal pastures at some distance from the settlement. In some cases each family may send off a few members with the herds. But in other cases certain families may concentrate on herding while others grow crops. This would necessitate some redistribution within the community.

Within the corporate structure of the agricultural society the family operates as a semi-independent economic unit and this may lead to slight differences in 'wealth' and some social stratification. Such differences may stimulate trade: more important members of the community will want to underline their position by obtaining 'luxury' goods, such as fine stones, pigments or shells. Certainly in South-west Asia there is a sharp increase in the amount of obsidian in circulation once farming gets under way. Both trade and inter-dependence between sections of the community may augment individual authority since more powerful members may act as the exchange or redistribution agents.

Inter-community exchange is probably more significant in this respect. It is less important in very uniform ecological areas where everyone will tend to produce the same range of food, and more important where the terrain is diversified and there is a variety of farming systems associated with various crops or animals. Specialisation will encourage exchange. Such exchange systems are found today among primitive groups like the Didinga and Acholi in East Africa. And crop-fish exchanging tribes are known from Melanesia and coastal New Guinea (Bronson 1972). The same effect will result where certain groups control and exploit non-agricultural raw materials, such as good quality stone. Where such exchanges are controlled by particular members of the community, their prestige and power will be considerably enhanced.

(4) Craft specialisation

Even at the level of a primitive farming economy the potential for specialisation and trading may stimulate new crafts. But although the term Neolithic (the New Stone Age) is still often defined as the advent of stone-using farmers and the invention of pottery, polished stone axes and weaving, there is no simple synchronisation. Food production and craft-specialisation do not necessarily go hand in hand. Crafts are adaptations, dependent upon the environment,

9

specific needs, economic and social pressures. There are hunter-gatherers who make pottery, who grind and polish stone tools. There are farmers who do neither. In the Tehuacán valley of Meso-America, the earliest cultigens are found around 5000 b.c., pottery 2300 b.c. and polished stone axes 1200 b.c. (MacNeish 1965). A range of factors are involved, differing from area to area. Permanence of settlement, concentration of population and increased settlement size may all promote increased craft-specialisation. The emphasis on individual family units and the resultant potential for individual 'wealth' may be another factor. Community interdependence and trade will be another since manufactured goods would be useful for barter.

Pottery, generally too heavy and fragile for nomadic people, will spread with sedentism. Pots for storage will be particularly useful for groups who collect or cultivate durable foods such as nuts, acorns, grass-seeds or grain. Where cooking is important, pots will be a great improvement on other receptacles.

Weaving, again, is more likely to develop under sedentary conditions. There would probably have to be a reasonably abundant and dependable supply of fibres, wool, flax or cotton. In the case of woollen textiles the craft can only have developed long after the beginning of sheep herding, for the earliest domesticated sheep had hairy coats (Flannery 1965). This means herders could not knowingly have selected for 'woolliness' and this trait must have emerged accidentally.

The development of polished stone axes would have depended on the environment and the sort of adaptations needed. It is often suggested that early farming would require forest clearance and that the polished axe evolved as a response to this need. But though this may have been true for some areas, clearance was probably far more frequently achieved by ringing the trees and then burning them. It may be that the development of polished axes had more to do with advances in carpentry and an increase in the range of wooden equipment. It may also be that many 'axes' are not axes at all, but hoes.

(5) 'Surplus' and 'leisure'?

Craft specialisation and innovation are often correlated with increased 'leisure' and 'surplus'. Such abstractions are hard to quantify. We have already seen that the !Kung bushmen only work twelve to nineteen hours a week – while we still battle for a thirty-hour working week. As Sahlins (1968) says, 'The amount of work *per capita* increases with the evolution of culture and the amount of leisure *per capita* decreases' and part of Boserup's thesis (1965) is that any agricultural innovation, though it increases output per unit of land, increases input in man-hours. It is reckoned that a simple slash-and-burn economy, requiring 500 to 1000 man-hours per year, brought little or no reduction to the average hunter-gatherer labour expenditure (Harris 1972). At most, rather than an over-all increase in leisure, there may have been longer 'blocks' of free time between such seasonal activities as planting, weeding and harvesting (Smith and Young 1972).

Similarly, what looks like a surplus often turns out to be a seasonal surplus, absolutely essential to tide the community over lean seasons or lean years: not a surplus at all, simply adequate in the long run. Nor is the food supply simply limited to what is necessary for eating: it must also be bartered for capital equipment and conserved as replacement funds (Wolf 1966, 6). More than this, no society provides purely for physical needs. 'The fact is that "Man does not live by bread alone", no matter how meagre the bread is' (Pearson 1957). Social obligations are part and parcel of the fabric of society – 'There is no disentangling bare subsistence needs from the total functional demands which the society makes on the economy' (Pearson 1957). So it may be argued that 'surplus' can only be regarded as relative and can perhaps only be defined in terms of the ways in which specific societies institutionalise part of the economy to support social requirements. Individual prestige or inter-community trade may play a role in institutionalising a 'surplus'.

By and large 'surplus' in a farming economy is more potential than real and usually requires some external pressure to bring it to life. In most farming societies 'the technical means for generating a food surplus were there; it was the social mechanisms needed to actualise it that were lacking' (Carneiro 1970).

We have now reached a point where many of the phenomena directly or indirectly associated with farming have been discussed. The emphasis has been on simple village-farming economies. It will have become clear that some of the innovations are directly associated with plant cultivation or animal herding and are the result of the extension of the range of these resources and the removal of some of the pressures of natural selection, while many others are secondary attributes, for example, territoriality, storage, etc. These may equally well be associated with certain hunter-gatherer groups. The division is not clear-cut: it is simply that the combination of primary and secondary phenomena results in cumulative change. The exceptions within hunter-gatherer societies become the rule within farming groups.

It will also have become clear that the elements all inter-lock, none stands on its own, and each is affected by and affects all the others. The easiest way to comprehend this is to see 'culture' as an adaptive system composed of a multiplicity of sub-systems, such as subsistence, technology, social structure and symbolic beliefs, each of which can then be further sub-divided and all of which are inter-connected. This is a theoretical model, one that will be elaborated in chapter 2 (p. 26).

(6) 'CIVILISATION'

A village-farming economy was until very recently the predominant subsistence pattern throughout the world. Only in certain relatively limited areas were there more complex systems requiring market centres, often in urban settings. Recently these more complex systems have spread at the expense of the earlier simple ones.

How the more complex systems develop is beyond the scope of this book; but the question of whether they were based on agriculture interests us. Civilisation has been defined in many different ways. 'The complex artificial environment of man, it is the insulation created by man, an artefact which mediates between himself and the world of nature' (Renfrew 1972, 13). 'It is the crystallisation of executive power which serves to distinguish the primitive world from the civilised. . . . Not the city but the state is the decisive criterion of civilisation' (Wolf 1966, 9). 'Civilised society is above all stratified society' (Sanders and Price 1968, 227). Neither urban-isation nor writing are essential to civilisation but it is usually associated with a high degree of technological ability and with monumental architecture. By these criteria no hunter-gatherer society has ever achieved 'civilisation'. The nearest perhaps were the North-west Coast Indians with their chiefdoms and complex rank system. But though definitions vary all authorities would agree with Adams (1966, 38) who says that it is 'a truism that complex, civilised societies depend upon a subsistence base that is sufficiently intensive and reliable to permit sedentary nucleated settlements, a circumstance that . . . in the long run has implied agriculture'. We may add to this that not only must there be farming but in most cases it must be diversified and intensive. The cause and effect be-tween population pressure, intensive farming, preferential control of resource areas, the effects of resource redistribution and the development of states is still in process of debate (among a multitude of others: Boserup 1965; Carneiro 1970; Sanders 1965; Sanders and Price 1968; Adams 1966; Coe 1961b, 1969; Flannery 1969; Renfrew 1972). Since civilisation – like farming – is an adaptive system there will be no one answer. In different parts of the world different combinations of factors will operate.

THE SPREAD OF FOOD-PRODUCTION

Once inaugurated, food-production spread fast. It took, for example, only 4000 years to spread from South-west Asia to the furthest parts of Western Europe. There are many reasons for this, of varying importance in different areas.

One is that farming communities did not develop in isolation. In many regions early attempts to domesticate plant or animal species occurred within a seasonal round of hunting and gathering. This seasonal movement facilitated contact between groups and the exchange of information and produce. In Meso-America different highland valleys experimented with different cultigens, there was some system of exchange and new cultigens appear quite suddenly in one or other of the valleys.

For more settled communities, for example in South-west Asia, transhumance, involving the regulated seasonal movement of herds, would have had the same effect. So would trade in non-agricultural commodities.

Farming also spread by colonisation. This would have been particularly rapid where swidden cultivation was practised. This is also known as slash-and-burn or shifting cultivation. Under swidden, the land is left fallow for longer than it is cultivated. Prior to the development of more intensive techniques involving fertilisation, ploughing or irrigation, long fallow would frequently have been necessary to allow soil regeneration. Swidden is an *extensive* form of exploitation, requiring a considerable amount of land per head of population. Since farm land was often restricted to favourable locales such extensive land use would immediately limit the size of the community. An increase in the population could only have been offset by a more intensive exploitation or by migration; and since the former requires a greater labour input, we may assume that migration was often the answer. Emigrant colonisers looking for new land would have had to bypass considerable tracts that were unsuitable for primitive farming. This was particularly the case where terrain was diversified. Colonisation therefore advanced in a series of leaps, and this speeded up the spread of farming.

Even where suitable land was less limited it would have been uneconomic to farm beyond a certain radius because of the time involved getting out to the fields. It is reckoned that for primitive farmers with no transport, the radius is about an hour's journey from the settlement (chapter 2, p. 31). So again, excess population would probably have hived-off.

The need to have some plots in cultivation and others lying fallow required a system of rotation. Some communities may have practised a cyclical rotation, returning to the same plots again and again with periods for regeneration between. But others may have moved on once the soil began to lose some of its fertility. Where there was little pressure on the land this linear shift may have been more convenient and this again would lead to a fairly rapid spread of farming (Harris 1972).

The spread was probably faster in areas of seed-crop cultivation. These protein-rich crops make far greater demands on soil nutrients than the starch-rich root-crops which have partially or totally lost the ability to form seeds. Herd animals also tend to retard regeneration, for though they are valuable as a source of protein and manure, their grazing on abandoned plots prevents the regrowth of woody plants (Harris 1972).

THE REST OF THE WORLD

In this book attention is focused on three areas: South-west Asia, Meso-America and Peru. In addition to these, Africa (particularly north of the Equator), India, China, South-east Asia and tropical South America could have been considered, but the evidence from these parts of the world is so uneven, often so slight and frequently so hypothetical, that there seems to be no way of subjecting it to any detailed or analytical treatment. It is all very well for Chang (1970b) to say, re China, that 'those seeking an understanding of, or writing about, Old World prehistory, would do well to avail themselves of the available evidence' when he then goes on to admit 'the facts remain meagre, their articulation remains essentially interpretative, and definite conclusions are therefore remote'.

It is not for lack of recent literature. Early farming in all these areas has been considered at greater or lesser length in the past ten years. It is rather a combination of two factors: a lack of modern archaeological excavation and the problem of the preservation of organic evidence in tropical regions. Poor preservation is a real problem when one is trying to establish the very minor shifts that mark the transition from hunting and gathering to cultivation, but it is not insurmountable. Chang (1968, 83) points out some of the possible sources of information: 'carbonised roots and tubers, identifiable plant protein crystals, pollen grains from the fenced gardens, and perhaps bamboo or wooden dibbles', while Gorman's work in Thailand has shown how much can be done if locations such as caves are sought, where preservation is somewhat better, and if minuscule organic remains are retrieved and indirect evidence such as pottery impressions or possible agricultural equipment is examined (Gorman 1969). The general lack of such evidence has led to some quite inspired theoretical reconstructions, for instance Chang's work (1968, 1970b) on China and South-east Asia and Lathrap's (1970) on tropical South America. But so far they remain virtually untestable. The information, such as it is, is summarised in Appendix A.

Four caveats about the areas studied in detail in this book. First, there is no reason to believe that they are the only centres of primary domestication. It seems very likely that there were other independent developments in, at least, North China, South-east Asia and tropical South America. Second, they are not necessarily the earliest. The only 'hard' evidence from other regions is from Spirit cave in north-west Thailand and it is by no means conclusive. If accepted it pushes cultivation in South-east Asia back to the eighth millennium b.c. and we may expect still earlier sites to be found. Third, several agricultural systems are coeval. Thus in South-west Asia there was mixed farming with cereals, pulses and herd animals, while roughly at the same time in Meso-America and Peru there was *milpa* cultivation of maize, beans and squash. Fourth, there is an archaeological bias in favour of seed-crops. Work has concentrated on the semi-arid regions of South-west Asia and Meso-America because preservation is excellent. These regions lack indigenous root-crops. Only in highland Peru are both seed-crops and tubers available. Here seed-crop cultivation does seem to take priority.

It would seem a fair assumption that since root-crop cultivation is considerably simpler than cereal cultivation it began at least as early, if not earlier. Digging up tubers gives an incomplete harvest, so what is missed simply sets a new crop in the disturbed ground. The timing of the harvest is less critical. The cultivator does not have to be completely sedentary, for once the crop is set and weeded it requires little attention. When another plant of the same type is required the cultivator simply cuts a tuber. The new plant is therefore a genetic duplicate and is not subject to the vagaries of genetic combination (Lynch 1967, 64).

Harris (1969, 1973) has suggested that one reason why it is difficult to establish early root-crop centres is that seed-crop cultivation is inherently less stable than root-crop cultivation and is therefore liable to expand at the expense of the latter. The greater stability of a root-crop system has three causes. Root-crops take fewer nutrients from the soil and therefore soil fertility is maintained. A greater density of plants grows on each plot which minimises soil erosion. Root-crops lack vital proteins and have to be supplemented by other resources, frequently aquatic. This tends to tie the system down to areas where these additional resources are available. There is evidence to suggest that rice expanded into South-east Asia at the expense of the indigenous root-crop system and that maize cultivation expanded into north-west Venezuela (Rancho Peludo), Colombia (Momil II on the lower Magdalena), possibly Ecuador (Chorrero) and perhaps also coastal Guatemala, in each case at the expense of an indigenous root-crop system (Lathrap 1970, 67; Reichel-Dolmatoff 1965, 78; Estrada and Evans 1963; Meggers 1966, 61; Green and Lowe 1967, 58).

In a recent paper, Harlan (1972) cautiously proposes that there may be a rather basic distinction between seed- and root-crop origins. He notes that what little evidence is available from tropical areas, for example from Africa south of the Sahara and north of the Equator, from South-east Asia and from tropical South America, suggests that individual root-crop species were brought into cultivation in different parts of a large territory. He calls these 'non-centers' in contrast to the seed-crop 'centers' of South-west Asia, Meso-America and perhaps North China where a whole galaxy of plants was brought into cultivation within a relatively confined area. He admits, however, that this pattern may simply be 'a reflection of the distribution of our ignorance. Do we have centers in those areas where substantial information is available and non-centers where we know too little?' Such speculations must be left until more information is available.

2 Theoretical Approaches

THE IMPORTANCE OF ARCHAEOLOGICAL EXPLANATION

The archaeologist, faced with the evidence he extracts from the earth, has three main objectives. He must describe the life of past societies. He must place them within a temporal and spatial framework. And he must attempt to explain how the society articulates and why it changes. In this chapter we are examining the third objective; the explanations – or hypotheses – that have been formulated about *How* and *Why* the transition to food-production occurred.

In the last few years there has been much debate about the function of explanation in archaeology and there has been a move away from implicit assumptions to more explicit theory. For some archaeologists an explanation is only considered satisfactory when it is deduced from confirmed or law-like generalisations (Watson and Watson 1969, 4; Watson 1973). But though, in the long run, this may be the ultimate aim, law-like generalisations about society are still few and far between and have often not been adequately tested. Indeed 'The degree and nature of regularity in sociocultural phenomena is still an open question; to state that no regularities have been found is just as important as to find regularities' (Chaney 1972),[1] and Hole (1973) says: 'There seems to be an imminent danger of believing one's cover laws especially when they have not been tested and when the one in question is only one of a long series of assumptions.'

Hypotheses are usually generated by, and tested on, the data provided by the first two objectives. The hypotheses in turn promote a new appreciation of available data or new insights for future in-

1 Even Patty Jo Watson, arch-proponent of law-like generalisations, admits that there are problems: 'It is easier to formulate laws in the physical sciences than in the social sciences because the objects and events of the physical sciences are more easily understood by man, of such magnitude in time and space as to be easily observed and manipulated in an experiment, and of such quantities that man can observe many examples of each type' (Watson and Watson 1969, 11).

vestigation so 'the path of development is a process of serendipitous theoretical hops leap-frogging a more myopic accumulation and testing of observations. It is the duty of theoretical hypotheses to outrun fact so that speculation o'erleaps the present information state and points the way, then careful accumulation of tested data will revise the validity of the theoretical position, which may then leap ahead again' (Clarke 1972b). In other words, the three objectives mentioned in the first paragraph are inter-related.

Generalisations = hypotheses = conceptual frameworks = theoretical frameworks = most explanations = models.[2] The title of this chapter could well have been 'Models' – avoided only because the word still seems to be shrouded in mystique. But a model is no more than 'any well-defined concept used to interpret data' (Clarke 1972b). It is more or less useful depending on how testable it is. If untestable it becomes an act of faith, heart-warming for the holder but not greatly relevant. Only when a model is testable can it be validated, revised or rejected.

Since a model is a 'well-defined concept' the underlying logical framework is consciously expressed. But this conscious expression is a fairly recent development. Many earlier archaeologists – and not a few modern ones – express views based on unconscious assumptions. They probably felt, as indeed did many historians, that if sufficient information were available, the 'facts' would 'speak', 'truth' would out and the problem would be resolved once and for all (Carr 1961, 7). But there is no such thing as 'truth': like beauty, it is in the eye of the beholder. It depends on how he conceives the situation, indeed it depends on his *pre*-conceptions. So one must try and establish the implicit assumptions, the particular framework of reference. 'Undoubtedly all theories concerning the past have such built-in assumptions' (Renfrew 1968). Is the writer an arch-diffusionist? Or, on the contrary, is he out to establish independent origins? Is he an environmentalist or does he come with an evolutionary bias?

If there is a bias, conscious or unconscious, in the way material is *interpreted*, the same bias will operate in *collecting* material. There cannot be a perfect, unbiased excavation. Although most archaeologists recognise this, most still feel that all one can do is to collect a general and reasonably comprehensive range of information, which can then be used as data to generate hypotheses. This has been derided as the 'vacuum-cleaner' approach (Hill 1972).

---

2 This is somewhat simplistic; some of the terms are used in a general and some in a precise sense – thus, in a more precise way, a model is said to generate hypotheses and tested hypotheses give rise to explanations.

Another approach, known as problem-orientated archaeology, is to formulate a particular hypothesis and then concentrate on extracting evidence that will help to prove or disprove it. Whereas the first approach is said to be 'inductive', this approach is 'deductive', but the distinction is far from sharp. The deductive approach has risks: alternatives may not be adequately tested, in which case 'we are likely to find we have set up a self-fulfilling prophecy whose outcome was never in doubt' (Hole 1971 – disputed by Hill 1972).[3] Certain classes of data which are not of direct relevance to the particular problem but which may be of interest to someone with a different problem may be ignored or glossed over.[4] On the other hand it often leads to a more critical approach to the extraction of information (Watson, LeBlanc and Redman 1971, 34).

Having warned the reader of the relationship between practical and theoretical archaeology, this chapter concentrates on some of the explanations or more explicit models for the transition to food-production.

CARL SAUER'S SOUTH-EAST ASIAN HEARTH

To start with, some untested and sometimes untestable offerings. If one proposed a scale ranging from testable propositions to 'acts of faith', then a good deal of Carl Sauer's book *Agricultural Origins and Dispersals* (1952) comes perilously near the latter end. The beginning is fine. Six necessary conditions for the transition from hunting-and-gathering to farming are proposed. First: the society concerned must already have a flourishing economic base – 'needy and miserable societies are not inventive, for they lack the leisure for reflection, experimentation and discussion'. Second: they must be orientated towards food-gathering rather than hunting and so be predisposed to agricultural experimentation. Third: they must be sedentary, for crops cannot be left untended. Fourth: they must live in wooded areas for grass sod is too tough for primitive tools.

3 Hole (1971) also suggests that hypotheses should be tested against analogous modern situations – where the evidence will always be more complete than for past societies. This opens up another vast area of dispute, viz., the role of ethnographic evidence, but that, fortunately, is beyond the scope of this book (Freeman 1968; Binford 1968d; Clarke 1972a).

4 So, for example, the publication by Hole, Flannery and Neely (1969) of their excavations in the Deh Luran area, in which an ecological hypothesis was formulated and tested, was criticised for not providing sufficient information on other aspects: 'Researchers who wish to consult it for certain kinds of information, or from viewpoints somewhat different from those the authors have considered important, will find the work unnecessarily difficult or even impossible' (Smith cited in Watson, LeBlanc and Redman 1971, 157).

Fifth: they must not live in large river-valleys for these, being subject to flood, require drainage and irrigation. And, finally, there must be a wide variety of plants and animals (Sauer 1952, 20). Sauer goes on to suggest that the innovating groups are likely to be 'some well-situated progressive fishing folk living in a mild climate along fresh waters' – for the lacustrine/riverine resources would underwrite a stable economy and a sedentary or semi-sedentary life style (Sauer 1952, 20). He makes the point that the initial domesticates would be multi-purpose plants set out around fishing villages to provide starch foods, substances for toughening nets and lines and making them water-resistant, and drugs and poisons. 'Food-production was one and perhaps not the most important reason for bringing plants under cultivation' (Sauer 1952, 27).

Many of these propositions are testable. Some have already been tested – both before and since Sauer's publication. Some have been contradicted: for example, marginal societies have been found to have ample leisure (Lee 1968); the initiating societies in the southern highlands of Mexico were not sedentary and lived in a semi-arid environment which by no stretch of the imagination can be classed as woodland – though it is not grassland either. But many of the propositions may be correct – for certain areas and certain farming systems.

But Sauer, rather than attempting to test his propositions either against available data or by going out to find new data, simply goes on to assume that these conditions were best met by the fishing-folk inhabiting South-east Asia. He suggests that they began by cultivating root-crops – vegetative reproduction being simpler than seeding. They raise dogs, pigs, geese and ducks. The problem of actually finding evidence is glossed over: 'At that time the ice caps were melting away, sea levels were rising markedly and hence rivers were filling their valley floors so that only chance locations not buried beneath sea or alluvium may be found' (Sauer 1952, 23).

Arch diffusionism then sets in: indeed he admits 'In the history of man, unless I misread it greatly, diffusion of ideas from a few hearths has been the rule; independent, parallel invention the exception' (Sauer 1952, 3). South-east Asia becomes the primary hearth for the whole of the Old World. There are secondary centres where, once the 'idea' has arrived, new plants and animals are brought into domestication: north China, west India, Ethiopia, West Africa and South-west Asia. So in South-west Asia, the olive, fig and date-palm, all vegetatively reproduced, are the first domesticates, then, later, seed-reproducing plants such as cereals are cultivated. The shift to seed-crops is 'as simple as this: where climatic advantage shifted from the root-plant to the seed-plant, the attention of the cultivators shifted from the former to the latter' (Sauer 1952, 71). All this he proposes, despite the fact that the evidence from Jarmo in South-west Asia, supporting early cereal cultivation and herding with no olive, fig or date-palm, lay in front of him.

In the New World, though 'a single center is unproved . . . it seems to me there is a case for one basic hearth' (Sauer 1952, 43) – a root-crop centre around the Caribbean. Even here the possibility lurks that the 'idea' may ultimately derive from the Old World – for there is the mysterious case of the blue and olive-green egg-laying chicken with black meat and black bones found both in South America (though never in Pre-Columban contexts!) and in South-east Asia (Sauer 1952, 58). To be fair, Sauer also mentions the appearance, in both the Old and New World, of gourds, cotton, sweet potato and coconut – and some of these parallels are indeed more difficult to explain. Cultivation spreads from the Caribbean to the Andean highlands, where other root-crops, not to mention the llama and the guinea pig, are brought into domestication, and then, in the region of the Mexican/Central American border, where the climate is marginal for vegetative planting, the switch to seed-crops occurs.

Most of this is a virtually untestable act of diffusionist faith and so Mangelsdorf (1953) attacks it: 'A theory almost entirely lacking in factual base may be stimulating and provocative and may be especially useful if it can be subjected to critical tests which would prove it wrong . . . [but] . . . if one sought, as an exercise in imagination, to design a completely untestable theory . . . it would be difficult to improve upon this one.'

JANE JACOBS – CITY INVENTION

We might look next at another untested, indeed little-known, hypothesis, proposed by Jane Jacobs (1969). An economist rather than an archaeologist, her hypothesis is only marginally based on available archaeological data.[5] It could be said to derive from an economic law-like generalisation. It has the virtues of being totally unexpected, of being testable, and of pointing to a line of evidence that needs following up.

5 Indeed the little data she does use is incorrect: Çatal Hüyük is mentioned as 'the earliest city yet found and the earliest known settlement of any kind to possess agriculture' – both statements wrong. So are her vague generalisations about the available archaeological information on the transition to farming in South-west Asia (Jacobs 1969, 47).

In the first chapter the well-worn path from farming, to village, to town, to – sometimes – 'civilisation' was traced. It was noted that you do not need to be a farmer to live in a village, and that you can be a farmer and not live in a village. It was never, however, suggested, as Jane Jacobs does, that you could be a hunter-gatherer and live in a city and that agriculture originated in such cities rather than in the countryside. A revolutionary idea and at first glance untenable. At second glance it still has weaknesses, but seems worth considering more carefully.

The opening law-like generalisation is: 'Rural economies, including agricultural work, are directly built upon city economies and city work' (Jacobs 1969, 13). Agricultural productivity and agricultural innovations stem from the city. Many of the examples she cites are weak. She mentions hybrid corns as originating in American cities. *Modern* hybrid corns may well be laboratory products but hybrids were already produced in the second millennium b.c. in Meso-America, with not a town in sight. 'Nobody knows just where the medieval three-field system began but this much is evident: it centred around cities' (Jacobs 1969, 25). But this simply means that the city acted as a stimulus, and the development may well have been initiated by rural populations. The initial generalisation therefore needs emendation: innovation *and/or stimulus* derive from the city.

Even accepting this, there is still a considerable leap involved in proposing that 'Agriculture itself may have originated in cities' (Jacobs 1969, 25). The argument unfolds: even in primitive hunter-gatherer societies particularly valuable commodities – fine stones, shells, pigments, etc. – are traded. A hunting-gathering group with a monopoly on such a commodity – and she uses obsidian as an example – can create and sustain a trading centre.[6] Other hunter-gatherer groups will barter natural produce against the prized commodity. The trading community will barter obsidian against specialised goods from other trading centres and will eventually act as a secondary depot for such goods. Since the settlement subsists both on its own hunting and collecting activities and on the natural produce brought in by traders, it may become both large and stable. But natural produce brought any distance would have to be reasonably durable, so meat would be brought in on the hoof. Not all the animals would need to be eaten immediately; some would

---

6 The great tell of Çatal Hüyük in Anatolia is her inspiration. Though so far the excavation has only uncovered farming settlements, the bottom of the tell has not been touched, and here the postulated hunter-gatherer settlements could still be uncovered (chapter 6, p. 158).

be herded together and might breed. Although again and again the whole lot might be killed off, eventually 'the stewards manage to keep fresh meat on hand permanently. They come in this way to possess . . . what we would call breeding stock.' Non-perishable seeds, nuts and beans also come in as barter – 'Seeds of many, many different kinds of wild grasses flow in to the city from wet soils and dry, from sandy soils and loamy, from highlands and from valleys, from river banks and from forest glades.' Not all the seed would be consumed immediately, it would be stored, spilt around the settlement, grow, and the mixing might lead to an extraordinary degree of cross-breeding and new, sometimes very successful hybrids.[7] The fact that certain patches of accidentally scattered seed gave higher yields than others and that not all the seed was needed for instant consumption could lead eventually to purposeful sowing. The argument goes on, but we can leave it here. Agriculture has begun in the trade centres, which she postulates are large enough to deserve the name of cities. Different centres experimenting with different plants and animals exchange information and produce. Agriculture spreads to the hunter-gatherer hinterlands – initially through the establishments of dependent daughter-settlements. Small farming villages develop, the cities may die, the villages go on.

It is very much taken for granted – indeed, the whole argument rests on the premise – that trade was carried out by people coming considerable distances. This assumption is rather dubious; it may well be that early trade was far more a matter of prized commodities passing from hand to hand.

Jane Jacobs' model is not simply a trade model. There are two essential ingredients: trade and a creative local economy. To work it needs many small cities: 'A city does not grow by trading only with a rural hinterland. A city seems always to have implied a group of cities, in trade with one another' (Jacobs 1969, 42). The evidence has yet to be found, but we shall see that Jericho, a great eighth-millennium settlement is hard to explain; that the unexplored basal levels of Çatal Hüyük in Anatolia must go back at least to the seventh millennium b.c.; and that, as Joan Oates (1972) points out, the basal levels of the great Mesopotamian tells, often situated at nodal trading points, remain untouched. Because it is so difficult to get at the base of the great tells excavators in search of early farming sites have concentrated on the small mounds and have uncovered small vil-

7 Dimbleby (1967, 82) also mentions that regularly used trackways – and, by extension, trade centres – would be potential meeting places for species from quite different ecological niches.

lages. But it may well be that these form only part of the settlement pattern at the transition from hunting-and-gathering to farming. The hypothesis can be tested. It may be found that an alternative hypothesis, one that Jane Jacobs ignores but which is inherent in her argument, is more applicable. The trade centres, like later cities, may not have been the primary innovators of agriculture, but may have been a great stimulus for the intensification and increased productivity of agricultural systems, just as trade itself has long been recognised as a vital ingredient in the diffusion and development of early farming (Renfrew, Dixon and Cann 1966; Flannery 1965; G. Wright 1969).

THE 'OASIS THEORY'

Next, a very well-known explanation. The 'Oasis Theory', propounded as early as 1908 by Pumpelly and again by Newberry in 1924, was popularised by Gordon Childe from the 1920s onwards (G. Wright 1971). However, it is rarely noted that, while Childe held to the theory right through to the final editions of *New Light on the most Ancient East* (1952) and *What Happened in History* (1954), in his final edition of *The Dawn of European Civilization* (1957a) he no longer mentions it. The 'Oasis Theory' is simply saluted in passing as a model that has been more or less tested, and, at least as formulated, found wanting.

In the 1920s there was very little information to go on. There was reasonably good evidence on climatic change at the end of the Pleistocene in Europe but no comparative evidence from South-west Asia or Egypt. No early sites were known from South-west Asia and only a couple (now found to be not so early) from Egypt. Nor were the distributions of potential domesticates well defined. Childe suggested that farming began where the potential plants and animals were available. In 1952 he considered that 'the conditions for the rise of a food-producing economy were . . . fulfilled in Afrasia'[8] – though Asia was probably more important (Childe 1952, 27). By 1954 he opted more firmly for South-west Asia (Childe 1954, 49). His second proposition was that Post-Pleistocene desiccation led to a concentration of man, plant and beast at oases, a concentration which 'might promote the sort of symbiosis between man and beast implied in the word "domestication" ' (Childe 1952, 25). 'The hunters whose wives were cultivators had something to offer some of the beasts they hunted – stubble on grain plots and the husks of the grain. As suitable animals

8 A belt running from the Atlantic to the Tigris.

became increasingly hemmed in to the oases by the desert, men might study their habits and instead of killing them off-hand, might tame them and make them dependent' (Childe 1954, 49).

This particular environmental model stands or falls on whether there is evidence of drastic desiccation. It falls: there is none (chapter 4). Furthermore, environmental determinism *per se* could never be a sufficient explanation (as Childe was well aware) for it does not explain why there were not similar responses to desiccation at earlier periods.

But this does not rule out changes in the environment as *an* explanatory factor. A great many models, directly or indirectly, willingly and sometimes unwillingly, incorporate an environmental factor. MacNeish recently postulated a series of environmental shifts and associated cultural adjustments in the highlands of southern Mexico and suggested a cause-and-effect almost the reverse of Childe's: in winter 'both man and beast were forced instead to cluster around the few well-watered areas, which again meant man further diminished the supply of game' (MacNeish 1971). Even Lewis Binford (1968b), while opting for a demographic model to explain the transition to food-production, ends up incorporating an important environmental sub-clause (p. 32).

Models incorporating environmental factors will be considered later, but first a model that remains obdurately 'cultural'.

BRAIDWOOD'S CULTURAL LEVELS

Robert Braidwood searched for evidence of desiccation during his first field-investigation in Iraq in the 1950s and found none. He reacted violently against the 'Oasis Theory' – 'I will tell you quite frankly that there are times when I feel it is plain balderdash' (Braidwood 1951). Later evidence established not major desiccation but some climatic shifts in the early Post-Pleistocene, but Braidwood considered them irrelevant. Only very recently has he somewhat modified his position (Braidwood and Braidwood 1969). So he erected a cultural model: farming was seen as the culmination of ever-increasing cultural differentiation, specialisation, and knowledge of habitat. It occurred within 'nuclear zones' where potential domesticates were available. He proposed a series of cultural levels: a food-gathering era with free-wandering hunting, at first with non-standardised, then with standardised tools; a food-gathering era with restricted wandering, hunting and some variation in standardised tool form within regions; then a food-collecting era with selective hunting and seasonal collecting with still more regional variation in tool forms; which developed into an intensified hunting and collecting, season-bound economy. In certain 'very specialised environments' this specialised food-collecting became so highly adapted that it allowed semi-permanent or permanent settlement. Finally the food-producing stage was reached: first, incipient cultivation within the zone of potential domesticates and then primary village-farming communities (Braidwood 1960).

There is nothing wrong with trying to formalise a series of socio-economic levels. Though the Victorian concept of evolutionary 'progress' is no longer acceptable, cultural evolution is still respectable – evolution in terms of increased complexity. 'Cultures have become cumulatively more efficient in their role of enabling the hominid species to survive, multiply and spread across the globe' (Clarke 1968, 87). In *Man and Nature* (1969) Patty Jo Watson and Richard Watson enlarge on Braidwood's levels, though in more detail and couched in more testable propositions.

The drawback to Braidwood's model is that he fails to distinguish between a description of regularities and cause-and-effect. The Watsons (1969, 5) carefully avoided this pitfall by stating that they were describing regularities of behaviour exhibited in nature, without considering cause-and-effect. Braidwood, however, brought in cause. He suggested that the process of change was inherent in human nature. The transition did not happen earlier because 'culture was not ready to receive it' (Braidwood and Willey 1962, 342), and 'the multiple occurrence of the agricultural revolution suggests that it was the highly probable outcome of the prior evolution of man and a peculiar combination of environmental circumstances'. But 'inherent human nature' is an untestable proposition. Binford (1968b) points out trenchantly: 'Vitalism, whether expressed in terms of inherent forces orientating the direction of organic evolution or in its more anthropocentric form of emergent human properties which direct cultural evolution is unacceptable as an explanation. Trends which are observed in cultural evolution require explanation; they are certainly not explained by postulating emergent human traits which are said to account for trends.'

THE SYSTEMIC APPROACH

Inherent in Braidwood's model, explicit in the Watsons' and basic to most recent models – whether they are attempting to explain cultural regularities or cultural change – is a systemic approach. Culture is viewed not so much as 'an assemblage of the same types that recurs at several distinct sites' (Childe 1956, 17) but rather as an adaptive system. The artefacts and modes of social organisation are seen as essential tools for dealing with environmental situations – both biological and cultural (Hole 1973). Culture comprises a series of inter-acting or articulated parts (sub-systems) which include the effective environment – that perceived and used by the human group under discussion[9] – economic activities, technology, social organisation, and religious beliefs. All of which act like a web of rubber-bands – pull one and all the others respond.

CYBERNETICS PRINCIPLES

General systems theory consists of a series of laws and methods to help investigate all types of physical, biological and cultural systems. One such law has been invoked to investigate how change occurs within the system. This is the first and second principle of cybernetics (Watson, LeBlanc and Redman 1971, 73).

The first principle is 'negative feed-back' – processes which promote stability in a system and counteract deviation over long periods of time (Flannery 1968). Thus, where the sub-systems are sufficiently elastic, any slight alteration in one of them will be counteracted by slight adjustments in the others. The system remains in equilibrium in the sense of a 'moving equilibrium whose over-all state is changing continuously along a trajectory at every point of which certain energy potentials are minimal' (Clarke 1968, 50). The last point in this quotation is a reference to the Law of Least Effort which assumes that societies attempt to obtain the maximum return for the minimum effort. This is obviously a relative concept: different societies construe 'Least Effort' in different ways, though in most cases minimisation of risk will play an important part.

But how then does major change come about? What makes the course of the trajectory alter? The second principle is 'positive feed-back' – processes that amplify deviation and cause the sub-systems to expand. This positive feed-back may begin as an insignificant or accidental kick. But what often happens is that because the sub-systems interact, innovation in one triggers off innovation in another. Changes in the sub-systems may go full circle and 'the multiplier effect is said to operate when [these] induced changes in one or more sub-systems themselves act so as to enhance the original changes in the first sub-system' (Renfrew 1972, 36). Positive

9 The food supply, for example, is not a matter of potential food-resources, not even of food-resources exploitable at a given technological level, but is primarily preferred exploitable resources (Lee 1968).

feed-back and the multiplier effect ultimately produce over-all changes in the structure of the society.

Flannery (1968) used these cybernetic principles to explain the transition to farming in the southern uplands of Mexico. He concentrated on a series of procurement systems – ways by which plant and animal resources were obtained. Each system was a component of the total eco-system. The 'negative feed-back', operating to ensure equilibrium, was partly imposed by nature, in that the plants ripened at different times and in different ecological niches and necessitated a seasonal procurement round, and partly by man, in that possible conflicts between the procurement systems were resolved by scheduling, i.e. by making a choice as to the form the seasonal round should take. Flannery considered that five major procurement systems were in operation, three plant and two animal. Seasonality and scheduling regulated which resources would be used at which time of year, regulated where the groups would be at any time of year and regulated the size of the groups at particular times of year. By and large the seasonality and scheduling militated against the intensification of one procurement system at the expense of the others. It resulted in a long-term *status quo* based on a 'broad spectrum' resource utilisation.

But then the second cybernetics principle came into play: the accidental kick. These human groups could have incorporated occasional cultivation into their cycle – a little weeding, or a little transplanting in order to increase the area in which a particular plant grew. The over-all equilibrium need not have been affected. But one of the cultigens had extraordinary genetic potential and responded vigorously to cultivation. The equilibrium was in danger. Wild maize (or teosinte) was a totally insignificant component of an insignificant grass-seed procurement system but it provided the initial kick in the positive feed-back loop. At first slowly, then, as hybridisation occurred, with astonishing speed, it increased in size and yield. When combined with beans, which rectified an amino-acid imbalance, and with squash, it had enormous subsistence potential. But the development of this procurement system conflicted with the old seasonal round. Eventually the procurement patterns altered and as the yield increased and the population expanded, there was no going back, the trajectory changed and then adjusted at a new state.

ECO-SYSTEM MODELS

The eco-system model is a particular type of systems model. The attention is focused on the inter-relationship between human organisms and their environment, on 'an idea of reciprocity, of a dialogue between cultures and their environments' (Sahlins 1964, 132). This ecological approach is frequently used. It has its limitations. It tends to lose sight of non-material aspects of the system. In South-west Asia, for example, the domestication of the large wild cattle was perhaps initially not undertaken for economic reasons. They may have been kept for religious or sacrificial purposes (Isaac 1970, 10). At Çatal Hüyük in Anatolia the lowest excavated levels contained evidence of a great bull cult and of domesticated cattle. It may well be that in the lower, unexplored levels there is evidence that the cult preceded domestication. Even though such a 'non-economic' explanation operates within the total cultural system it might easily be overlooked in an ecologically orientated hypothesis.

TECHNICAL LEVEL AND 'BROAD-SPECTRUM' ECONOMY

When Flannery uses eco-system models to explain developments in Mexico and South-west Asia he incorporates at least three explicit or implicit hypotheses – all of which are widely accepted (Flannery 1969).

The first is that the transition to food-production only occurs when potential domesticates are present. This underlies virtually all models. Not only *where* domestication occurs but *what* is domesticated will depend on the potential resources available. (*What* and *where* are dealt with in chapter 5.)

The second, often only implied, is that the level of technical competence must be sufficient for a systematic and intensive utilisation of resources. Technology includes not only tools and associated techniques but also 'a flexible repertoire of skills, knowledge and methods for attaining desired ends and avoiding failure under varying circumstances' (Merrill cited by Harris 1972). In some cases the technology may involve potential 'pre-adaptations' to agriculture, such as compound tools, grinding equipment or storage facilities.

The third is that there must be a 'broad spectrum' economy whereby a combination of technical ability and environmental availability allows a wide variety of resources to be tapped. This broad spectrum economy figures in many other models: Braidwood's South-west Asian 'food-collectors' and 'incipient cultivators' operate within such a system. Sauer's insistence that his originating centres must have a wide range of plant and animal resources points in the same direction. Recent work in Thailand again suggests that a broad spectrum economy lies behind the emergence of horticulture (Gorman 1971, see Appendix A).

This broad spectrum economy is considered important because it presupposes an intimate knowledge of available plants and animals, a variety of ecological niches to which plants can be transplanted once experimentation has begun, and, usually, a well-defined and regionally circumscribed seasonal round. The seasonal round allows contact between groups. In particularly favourable situations (for example, where a variety of ecological zones are closely packed together) semi-permanent or even permanent settlements will be possible. In general the system will be stable, for the failure of one resource will be counteracted by slight adjustments in the procurement system. However, sometimes a broad spectrum economy will result in near-optimal exploitation and then, since there is no large risk margin, the system will be delicately poised, and will be very susceptible to pressures, and perhaps to innovations. Finally, within the wide range of available resources there may lurk plants or animals which have a genetic potential for high yields. These may provide the initial 'kick' leading to specialisation and domestication.

Both the second and the third hypotheses need more testing before one can be sure that they are universal pre-requisites. They may hold for seed-crop cultivation, but what about root-crops? Despite Gorman's work in Thailand far too little is known about the conditions under which root-crop cultivation emerged.

The situation is even less clear where animal domestication is concerned. There are many man–animal relationships and it is often not meaningful to draw lines between loose herding, game culling, taming, restraint and selective breeding. For most of these practices the skill of the trained hunter would seem to be the only technical competence necessary. It may, however, be true that domestication – in terms of close control and breeding – is more frequently associated with broad spectrum economies and is most viable when practised in conjunction with plant cultivation. The large number of resources reduces the risk and there will be little need for mobility. In contrast, where there is a 'specialised' economy, with only a limited number of resources, exploitation will be intensive rather than extensive, and the risk, should the staple fail, will be high. In such circumstances mobility may be important and where migrating herds are the economic mainstay, a loose herding system rather than a system involving close contact (and breeding) may be preferable (Sturdy 1972). A great deal more data is needed on the conditions favouring different kinds of animal exploitation – including domestication.

ENVIRONMENTAL POTENTIAL

Harris (1969) has formulated a predictive model to assess the potential environments within which broad spectrum and 'specialised' economies are likely to function. It is a case of 'environmental possibilism' rather than 'determinism'. Specialised hunters, involved in the intensive exploitation of a limited number of species, will occupy specialised natural eco-systems where there is a low plant and animal diversity but a large number of each species. The broad spectrum economies will occur within generalised natural eco-systems where there is a large variety of plant and animal species, each represented by a small number of individuals. The latter are particularly associated with transitional zones, between forest or woodland and steppe, savanna, river or coast or on the margins between upland and lowland – whether simply small intermontane basins or major physiographic units.

Within such transitional zones, Harris tries to pin-point potential areas of seed- and root-crop cultivation. Many seed- and root-crops have in common that they are adapted to climates with well-marked seasons – 'In so far as they provide concentrated food-resources in the form of seeds, fruits or enlarged roots or stems, man is in effect exploiting a range of adaptations which enable the plants to survive periods in which growth is curtailed by drought or cold' (Harris 1971). Some seed-crops, for example wheats and barley, are adapted to the arid sub-tropics; others, including maize, rice, millet and sorghum as well as non-cereal crops such as cucurbits and some beans, are adapted to tropical regions with a long dry season (five to seven-and-a-half months), where the deciduous woodland, savanna or xerophytic shrub vegetation provides an open canopy. Though there are root-crops which are remarkably drought resistant, on the whole lowland root-crop cultivation is better adapted to a shorter dry season (two-and-a half to five months), and to the light tree canopy provided by the semi-evergreen or deciduous forests (Harris 1973).

Another environmental model, site catchment analysis, attempts, as the name suggests, to assess the potential resource exploitation from a given site. It is based on the idea that the area exploited can be construed in terms of 'work distance'. For example, with hunting or loose herding (on foot) a two-hour range from the site is feasible, for early farming (again, without wheeled transport) probably one hour (Jarman 1972a). This concept allows a very detailed analysis of site potential which can then be re-defined in terms of technical ability and cultural food preferences. When it becomes clear that a site territory could not provide resources for the whole year, one can look for sites with complementary catchment areas and thus arrive at an *annual* territory. Since different resources will be exploited at different sites within the annual territory the artefact assemblages may differ. An understanding of the seasonal inter-connections between sites may therefore lead to the elimination of some previously postulated 'cultures'. There are difficulties in applying site-catchment analysis. One is that environmental resources may have altered during the last several thousand years. Another is the problem of knowing how representative the sample is. A third is that there is no guarantee that two sites belonging to the same cultural tradition were actually occupied at the same time.

A third model attempts to study the processes of choice and decision that may occur if the environment changes. This decision-making model is called 'game theory'. It introduces again the Law of Least Effort (p. 27), the assumption that 'the best general rule to the behaviour of primitive farmers is that they work to get the maximum return for the minimum effort' (Nye and Greenland cited in Coe 1969). The maximum return must be construed in terms of the most adverse conditions – the leanest seasons or worst years. By considering a system at a particular time and in relationship to its past trajectory one can try to simulate the changes in the economic system that would result from changes in the environment. It 'may well prove possible to "game" the optimal or least-risk schedule of resource exploitations within the annual routine of a hunter-fisher-gatherer band or its "best moves" through a series of environmental changes' (Clarke 1972a).

DEMOGRAPHIC MODELS

Having considered hypotheses about the sort of conditions under which the transition to food-production might occur, and the dynamics – using the cybernetic principles – of how the change might come about, there is still at least one unanswered problem. *Why*, once 'positive feed-back' had arisen, was it allowed to continue? Why did the multiplier effect come into play? We can accept that food-production is a more intensive form of exploitation; as such it probably involves a *per capita* increase in labour. Thus, according to the Law of Least Effort, it will not be undertaken except under pressure. Following this line of argument Meyers (1971) suggests that only when the entire system is under pressure will it be predisposed to change so that 'positive feed-back' can operate.

Lewis Binford (1968b) formulates a model incorporating such

pressures. He suggests, using modern ethnographic parallels, that where the environment and population are stable, population growth and food resources remain in equilibrium well below the carrying capacity of the region. Through a system of 'negative feed-backs', pressures and the need for change are avoided and the population remains well above starvation level. Pressures allowing positive feed-back to operate only arise when either the environment or the demography alter.

Binford concentrates on the demographic rather than the environmental pressures. Such pressures must not, as Smith (1972) points out, be equated with over-all population size, not even with population density, but with density 'in relation to the carrying capacity of the area concerned. In simpler societies at least, it is the number of people per square meal rather than per square mile.'

Binford differentiates between *internal* and *external* demographic pressures. Internal pressure is likely to occur in optimal areas where food procurement is almost too successful and permits a large growth in population. It is likely to be rectified either by some form of artificial control or by emigration. Either way the equilibrium within the area is maintained. But emigration into more marginal areas already occupied by less sedentary groups will result in *external* demographic pressure. The resultant stress may be relieved by a drastic reduction in the birth rate/life expectancy leading to a decline in population. Or else by change, in terms of more intensive exploitation of available foodstuffs to maintain the increased population. Such external demographic pressures would be recurrent and would provide an explanation for successive adaptations.

Binford uses the shift from hunting and gathering to food-production to illustrate his hypothesis. He postulates adaptations in optimal areas leading to an increased reliance on aquatic resources – fish, molluscs and migratory fowl. These adaptations required the development of food storage facilities 'linked to the highly seasonal nature of migratory fowl and anadromous fish' (Binford 1968b). Utilising resources within a small geographical area and using stored resources to counteract lean seasons it was no longer necessary to move around. Groups could become sedentary, there was then no selective advantage in widely spaced births and the population could increase. The resultant population pressure was relieved by migration to neighbouring regions which, though more marginal and therefore inhabited by more mobile groups, were the natural habitat of potential domesticates. Here the immigration upset the existing balance, threatening to take the population above the carrying capacity. The result, in some cases, was a shift to a more intensive exploitation of available resources – including domestication.

This model, as Binford stresses, still needs a lot of testing. Right at the beginning there is an inherent problem: why did the human groups begin to depend on aquatic resources? Renfrew (1972, 480) sagely remarks: 'In such explanations there is often opportunity to wonder what caused the cause.' Binford (1968b) says rather vaguely 'this shift [was] probably linked to world-wide changes in sea-level' – implying that this created 'new' favourable micro-environments. But quite apart from introducing an environmental factor to account for demographic pressures, such conditions would hardly be novel – sea-levels have changed time and time again.

One may question why, if there was a threat of population pressure in an optimal area, it was not counteracted by artificial control or by intensification of production. Why was migration the most viable solution? Must some other variable be included?

Accepting migration as a solution, is there any evidence of optimal areas with sedentary folk adjacent to marginal areas in which the initial domestication began? Binford mentions coastal groups in Meso-America but they were few and far between at the time that the first attempts at plant manipulation occurred in the highland valleys and, as Meyers (1971) points out, the adjustments necessary to allow tropical coastal people to adapt to the semi-arid inland valleys would have been enormous. Perhaps Binford's concept of an optimal environment is too limited. It has been suggested that near-optimal exploitation may occur in a variety of generalised natural eco-systems, so long as one or more 'gregarious' staples are present. These may be aquatic resources, herd animals or 'gregarious' plants such as cereals (Clarke 1968, 335). Flannery (1969) proposed the oak-pistachio and mixed oak woodlands of South-west Asia as optimal areas. He considered that cultivation was an attempt to produce artificially 'around the margins of the *optimum* zone, stands of cereals as dense as those in the *heart* of the optimum zone'. (This again brings in an environmental factor, for the oak-pistachio woodlands undoubtedly expanded in Post-Pleistocene times.)

If there are such adjacent optimal/marginal areas, is there evidence of cultural encroachment from one area into another? Or of population pressure? Or of an imbalance of resources?

Finally, even if all these conditions existed, why, again, was the response in terms of increased productivity (involving more work) rather than of artificial control?

Meyers (1971) comes up with an alternative demographic model which has the virtue of economy and gets round the necessity for neighbouring optimal/marginal zones and of migration from one to the other. He accepts Binford's postulate that in an optimal area successful adaptation is likely to lead to a rise in population. This, if left unremedied, would threaten to exceed the carrying capacity of the area. Binford considered the threat would be alleviated either by cultural control or, more probably, by emigration. But Binford was basing his assumptions on ethnographic examples primarily from *marginal* areas with little potential for adaptation. What would happen in an *optimal* area where the potential for adaptation was present but the possibility of emigration was removed or reduced? Where, for example, the surrounding areas were already populated by similar groups? Since the population pressure could not be adjusted by emigration the alternatives would be artificial control or adaptation leading to more intensive exploitation. If potential domesticates were present, the exploitation could take the form of plant or animal manipulation. So *internal* pressures in an *optimal* zone could lead to the same result as Binford's *external* pressure in a *marginal* zone. Meyers considers that the upland valleys of central Mexico constitute optimal areas. Similar groups inhabited the surrounding valleys and 'the presence of high mountain walls and tropical jungles at the exit of the valley[s] into the coastal plain[s] would tend to restrict emigration as a solution to the demographic problem' (Sanders and Price 1968, 109). So population pressure leads to internal adaptation; the society is thereby predisposed to change and positive feed-back may not be counteracted. Meyers does not bring in any environmental factors – but here again the demographic pressure may go hand-in-hand with Post-Pleistocene environmental changes (MacNeish 1971).

This model, like Binford's, needs more testing. Can the semi-arid valleys of central Mexico really be considered optimal environments? Is there evidence of population pressure or of food resource imbalance?

Like Binford, Meyers neglects the possibility that population pressure within an optimal area could lead to more intensive exploitation even when the alternatives of cultural control or migration were available (Bronsen 1972).

This possibility is brought out in a third variant of the demographic model. Smith and Young (1972), in discussing the development of food-production in South-west Asia, suggest that despite population pressure there would be a reluctance to move away from optimal areas: 'Through sedentism man had, in the meantime, developed certain new social and economic patterns that had become cultural norms. We might expect a reluctance to deviate from these norms. . . . Under cumulative pressures resulting from the inter-action of his social, economic and environmental circumstances, all influenced by increased population densities, he gradually began more and more to manipulate the plants and animals with which he was now so familiar.'

A lot of explanations have been examined. Some have been rejected, many have been left with question marks. Further evaluation will have to wait until the evidence has been assembled in the next chapters. Even then there will be no final answer: ' "Truth" is just the best current hypothesis and . . . whatever [we] . . . believe now will ultimately be proved wrong' (Flannery 1967b).

3   The Recognition of Domestication

Between the time a site is abandoned and the time that it is excavated, sometimes thousands of years later, a great deal of the evidence disappears. Unless conditions of preservation are particularly favourable, either very wet, very dry or very cold, most of the organic matter (plant remains, fur, meat, hides and wooden objects) will decay. Gordon Childe (1956, 10) likened the situation to a fat mail-order catalogue covering a great quantity of material goods from which all the pages featuring perishable objects are torn out. A very slim volume remains.

What then can the archaeologist find that will show that plant or animal domestication is under way? How can he tell that a hunting-gathering economy is being supplemented or superseded by cultivation or herding?

Three main groups of remains may yield information: man-made, animal and plant.

MAN-MADE REMAINS

It would be quite reasonable to consider many domesticated plants as 'man-made'. Maize, for example, and many root-crops have been tampered with to such an extent that they can no longer reproduce without human intervention. But in this chapter the term is restricted to inanimate creations, whether immovable, like houses or pens, storage pits or parching ovens, or movable, mainly equipment.

Rather surprisingly, in view of the potential range, there is no one artefact that immediately demonstrates that domestication has begun. Some, however, when found together, make it very probable.

(1) PERMANENT SETTLEMENT AND POTTERY

Permanent settlement used to be considered synonymous with

farming. But in the introduction (p. 7) this was shown to be untrue. It simply indicates a fairly sedentary life-style and a reasonable supply of plant and animal resources within easy range. At Eynan in the Upper Jordan valley a settlement with fifty houses was based entirely on the exploitation of local wild resources. In contrast, in the Tehuacán valley of Mexico, where resources were scattered, cultivation was incorporated within the seasonal round and even after 3000 years of plant cultivation there was not a single permanent settlement. These examples do not invalidate the proposition that eventually farming came to underwrite a sedentary life on a scale inconceivable with only a hunter-gatherer economy. It is simply that at the transition to food-production, settlement is not a sensitive indicator.

The same is true of pottery. Being heavy and fragile it is generally associated with sedentary communities. But, again, they need not be farming communities. In Japan the pre-Jomon hunter-fisher-gatherers made pottery over 12,000 years ago, 8000 years before the introduction of farming to the island (Chard 1972). Nor do all sedentary farmers make pottery. There is no pottery associated with the earliest farming settlements in South-west Asia.

Pottery, like settlement, is not a reliable indicator of the economic transition. It only gradually becomes associated with food-production and village life and is then invented and re-invented over and over again at different times and places.

(2) MAN-MADE EVIDENCE OF ANIMAL MANIPULATION

Primitive herd manipulation does not require specialised equipment. Where animals are constrained there may be traces of compounds or stalls. However, in order to prove the function of such buildings non-artefactual remains such as dung, fly pupae or fodder usually have to be present.

The presence of milk or cheese strainers would be good evidence that herds were kept; but non-perishable strainers are usually made of pottery, and pottery often only appears some time after herding has begun.

(3) MAN-MADE EVIDENCE OF PLANT CULTIVATION

There is more potential evidence for plant cultivation but it is rarely totally definitive.

Storage pits are frequently found within settlements. But what was stored? It could have been wild seeds or nuts. One can excavate clay-lined pits, perhaps filled with ash, and they may have been used for parching primitive cultivated grains in order to separate the seed from the glume, but again, one needs to find the grain in order to be certain. And even that may not solve the problem, for at the small tell of Mureybit in southern Syria there were a series of well-made, clay-lined, ash-filled pits containing grain. Morphologically the grain was wild, but it may be that cultivation had not been under way long enough for genetic change to occur.

Unlike herding, most forms of plant cultivation require fairly specialised tools such as digging-sticks, sickles, mortars and pestles, querns and grinding stones. But none are essential and all may be used by non-farming groups. Digging-sticks may be used for root-grubbing. Sickles – usually stone insets in a bone or wooden haft – may be used for gathering wild grasses or reeds. A silica gloss, often found on the stone insets, may result from cutting gramineous wild plants or reeds. A mortar and pestle or quern and grinding stone may be used to crush cultivated or wild grain, to pound acorns, to grind pigment or even to pulp meat.

Ground and polished axes are sometimes thought to indicate farming activity, the need to clear the undergrowth and scrub and to break up the soil. But though a ground stone axe may be more efficient than a chipped one it is not essential for agriculture. Often the clearance would have been done by burning. Ground stone axes may be found in non-farming contexts – for example, in Australia 20,000 years ago (Golson 1972).

It may sometimes be possible to distinguish the function of tools by examining the wear-patterns of the working-edge under a microscope. This may show what sort of substance the tool was used on; whether for example a stone celt was used for chopping down trees or had been pushed through the earth. This is a relatively recent approach, with considerable potential.

There are specialised pottery forms associated with the processing of cultivated plants. In tropical South America bitter manioc bread is made on special pottery griddles. But, like the cheese-strainers, they may be a fairly late innovation (Appendix A, p. 228).

ANIMAL REMAINS

Most of the evidence of animal manipulation comes directly from a study of the bones. Occasionally there may be other, more indirect evidence. Dung, fly pupae or fodder found inside a man-made enclosure probably indicates herding activities. Where the dung is found inside a cave, even alongside man-made artefacts, its significance is more dubious. Llama dung found in the Ayacucho cave of upland Peru may be from herded animals or might be wild animal dung brought in for fuel. So too, the dung sometimes found in mudbricks may be from wild animals.

Occasionally animal remains indicate activities other than animal manipulation. Concentrations of rodent bones or insect remains may suggest grain storage – though not necessarily of cultivated grains. Some molluscs favour cultivated fields; some insects even indicate specific crops.

Bones are the main source of information on animal manipulation. The initial problem is to define the type of manipulation one is looking for. In the first chapter animal domestication was defined as manipulation that resulted in genetic change. It was left open whether these changes were 'accidental' results of herding and constraint or were due to selective breeding. Recently Higgs and Jarman (1972) have distinguished between animal husbandry 'where some form of intentional conservation was practised' and domestication 'where intentional, purposeful breeding can be demonstrated'. By this definition early sheep and goat herding in South-west Asia would almost certainly be regarded as a form of animal husbandry. But the categories are not water-tight. The primary aim may have been the conservation of the meat supply but it is highly probable that herd culling was practised from an early date in order, among other reasons, to improve the stock. Since no hard-and-fast line can be drawn, a rather arbitrary definition will be employed. The emphasis will be on evidence of animal manipulation that takes the form of fairly close control, i.e. herd constraint, in association with some degree of selective breeding. Thus any morphological or osteological changes may either be the effect of constraint or of breeding.

The problems associated with actually extracting the bones from the soil and obtaining a reasonable sample have been recently analysed by Payne and Uerpmann (Payne 1972a, 1972b; Uerpmann 1973). Here we will concentrate on interpreting the evidence after it has been extracted.

(1) Changes in animal size

Domestication frequently affects the perishable parts of animals; there may be changes in meat weight, in wool or hair structure or in the enlargement of udders. All these are lost to the archaeologist. Attention therefore has concentrated on changes in bone structure.

Much evidence has been carefully accumulated in the last decade, and most of it has been sharply criticised in a paper by Jarman and Wilkinson (1972).

One assumption has been that domestication initially leads to a decrease in size. Various explanations have been given for this. It could reflect the genetic isolation that occurs if animals are segregated from the rest of their species. It has been found that when an animal species – wild or domesticated – is isolated on an island, thus curtailing the gene flow, one of the effects, on all but the smallest species, is a decrease in size (Berry 1969). However, it is not clear whether these insular developments are solely a matter of isolation or whether they are also a reflection of environmental pressure. For at Chillingham in England, where White Park cattle have been bred in isolation for 700 years there seems to have been no change in size. It would also seem that there is considerable constraint on inter-breeding between wild populations even when there are no physical barriers. When wild mouflon were introduced to the island of Lambay in Co. Dublin, there was no inter-breeding with the local domesticated sheep, despite freedom of access, over a period of twenty years (Jarman and Wilkinson 1972).

Size decrease could also result from malnutrition or from over-crowding if animals were penned or their grazing were restricted. Or it may be that smaller animals were selected because they were more docile – though docility seems to be more a matter of behavioural adaptation than of size (Jarman and Wilkinson 1972).

Or the decrease in size may have a more purposeful economic motive. It may have been advantageous, under primitive conditions, to keep many smaller animals in order to get a reasonable number through the lean season rather than fewer, larger animals which would be less likely to survive (Jarman and Wilkinson 1972). In what sounds like a riddle Higham (1967) has noted that the same amount of hay keeps seven cows for two years or three cows for two and a half years and that seven cows kept for two years give 40% more meat.

Even if we accept that for one reason or another primitive domestication often leads to a decrease in size, there still remains the problem of distinguishing between decrease due to domestication and decrease due to other causes. Differences in bone size may also be a reflection of the age or sex of the animal. In wild animals there is often considerable sexual dimorphism and the males are much larger than the females. Size also varies with latitude. Bergmann's Law formulates that animals in colder latitudes are larger than those in warm ones. North-west European wild cattle are larger than those of South-west Asia. It is therefore totally misleading to compare cattle bones from the two areas and then conclude that because the latter are smaller they are domesticated. Environmental change within a region may also affect the size, though not necessarily in a uniform way. In post-glacial Europe bears and wild cats decreased in size, badgers increased and foxes remained the same (Payne 1972b). It is essential that any comparisons be made with a representative sample of the wild species from the same area and the same period. Such comparative material is hard to find.

(2) Increased variability

There may be an increase in variability in domesticated stock. This may be due to genetic isolation (Herre 1969) or be correlated with the increased docility of domesticated animals (Belyaev 1969). Since variability is hard to quantify and as there is considerable variability in wild populations it is not a particularly useful criterion.

(3) Bone formation

If animals – wild or domesticated – suffer from malnutrition the density of the bones may decrease. X-rays of Scottish hill sheep grazing on inadequate pasture show a thinning of the cortex and rarefaction of the cancellous bone, particularly in the skull, jaw and cervical vertebrae (Brothwell, Molleson, Gray and Harcourt 1969). Domestication may affect the crystalline structure of the bones. Recent experiments seem to demonstrate that in wild animals the crystals are unaligned, while in domesticated animals they are aligned both perpendicular to the joints and in a radial fashion. It is this alignment that gives the bones their characteristically greasy feel. The alignments show up when polarised light is passed through thin slices of bone. Where they are aligned, a rotation of 90° changes the colour of the observed light quite dramatically to bright yellow and blue. When unaligned, no changes are seen (Drew, Perkins and Daly 1971). Why such changes occur and whether they occur under all conditions of domestication has not yet been established.

The main problem with all morphological and osteological changes is that it takes time for them to occur. The length of time depends on whether a simple genetic mutation requiring only a few generations is involved, or whether it is a more complex mutation taking much longer. It will also depend on the life-span of the various species and the degree of selective pressure. Pigs running semi-wild in the woods will continue to resemble their wild ancestors long after special breeds of the more closely herded sheep or cattle have emerged (Chaplin 1969). This means that none of the changes so far mentioned will indicate initial attempts at herding and breeding.

(4) PHYSICAL CHANGES IN SELECTED SPECIES

Bearing in mind all these caveats, we may still examine morphological and osteological changes in certain species. Only those animals that formed part of the early farming complex of South-west Asia will be considered. In the Mexican centres no animals were domesticated, and though the llama and guinea pig were domesticated in Peru, no one seems to know, or at least to publish, much about what captivity does to a llama or a guinea pig.

(a) Sheep and goat

Sheep and goat are the earliest domesticates to show morphological changes. It is quite possible that gazelle were herded as early or even earlier but there were no associated changes in physique (Legge 1972b).

The first problem is that 'As the Old Testament suggests, it is not always easy to separate the sheep from the goat' (Hole, Flannery and Neely 1969, 267). There are relatively few diagnostic features. The bones of the feet, particularly the first and third phalanges and the distal metapodial, provide the most reliable criteria (Payne 1969; Ducos 1969; Hole, Flannery and Neely 1969, 267). Skulls and horns, particularly of the males, are also diagnostic. Rams have skulls that are elongated and bent over towards the rear and have heavy, almost solid horns, while goat skulls are short and straight in the rear and the horns are long but relatively light (Reed and Schaffer 1972). These differences are connected with the combat behaviour of the two species: goats stand and clash horns, sheep charge at full run. If goats behaved like sheep they would 'snap their horns, addle their brains and possibly crush their skulls' (Reed and Schaffer 1972).

The goat, *Capra hircus*, is thought to descend from the Persian bezoar, *Capra aegagrus*. With herding and breeding the animal becomes much smaller and the large scimitar-shaped horns are gradually reduced to a small upright form (Murray 1969). The archaeologist rarely finds the outer cover of the horn. He works with the inner, bony core. The cross-section of a wild goat core tends to be quadrangular, but an early mutation results in the flattening of the medial surface so that, in section, it first becomes triangular or almond-shaped and later becomes plano-convex. Perhaps a little later still the horns tend to become twisted (Hole, Flannery and Neely 1969, 277).

There have been attempts to detect changes in other parts of the anatomy, particularly the vertebrae and pelvis (Boessneck 1969), but with the considerable variation in primitive stock these are often hard to establish.

The sheep, *Ovis aries*, probably derives from the urial, *Ovis orientalis*, though the mouflon, *Ovis musimon* ssp., may have played some part in its ancestry (but see p. 103). Wild sheep are hairy, and the sheep would at first have been kept for meat or perhaps milk, not for wool. Selection for woolliness takes time, for alterations in two types of skin follicles are involved, the primary follicles producing the hair and the secondary follicles producing the wool fibre (Reed 1960).

It has been suggested that an early mutation in some herded populations resulted in the female losing her horns (Flannery 1965). This assumption was questioned when a hornless female skull was found among a wild sheep population at Suberde in Anatolia (Perkins and Daly 1968). However, it has also been queried whether the Suberde sheep really were wild!

(b) Cattle

The ancestor of the South-west Asian domesticated cow, *Bos taurus*, is the aurochs, *Bos primigenius*, a huge beast which sometimes stood five feet at the withers, had horns three feet long and weighed a ton. A smaller wild version, with shorter horns, once believed to represent another wild species, *Bos longifrons* or *Bos brachyceros*, is now usually thought to be the smaller female aurochs.

The main difference between *Bos taurus* and the wild aurochs is one of size. This is difficult to quantify. Too often the South-west Asian *Bos taurus* has been compared with the north-west European *Bos primigenius* but, as mentioned above, this makes no allowance for Bergmann's Law. There may also have been a post-glacial decline in the size of the South-west Asian aurochs. Add to this the problem of considerable sexual dimorphism and it becomes clear that precise differentiation between domesticated and wild cattle requires a substantial collection of local, contemporary fauna (Grigson 1969).

The post-domestication decrease in size is presumably due to malnutrition and indeed the bone structure shows, more than in the other species, a considerable decrease in density.

Though the shape of the skull remains virtually unchanged, the muscle ridges are weaker. The joint facets become less well defined and there is a reduction in the number of tail-vertebrae (Berry 1969) – though the chances of finding an intact tail and being able to count all the vertebrae are not large!

(c) *Pig*

The domesticated pig, *Sus scrofa*, of which several sub-species are known, probably derives from a similar variety of wild sub-species. It may well have been independently domesticated in many areas. The South-west Asian pig is very similar to the South-east Asian wild boar, *Sus vitattus*.

One of the early effects of domestication is a foreshortening of the tusks and jaw resulting in a shorter snout and smaller teeth (Murray 1971). In particular, the late-developing teeth, the third molar and to a lesser extent the second, become much shorter (Reed 1961). There is also a slight over-all decrease in size, and, as in cattle, the joint facets are poorly defined and the tail vertebrae reduced.

(d) *Dog*

It is generally agreed on both anatomical and behavioural grounds that the domesticated dog, *Canis familiaris*, is descended from the wolf. In South-west Asia its ancestor is the small Asiatic wolf, *Canis lupus L.*, which, from the Palestinian cave evidence, seems to have become considerably smaller in the post-glacial period. As with the pig, the jaw becomes shorter and the teeth smaller and more crowded – though it must be admitted that not too much is known about teeth-crowding in post-glacial wolves. Since the jaw width remains the same, the foreshortening results in a blunter muzzle (Clutton-Brock 1969).

(5) CHANGES IN AGE/SEX STRUCTURE

By establishing the degree of eruption and amount of wear on the teeth, the state of the skull sutures, the degree of antler development (where applicable) and the degree of bone fusion, one can estimate the age of an animal fairly accurately (Chaplin 1971, 76; Uerpmann 1973). There is still not enough information on precisely *when* various bones in the different species fuse but, for example, the first and second phalanges and the distal metapodia fuse relatively late. More specifically, three stages of bone fusion have been

recognised for the pig. Some bones fuse at one year, some at two
and some at three and a half (Uerpmann 1973).

The sex of the animal is determined primarily by differences in
size and by morphological differences. In pigs the development of
the canine is sexually determined. In ruminants horn cores, pelvic
bones and metapodia can be sexed. Pelvic bones provide the most
reliable information. Metapodia are difficult to work with and horn
cores are differentially preserved. For example, female goats have
harder and more resistant horn cores than males and will be over-
represented, while female sheep often lack horns and have lighter
frontal bones than the males and will therefore be under-
represented. With cattle, castration affects the sexual determination
of the horn cores (Uerpmann 1973).

Using all the available information it should be possible to
establish the approximate ratios of young/old and male/female in a
sample. Changes in the ratios will be due to selection, natural or
human, and, since no genetic mutations are involved, the changes
will quickly become apparent. This means one can focus more sharply
on any shifts in the pattern of animal manipulation. In South-west
Asia, for example, age/sex differences, probably marking the transition to herding, show up in samples dating between 8500 and 7000
b.c., whereas morphological or osteological changes are not firmly
indicated until around 6500 b.c. – with the exception, perhaps, of
the hornless female sheep from Ali Kosh, dated 7000 b.c.

The reason why herding is likely to affect the age/sex structure
is that under primitive conditions it is difficult to keep animals
alive through the winter months when food-supplies are short. Moreover, as noted earlier, it is more economic to keep a large number of
animals for a relatively short time than a smaller number for
longer. For one or both reasons, a large proportion of the herd
may be killed off in autumn. Often about half the herd will be
despatched before reaching maturity. There will also be a strong
bias against the males, for the females are more docile and, more
important, need to be kept for breeding. There will therefore be a
considerable difference between the age/sex pattern of a wild population and a herded one.

However, if the purpose is to establish changes in animal manipulation, the comparison is not between herded and wild populations
but between herded and hunted. It is often assumed that a hunted
population will resemble a wild one. Sometimes this may be true.
But sometimes hunting may be very selective. The age/sex pattern
of the hunted population may then either be different from both a
wild or a herded population, or it may be very similar to a herded

pattern. At Nahal Oren in Israel the age structure of the gazelle population found in levels dating from about 12,000 to 8000 years ago falls well within the range of a herded population (Legge 1972b). No morphological changes were recognised and there are no statistics on the sex structure. Is this a case of selective hunting or of loose herding? A more curious example comes from the cave of Shanidar in Iraq. The first human occupants, around 45,000 b.c., were Mousterian hunter-gatherers. The associated sheep or goat bones show a very high percentage of immature animals – statistically no different from the herded population of the neighbouring camp site of Zawi Chemi Shanidar occupied 36,000 years *later*! Around 30,000 b.c., the cave of Shanidar was reoccupied by Baradostian groups and the sheep/goat age pattern reverts to that of a 'normal' hunted or wild sample (Bökönyi 1969). As Payne (1972b) notes: 'Evidence that we would readily accept as showing that the sheep at a Neolithic site were domesticated might as readily be rejected if the site were Mousterian, or the animal gazelle.'

The significance of age/sex changes has therefore to be treated with some caution. But it is probably reasonable to infer herding practices at a site where potential domesticates show a change in the age/sex structure, including an increased percentage of immature stock, while the other species continue to show a more random age distribution. At Ali Kosh in Iran the age curve for both 'wild' and 'potential domesticates' remained similar up to the age of two then diverged significantly with 73% mortality of immature animals among the potential domesticates[1] and only 42% among the wild (Hole, Flannery and Neely 1969, 286).

(6) The conversion of bones to meat

Having established, with a greater or lesser degree of certitude, which bones at a given site are from domesticated animals and which from wild, the next step is to convert these to percentages by species of the total meat diet. A rather primitive method is to add up all the identifiable bones; take the total to represent 100%; then count up the bones of each species and express this as a percentage of the whole (fig. 1, top left). This presupposes that the pattern of bone survival, the number of identifiable skeletal elements and the butchering techniques are all constant for all the species. This is patently not the case. A pig has forty-eight foot bones, a dog fifty-two to fifty-eight, a cow twenty-four and a horse twelve. A wild sheep or

1 The problem of what constitutes a potential domesticate is considered in chapter 5, p. 89.

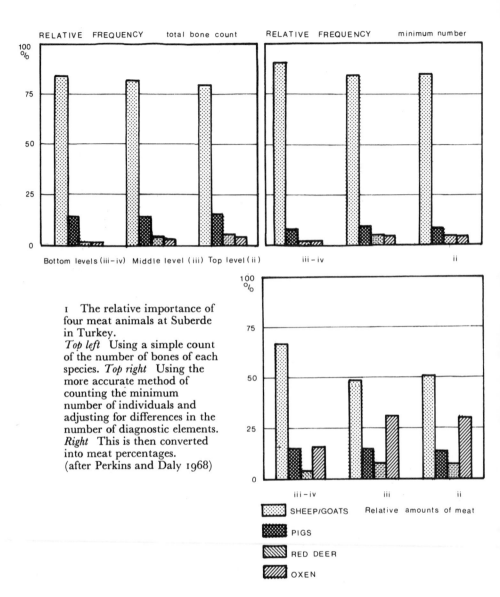

RELATIVE FREQUENCY   total bone count   RELATIVE FREQUENCY   minimum number

Bottom levels (iii–iv) Middle level (iii) Top level (ii)   iii–iv   ii

1 The relative importance of four meat animals at Suberde in Turkey.
Top left Using a simple count of the number of bones of each species. *Top right* Using the more accurate method of counting the minimum number of individuals and adjusting for differences in the number of diagnostic elements. *Right* This is then converted into meat percentages.
(after Perkins and Daly 1968)

SHEEP/GOATS   Relative amounts of meat

PIGS

RED DEER

OXEN

goat killed out hunting will often be brought back intact and all the bones will be present. A wild aurochs, weighing a ton or so, is likely to be butchered on the spot, the leg bones would be cut out and discarded and only the incomplete carcass would be 'schlepped' back to camp. Many other examples could be quoted to show how inaccuracies creep in (Perkins 1969, Perkins and Daly 1968, Higham 1967, Payne 1972b).

A better solution is to work out the minimum number of animals present and express these as percentages. In this case the most abundant diagnostic bone is used, usually the distal end of the tibia (inner lower leg bone). These are separated into left and right, are checked for pairs and are counted (Flannery 1967). For reasonable accuracy at least three hundred bones are needed (Payne 1972b). A further refinement may be added by working out the number of diagnostic elements for each species, counting the number of diagnostic bones and adjusting this figure by multiplying by the reciprocal of the number of diagnostic elements per species (fig. 1, top right) (Perkins and Daly 1968).

More pertinent than the percentage by species is the translation of this bone percentage into meat weight, for this will indicate the economic importance of each species (fig. 1, bottom). The meat weight is roughly half the live weight for long-legged animals, such as sheep, deer, etc., and three-quarters that of short-legged animals such as pig and bear (Daly 1969). Wild sheep or goat are calculated to give about 77 lb. of edible meat, a pig or deer about 220 lb. and an aurochs about 1000 lb. One dead aurochs would therefore be the equivalent of about thirteen sheep or goat, though for the hunter this bounty would be somewhat offset by the difficulties in hunting the animal, getting the carcass home and preserving the excess meat.

Where plant remains are sufficiently well preserved to allow calculations of quantities consumed, as in parts of Mexico and Peru, the meat volume can be expressed in litres and so be directly compared to the volume of plant food (MacNeish 1967, 296). This gives an idea of the relative importance of the different food resources within the total economy. This can be further refined by analysing the nutritional values of the various plants and animals[2] (Flannery 1969; J. Renfrew 1973, 190). One must remember that animals may be kept for reasons other than meat, though it is likely that for early herders meat was the primary objective. Lack of wool would have precluded use for textiles, and animals were not initially used for traction or transportation. Early domesticates would have given only a limited amount of excess milk. Blood, however, may have been consumed as it is among some modern African pastoralists, and some animals may have been kept for ritual purposes.

By such tortuous means does one arrive – sometimes – at a fairly

2 Animals are primarily a source of protein, cereals of carbohydrates and vitamins B and E, pulse crops provide vegetable protein and carbohydrates, oil-seeds provide both oil and protein and many nuts are rich in fats and proteins (J. Renfrew 1973, 190).

accurate idea of the relative importance of different activities: hunting, herding, plant cultivation and gathering (fig. 29).

PLANT REMAINS

(1) Retrieval of evidence

It is a great deal more difficult to get a reasonable sample of the plant diet of early farming communities. Only in bogs, or where the soil is frozen, or in arid or semi-arid regions is preservation good. And in the semi-arid regions – particularly important for the Old and New World centres under review – additional protection usually has to be provided by caves or rock-shelters.

Under such conditions seeds, plant fragments and pollen may be preserved. Sometimes there are quids – masticated plant fibres. Sometimes there are coprolites – faeces – which may show not only what was eaten, but how it was prepared (Callen 1969). For example, in Mexico the early, tiny domesticated maize cobs were often eaten whole. Later on the kernels were taken off the cob and ground into flour. Beans were at first eaten young and green, later on they were eaten soaked when more mature. Pumpkins and squash were first gathered for their seeds and only later for their flesh (MacNeish 1964).

This is preservation under optimal conditions. In less-favoured regions a certain amount of information can be obtained by examining coarse pottery, mud-bricks or building clay for plant fragments intentionally included as filler or accidentally incorporated. Though the organic matter will have completely disappeared, very precise impressions are often left behind. Sometimes, in addition to the impressions, silica skeletons may be found. The silica forms part of the cell walls of the epidermis or glumes and may remain intact long after the rest of the plant has decayed. Such skeletons may also be found in ash deposits (Helbaek 1969b). More frequently, grain may be found that has been carbonised by proximity to heat and so preserved, though considerable allowances have to be made for the effect of heat on the shape, size and proportions of the grain (J. Renfrew 1973, 13).

In the last few years a much more systematic method for retrieving carbonised plant remains has been used. This is by flotation. One way of achieving this is to put the excavated earth into a liquid of intermediate density, either a salt solution or a heavy organic liquid such as toluene or carbon tetrachloride. The lighter carbonaceous seeds will separate from the heavier earthy material. The carbonised material will float, the soil minerals will sink. However, this method is often not practicable in the field (Charles 1972).

Froth flotation is generally more useful. The excavated earth plus seeds, etc., is placed in a container of water. When kerosene or paraffin is added, the organic particles become water-repellent and air-avid. Air bubbles are passed through the mixture and the air-avid particles attach themselves to the bubbles and are lifted to the surface. The stabilised froth has only to last long enough to allow overflow and separation (Charles 1972; Jarman, Legge and Charles 1972). Not only is a great deal of evidence retrieved but there is little risk of damage. Sampling at Knossos on Crete provides a good illustration of the virtues of this method. Without flotation the plant sample would have consisted of one large cache of several hundred wheat grains from the lowest level and less than a hundred seed grains from the next nine levels. With flotation, non-cereal plant remains were retrieved from the lowest level and several hundred more seeds from the other levels (Jarman, Legge and Charles 1972).

(2) POLLEN ANALYSIS

Most of the information on early cultivation comes from seeds or plant fragments, but pollen can be a useful adjunct. It survives well in very dry or very wet conditions – where oxidation is limited or absent – or in acid soils, but not, or hardly at all, in calcareous or neutral soils.

Pollen from different trees and plants is distinguishable under a microscope. Cereal pollen, for example, can be differentiated from wild grass pollen. Unfortunately not all plants and trees drop pollen equally, for some are wind-pollinated, some insect-pollinated and some are self-pollinating (Dimbleby 1967, 117).

Sometimes pollen that has blown into cave or settlement sites will be preserved. Sometimes, where an old land-surface has been protected by an earthwork or some other structure, pollen from the old surface will provide clues to the original vegetation covering. But from the point of view of establishing changes in the economy the most exhaustive evidence comes from pollen deposited over a long period of time in gradually accumulating bog or lake sediments. The pollen will have blown in from the surrounding region and will give a generalised picture of how the landscape evolved. A core is taken through the sediment and samples are extracted at intervals. The changing percentages of the various plant and tree species are represented on a histogram so that one can visualise the development through time (fig. 8). This vegetation sequence has to be tied-in with the cultural sequence: sometimes artefacts are found in the sediments; more often carbon-14 dating provides cross-references. Because some cultivated plants, for example wheat and barley, are primarily self-pollinating the pollen evidence may often be indirect. An abrupt decline in the number of trees and a sudden rise in plants like plantain or goosefoot will suggest clearance and grazing. A decline in tree pollen and a rise in crop-weed pollen will indicate cultivation. Where swidden cultivation is practised and the land is left fallow there will be a re-colonisation by scrub and trees and then, perhaps, another human onslaught will be marked by an abrupt recession (Dimbleby 1969).

(3) SEED AND PLANT REMAINS

Cultivation, with the attendant element of human selectivity, conscious or unconscious, frequently results in genetic changes. Just as with animals, such morphological changes can be important indicators of the transition to food production. The genetic mutations take time and the length of time will depend on the complexity of the mutation. Some mutations, like the toughening of the rachis (the axis between the ear and the stem) or the freeing of the seed from the husk, are fairly simple and may take only a few generations. Changes in plant morphology will therefore often become apparent more rapidly than changes in bone structure.

Even so, there will be an intermediate stage where plants are sown and harvested but show no morphological change. Helbaek (1966b) has therefore distinguished between 'cultivated' plants that have been sown and harvested but show no morphological alterations, and 'domesticated' plants where morphological change has occurred.

Although many, probably most, plants are affected by human selection and do change morphologically, there are, as always, exceptions. Domesticated spelt wheat, *Triticum spelta*, retains, unlike most of the domesticated wheats, a very brittle rachis and has to be harvested before it is fully ripe. It has also retained its husks so that a special mill has to be used. In compensation it has winter hardiness and resistance to smut, bunt and fungi (Jarman 1972c).

Morphological changes in some of the more important Old and New World crops are considered below.

(4) SOUTH-WEST ASIAN CROPS

The most important early crops in South-west Asia were barley, *Hordeum distichum*, emmer wheat, *Triticum dicoccum*, and einkorn wheat, *Triticum monococcum*. These were supplemented by pulse crops such as horse beans, field peas, lentils and vetch. The cereals are winter grains adapted to a regime with well-marked wet and dry seasons. They germinate and grow quickly during the spring rains, then ripen fast and disperse their seeds. The seeds are large, both in order to survive the dry summers and to aid germination when the rains come. The seed size is, of course, an advantage to the human collector. As the wild stands often extend over several kilometres and in both growth and total mass are sometimes hardly inferior to cultivated stands it is not surprising that their potential was recognised early (Zohary 1969). Though the harvesting period is short, often no more than two weeks, the fact that the stands occur at various altitudes and in various ecological niches means that they ripen at slightly different times and, by moving up the hillslopes, men could prolong the harvest by another two to four weeks.

But from the human point of view the wild grains have certain disadvantages. The first is that they are not easy to harvest. Part of the plant's mechanism to facilitate seed dispersal is to have a very brittle rachis which shatters when touched. Theoretically, a single mutation can produce a tougher non-shattering rachis. This mutation must have happened over and over again in nature but since it impeded seed dispersal it would have been at a disadvantage. However, human collectors using sickles would have unconsciously selected in their favour for they would have stayed intact longer than the plants with brittle rachis. Such unconscious selection may well have occurred in South-west Asia where stone inset sickles were used by Post-Pleistocene gatherers. In other parts of the world, for example the south-west of North America, where grass seeds were simply knocked into baskets, the collection would be similar to wild dispersal and there would be no bias in favour of tough-rachis mutants (Wilke, Bettinger and O'Connell 1972). If the seeds harvested by sickle are sown, either accidentally or purposefully, the crop should yield a disproportionate number of tough-rachis plants. Gradually the tough-rachis mutant will become dominant, with man rather than nature ensuring the seed dispersal. As cereal crops are mainly self-pollinating, the mutant strain can rapidly be stabilised and can exist alongside wild stands without running the risk of being constantly swamped by the brittle-rachis form (Zohary 1969). This reconstruction of how the mutation occurs suggests that even collected wild grains found on sites will have a higher proportion of tough-rachis than a normal wild population. Thus only when most, or all, have tough rachis, or where there is evidence of other morphological changes can one really be sure that domestication has begun.

A second disadvantage of wild grain is that it is difficult to remove the grain from the tightly-fitting husks. It can be done by parching the grain prior to grinding and this may have been the function of many of the clay-lined pits, sometimes filled with ashes, which are found on early farming sites. But another mutation frees the grain from the husk, giving rise to 'naked' varieties which can be threshed.

A third disadvantage is that the wild cereals tend to flourish on poor and thin soils among rocks, on uneven terrain and on hillsides (Hawkes 1969). Harvesting is therefore difficult. When crops began to be cultivated there would have been a tendency to plant close to the settlement on less rocky and uneven ground. The soil around the settlement was probably enriched by the deposition of decaying organic matter – faeces, plant-remains etc. – and would have been particularly fertile. It may also be that the first experiments in cultivation were undertaken by groups living just outside the natural habitat of the wild grasses, in an attempt to reproduce this excellent food resource. Either way the plants would be removed to new environments and this would encourage new adaptations and hybridisations. Although cereal grasses are generally self-pollinating, cross-pollination can occur, not only between the wild and domestic varieties but also with other wild species. Usually the hybrids are sterile, but not always. The successful hybrids then back-cross with the cultivated species, resulting in effective introgression (Zohary 1969).

(a) Barley

Barley was one of the most important early crops. The two-row hulled barley, *Hordeum distichum* L., derives from the two-row barley, *Hordeum spontaneum* Koch. The two are so closely related that hybrids are fertile. The main difference is that the wild variety has a brittle rachis, while the domesticated form has a tougher one. The grain also becomes larger and the shape, attitude and hairiness of the sterile spikelets alter (J. Renfrew 1973, 75).

The husks of the wild barley are attached to the grain surface and no amount of threshing can remove them. An early mutation gives a 'huskless' or naked form and the pales become wrinkled. It is not entirely clear whether the earliest naked barley is the domesticated two-row *Hordeum distichum* var. *nudum* or the domesticated six-row *Hordeum vulgare* var. *nudum*. Helbaek (1966a) considers that there is no evidence of naked two-row barley and that it is all naked six-row (fig. 2). However, there are naked grains from Ali Kosh and Beidha that could be either (J. Renfrew 1973, 70).

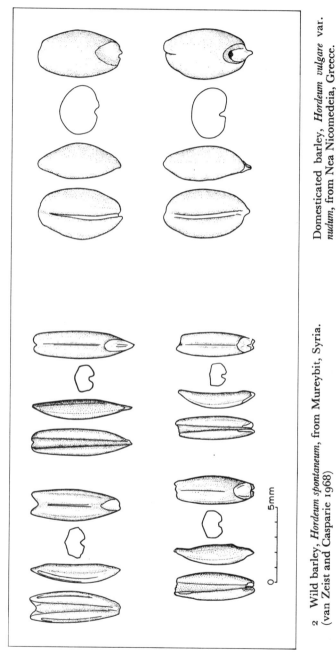

5mm

2 Wild barley, *Hordeum spontaneum*, from Mureybit, Syria. (van Zeist and Casparie 1968)

Domesticated barley, *Hordeum vulgare* var. *nudum*, from Nea Nicomedeia, Greece. (van Zeist and Bottema 1971)

The early domesticated six-row barley is all of the naked type, *Hordeum vulgare* var. *nudum*. The six-row form is generally regarded as a derivative of the wild two-row *Hordeum spontaneum* for it only needs a single mutation for the lateral flowers of the two-row barley to become fertile.[3] However, to arrive at the naked form two other mutations are also necessary, one to promote the tough rachis and one to engender the naked grains. As Jane Renfrew points out (1973, 71): 'It is strange that the hulled form occurred later than the naked variety. . . .' An alternative suggestion is that the naked six-row barley derives from the wild hulled six-row barley, *Hordeum agriocrithon*, found in Tibet. But if this is so it is curious that this wild form does not turn up on any of the early sites (J. Renfrew 1969). It may even be that this 'wild' six-row barley is the result of a secondary hybridisation between wild two-row *Hordeum spontaneum* and cultivated six-row *Hordeum vulgare* (Zohary 1960). Very small quantities of domesticated hulled six-row barley turn up on sites dating around 6000 b.c., but it does not become important until farming begins on the Mesopotamian alluviums in association with irrigation. It seems to require much more water than other barleys (Helbaek 1966a, 1969a).

(b) Wheat

Two major forms of hulled wheat were cultivated right from the beginning: the small diploid einkorn *Triticum monococcum* L. and the much larger tetraploid emmer, *Triticum dicoccum* Schübl. A third form, more complex hexaploid wheats *Triticum aestivum* L. and *Triticum compactum* Host., is found a little later.

The relationship between different wheat species, wild and domesticated, has been clarified by the study of the chromosome composition. The diploids have 14 chromosomes and only the A genome; the tetraploids have 28 chromosomes and have both A and B genomes; the hexaploids have 42 chromosomes and have A, B and D genomes. The diploids are therefore the most primitive form; the tetraploids arise through hybridisation between the diploid wheat and another diploid species with the B genome; the hexa-

---

3 In the wild two-row form the infertile lateral spikelets have an important function for they help to wedge the grain into the ground and so protect it against drying out, grazing animals, rodents, etc. But once the rachis has toughened and the seeds no longer disperse naturally this mechanism has no function. The lateral spikelets are either reduced or become fertile – hence six-row barley. Another redundant mechanism is the long rachis internode which formed the point of departure for the seed. With domestication it becomes shorter, allowing the ears to become denser (Zohary 1960).

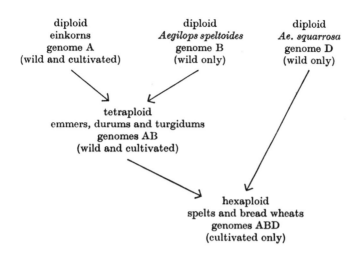

3   Cytogenetic relationships of wild and domesticated wheats.
(Reproduced from 'Origin of South-west Asian cereals' by David Zohary, in *Plant Life of South-west Asia*, ed. P. H. Davis, 1971, The Botanical Society of Edinburgh.)

ploids followed as a result of the hybridisation of tetraploid wheat with another diploid donating the D genome (fig. 3) (J. Renfrew 1973, 41).

Domesticated diploid einkorn, *Triticum monococcum*, derives from the wild *Triticum boeoticum* Boiss. which comes in a variety of forms. A rather small one-seeded form, *Triticum boeoticum* spp. *aegilopoides*, flourishes in cool conditions, while the larger two-seeded form, *Triticum boeoticum* spp. *thaoudar*, is found in warmer areas. Both wild forms are found on early farming sites (Zohary 1969).

Domesticated emmer *Triticum dicoccum* Schübl. derives from the wild form *Triticum dicoccoides* Korn., which in turn derives from the crossing of wild einkorn, *Triticum monococcum* Boiss. and a species of Aegilops grass, probably the ancestor of the present-day *Aegilops speltoides*.

Both domesticated einkorn and emmer are so close in form to their wild progenitors that hybrids are completely fertile. In both cases the rachis becomes tougher than in the wild varieties but still remains rather fragile. Both retain their glumes, which makes it hard to get at the grain but easier for the archaeologist to identify the carbonised remains! (Helbaek 1960). The seed size increases and the shapes alter slightly[4] (figs. 4, 5) (Zeist 1972; J. Renfrew 1973, 48).

4 With the increase in seed size and the decrease in chaff, cultivated einkorn threshes out to about 75% grain, compared with 46% for the wild form (Harlan 1967).

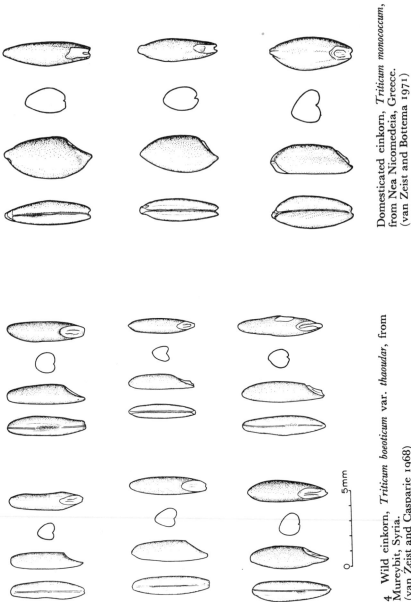

Domesticated einkorn, *Triticum monococcum*, from Nea Nicomedeia, Greece. (van Zeist and Bottema 1971)

4 Wild einkorn, *Triticum boeoticum* var. *thaoudar*, from Mureybit, Syria. (van Zeist and Casparie 1968)

5mm

The third form of wheat, the hexaploids, comes in two main sub-groups: bread wheat, *Triticum aestivum* L., and club wheat, *Triticum compactum* Host. They are usually considered to be the result of a hybridisation between emmer and a goat-grass, probably a form ancestral to *Aegilops squarrosa*. But it has recently been pointed out that such a cross gives rise to something resembling *Triticum spelta* rather than *Triticum aestivum* or *Triticum compactum*. *Triticum spelta* only appears late in the archaeological record. Perhaps 'the several species or sub-species of hexaploid wheats . . . had separate origins at various times and places' (Jarman 1972). The addition of the D genome considerably widens the adaptability of hexaploid wheats – they can endure extreme continental conditions or sub-humid temperate climates (Zohary 1971). The hexaploid wheats have a tough rachis and are naked; the kernels are loose within the spikelet at maturity and can easily be separated.

(c) *Pulse crops*

There is a great deal of literature on the various winter cereals, much less on the pulse crops which, though perhaps subsidiary, were very important. They not only provided a source of vegetable protein but also acted as a fertiliser, for when the root nodules decay nitrogen is released into the soil.

Early cultivated pulses in South-west Asia include horse bean, *Vicia faba*; field pea, *Pisum sativum* var. *arvense*; lentil, *Lens esculenta*; bitter vetch, *Vicia ervilia*; and chick-pea, *Cicer arietinum*. The little that is known about the morphological effects of domestication on these crops is well summarised by Jane Renfrew (1973, 108).

(5) NEW WORLD MAIZE-BEAN-SQUASH TRIAD

There is a very different and far greater range of cultigens in the New World. It took far longer before they played any major role in the economy: only after several thousand years of cultivation was there an abrupt jolt forward. This was associated with an increase in maize yield and with the emergence of a viable triad: maize, beans and squash. This threesome eventually dominated the economy, both in Meso-America and Peru.

Probably the reason that it took so long was that primitive cultivated maize was an unrewarding plant. It has been estimated that major reliance on maize is only practicable when there is a return of 200 to 250 kilograms per hectare. This was far beyond the possibilities of primitive maize and, even by 1500 b.c., after several

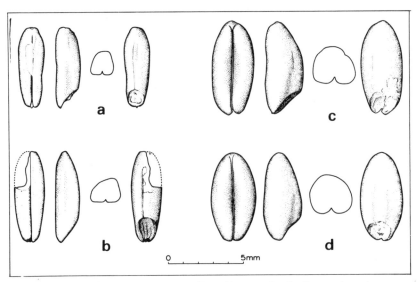

5 **a** & **b** Wild emmer, *Triticum dicoccoides*. **c** & **d** Domesticated emmer, *Triticum dicoccum*. Both from Cayönü, Turkey. (van Zeist 1972)

thousand years of cultivation, such a return was only achieved under the very best conditions. In comparison the wild cereals of South-west Asia could yield 500 to 800 kilograms per hectare in a good year (Flannery 1972).

For several thousand years there was little specialisation; instead a perhaps rather desultory cultivation of a wide range of cultigens. Apart from maize, beans and squash, there were avocados and peppers, black and white zapotes, coyol and perhaps amaranth, fox-tail millet and fruit-trees like chupandilla. Many of these were non-essential foodstuffs, or not foodstuffs at all. Chili peppers would have been used as a condiment, wild squashes which are 'virtually seed bags with an exterior layer of thin, stringy flesh' (Whitaker and Cutler 1965) would have been valued for their seeds, while bottle-gourds made handy containers.

There is not much information on morphological changes in the more minor cultigens. Avocado seeds, *Persea Americana* Mill., from the Tehuacán valley in Mexico changed from a nearly spherical shape in the early levels to a more elongated form and also increased in size (Smith 1965).

Peppers, *Capsicum*, found early in both Peru and Mexico, show an increase in both over-all size and seed size. At Huaca Prieta in northern Peru, in the earliest levels, there are both orange and red fruits. This colour variability is another indication of domestication –

wild orange fruits are not known. Domesticated peppers also lose their deciduous character, the fruit is no longer shed and seed dispersal is therefore reduced (Pickersgill 1969).

In the Tehuacán valley, seeds from the chupandilla tree, *Cyrotocarpa procera* HBK, increased in size, though, as there were no other morphological changes, this may simply reflect the conscious selection of the larger wild fruits. The same may be true for Foxtail millet, *Setaria geniculata beauvais*: coprolites from Tamaulipas in north-east Mexico contained some grains that were larger than usual (Callen 1967). Although large amounts of amaranth, *Amaranthus leucocarpus*, were eaten in the Tehuacán valley there was no change in seed size; it may be that when cultivated it simply produces more seeds, but this the archaeologist cannot ascertain (Jones 1953).

(a) Maize

Of the three crops that came to dominate the economy, maize shows the most startling changes. Darlington (1963, 144) talks of 'the altogether extravagant process of evolution entailed in the domestication of maize'.

There is no wild maize today. Either the wild form has been swamped out of existence by the highly successful cultivated form, or there never was a wild form and the ancestor of domesticated maize was a rather insignificant grass called teosinte (*Zea mexicana*). The tiny cobs, no more than nineteen to twenty millimetres long, found in the early levels of the caves in the Tehuacán valley in Mexico (fig. 6) are probably very early cultigens. They usually have only eight rows of tiny kernels, each partially enclosed in a glume. Each cob is again partially enclosed in a few husks. The spikelets are uniformly paired and attached to a fragile rachis, making seed dispersal easy. They seem to be bi-sexual: male above, female below (Galinat 1965; Mangelsdorf, MacNeish and Galinat 1964). In the Tehuacán valley this primitive maize is found at 5000 b.c. and for a long time it remained an insignificant cultigen.

It was only around 1500 b.c. that there was a relatively sudden boost in size and variability. The reason for the rather slow development was probably that the favourable genetic changes were all polygenetic and required considerable crossing and back-crossing. Stabilisation would be slow because maize is wind pollinated, which means that 'improved' stands would constantly be bombarded with wild pollen (Flannery 1972). The enormous genetic variability found today in maize is the result of a genetic flexibility caused by the introgression with wild relatives. At Tehuacán around 1500

6 **a** Primitive maize **b** Teosinte **c** *Tripsacum*
(From 'The Origins of New World Civilization' by Richard S. MacNeish.
Copyright © 1964 by Scientific American Inc. All rights reserved.)

b.c. the first known hybrid emerges, probably through the back-crossing with teosinte (fig. 6) (Galinat 1965). The gene pool increased and, with it, the variety. Very quickly, several races emerged, including two still found today, Nal-Tel and Chapalote.

The over-all effects of domestication include the separation of the male and female elements. The tassel terminating the main stalk becomes entirely male, 'a lax plume whose moving branches shed their pollen into the wind' (Galinat 1965). The pollen becomes larger. The ear, which terminates the lateral branches, becomes female. The number of kernel rows increases enormously and so does the size of the rachis (cob) to which they are attached: a modern corn cob is ten times as large as the wild or early cultivated examples from Tehuacán. There are hundreds of large kernels. The glumes are usually reduced to the base of the kernel so that the individual seed is naked. But the whole ear is then protected by many overlapping husks. The silks (styles) then extend beyond these husks and so remain exposed to the pollen. The husks make harvesting easy but totally prevent seed dispersal. Modern maize is completely dependent on man.

(b) Beans

Beans were one of the early cultigens in both Meso-America and Peru. They were very important as a complement to maize. The principal maize protein, zein, is an amino-acid which is deficient in lysine. The *a* and *b* globulins in beans make up for this deficiency (Kaplan 1965). Beans are also important because of their high protein content, 22% in dry native beans. The New World lacked animal domesticates and therefore had to depend on hunting for any meat protein (Kaplan 1965, 1967).

There are eighty-four species of bean in the New World, of which four were, and still are, important food crops: the common bean, *Phaseolus vulgaris* L. (which includes navy beans, red kidney and pinto); tepary beans, *Phaseolus acutifolius* Gray var. *latifolius* Freeman; runner beans, *Phaseolus coccineus* L.; and small lima beans, *Phaseolus lunatus* L., also known as sieva. The last are found in Mexico and are related to the large lima, *Phaseolus lunatus* var. *microcarpus* Bentham, found in coastal Peru. Following domestication these beans show three major morphological adaptations. The size increases – both seed and pod size. The seeds become more permeable in water, allowing germination to start earlier. The seed dispersal mechanism becomes less efficient. In the wild varieties the pod is dehiscent along both sutures and when ripe it twists, ejecting the seeds violently. With domestication the parchment layers are reduced so the expulsion is less violent. A fourth characteristic is that while wild beans are perennial, domesticated beans are annuals. This trait, however, leaves no evidence. Another, probably early change, which the archaeologist cannot recognise, is a transition from a vine to an erect bush; the vast profusion of lateral branches found in the wild species would definitely be a disadvantage to cultivators, particularly where the beans are grown in conjunction with maize (Kaplan 1965).

(c) Squash

Like beans, squash comes in many varieties. Early domesticated varieties were pumpkin or summer squash, *Cucurbita pepo* L.; cushaw squash, *Cucurbita moschata* Duch.; walnut squash, *Cucurbita mixta* Pang.; and winter or turban squash, *Cucurbita maxima* Duch. There is also the related bottle gourd or calabash, *Lagenaria siceraria*, used mainly for containers. The effect of domestication on all these forms is to increase the seed size (Cutler and Whitaker 1961).

There is still much work to be done on the effects of domestication on particular plant species. But slowly it should become possible, using this and all the other categories of evidence, to focus more closely on the transition to food-production, to ascertain what plants and animals were involved and to visualise the relative importance of each within the total economy.

4 The Significance of Climatic Change

Climatic fluctuations rarely affect human subsistence patterns directly. They operate indirectly by altering the environment. So in discussing climate as a factor in the transition to food-production three variables have to be examined. One: were there climatic fluctuations in the regions under discussion at the operative times? (This involves a further problem of defining what constitute 'operative times'.) Two: if there were changes what effect did they have on the environment? And three: if the environment was affected did this bring changes in the human subsistence activities?

This chapter concentrates on the first two questions: were there climatic or environmental changes that might have played some part in the development of a food-producing economy? The third question can only be answered after the archaeological evidence has been assembled.

Studies in climate as a possible factor have usually concentrated on the major climatic fluctuations associated with the recession of the Pleistocene ice sheets over North America and Northern Europe. It has frequently been noted that, at present, evidence of early independent food-producing economies in widely scattered parts of the world first appears in the early Post-Pleistocene.

Such cause and effect is hard to establish. The areas in which the transition to food-production is recorded lie far to the south of the maximum extent of the ice-sheets. The effect of the recession can, at most, only have been felt indirectly. Attempts to correlate changes in the climatic regime of South-west Asia with Late Pleistocene and early Post-Pleistocene climatic developments further to the north have not been notably successful.

It is true that the data on major climatic fluctuations in South-west Asia, Meso-America and upland Peru is very inadequate, but even if the coverage were better it remains questionable whether this is the right approach. First of all climatic change means little unless it is related to detailed local morphology. Thus an increase in rainfall will affect certain areas far more than others. For example, in South-west Asia the areas lying between the present-day 250 and 200 mm. isohyets would be particularly sensitive to relatively small increases in rainfall because the sparse vegetation covering permits rapid erosion (Raikes 1967, 44). Cohen (1970), working in Anatolia, states: 'Whether or not one postulates more or less moisture for the early Holocene (Post-Pleistocene), it seems clear that the ecological situations in . . . marginal areas have not been defined with any accuracy, *nor will the relationship between such areas and their accompanying sites be determined by general statements on the climate of the Near East*' (italics added).

Secondly, while some changes in the environment may be caused by major climatic fluctuations others may be the result of very local phenomena. Thus the creation of favourable micro-environments with aquatic resources and a wide range of fauna and flora close at hand *may* in some instances be linked to the general Post-Pleistocene rises in sea-level and the flooding back of rivers (Binford 1968b). And the exposure of fertile alluviums *may* often be related to a general Post-Pleistocene recession in inland lake levels (Cohen 1970). On the other hand, alluvial deposition or erosion, or the formation of lagoons or lakes might result from quite minor changes in coastal or riverine morphology, or from a series of very dry years, or a spate of torrential downpours, or even local over-grazing.

In sum, it may be more profitable to shift the emphasis to 'the primary geological (and analogous) evidence while shelving its secondary climatic connotations' (Vita-Finzi 1969a).

Unfortunately studies in what Vita-Finzi (1969a) calls 'geological opportunism' (as opposed to climatic determinism) are few and far between. Cohen (1969, 1970) has studied the alluvial deposits of the Konya-Ereğli and Burdar basins in Anatolia. He has linked the establishment of early farming sites such as Aceramic Hacilar and Çatal Hüyük East with the exposure of fertile alluviums following the recession of the lakes in the early Post-Pleistocene. He also indicates the fallacy of construing local environments in terms of the present situation, even in areas where there is no indication of climatic change. He points out that great tracts of the Konya basin are today salt impregnated and could not support stands of wild barley or emmer wheat. But this salinity is largely the result of quite recent irrigation works, and in the early Post-Pleistocene when the lake receded the alluvial soil probably supported a fairly luxurious grass cover, adequate for the pasturing of the great cattle herds of Çatal Hüyük. Wild cereals could have been available locally and areas with a high water table would have been very suitable for cereal cultivation.

Another detailed study is Raikes' (1966) work on the rise and fall of the village of Beidha in Jordan (chapter 5, p. 133).

This type of environmental approach still remains largely un-developed and we are therefore forced in this chapter to assemble a fairly motley collection of information on local changes in climate or environment.

The coverage in this chapter, particularly for America, is by no means exhaustive; it is more by way of a sample, trying to illustrate the scope of different types of evidence. For South-west Asia a much fuller documentation is to be found in Perrot (1968, 299) and Far-rand (1971).

SOUTH-WEST ASIA

Fig. 7 shows the distribution of sites from which there is evidence of the early manipulation and domestication of plants and animals. They are set against the background of present day climatic/environ-mental zones. It is noticeable that the distribution more or less coincides with the Mediterranean and Warm Temperate climatic zones. The Mediterranean zone forms a great arc curving north through the coastal hills of Israel, Jordan, Syria and the Lebanon, then swinging east along the Tauros mountains of Turkey, then south through the Zagros mountains of Iraq and Iran. A narrow belt hugs the south Anatolian coast and includes Cyprus, then swells out around the Aegean basin. In all these areas the climate is warm throughout the year, with less than 30 days of frost. The rain, mainly the result of cyclonic activity, is very seasonal, con-centrated in the winter months and varying from 250 to 1000 mm. per annum (Butzer 1970, 41). In general the vegetation is – or would be were it not for over-grazing and deforestation – open woodland with oak, juniper, hawthorn and wild pear. There are stands of winter cereals. It is the natural habitat of wild sheep and goat, cattle and pig – though all are tolerant of a wider range of climate (chapter 5).

The Warm Temperate zone lies to the north of the Mediterranean zone. Temperatures are more extreme, with 30 to 120 days of frost per annum. The natural vegetation is grassland with stands of de-ciduous or mixed forest – black pine, juniper and evergreen oak (Butzer 1970, 41).

But this is the present-day climatic/vegetation zoning. What was it like 11,000 years ago when these sites were occupied? Today many of the sites are right on the edge of the Mediterranean zone

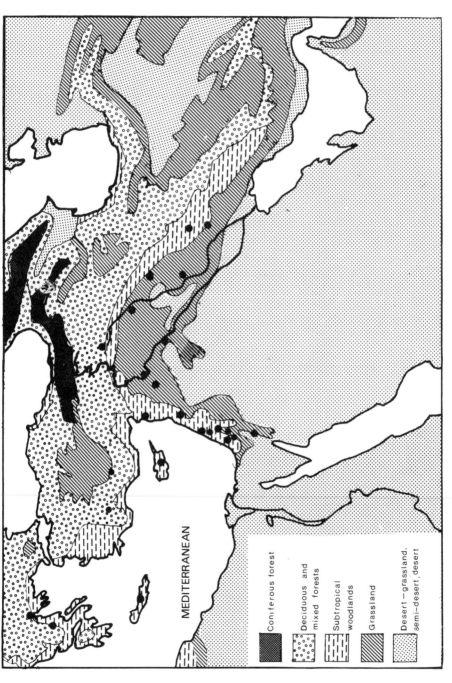

7 Map showing modern vegetational/climatic zones in South-west Asia and the Aegean. The dots indicate the location of seventh and sixth millennia b.c. sites with herding and/or cereal cultivation. Site names are given on figure 19. (after Butzer 1971, with additions)

MEDITERRANEAN

Coniferous forest

Deciduous and mixed forests

Subtropical woodlands

Grassland

Desert—grassland, semi-desert, desert

and are very marginal for dry farming. Were they marginal then?

11,000 years ago corresponds to the end of the Pleistocene, to the time of the final recession of the ice-sheets over Europe. It is for this reason that archaeologists have been tempted to see a connection between this climatic phenomenon and early food-production. But it is not reasonable to focus exclusively on this point in time. Food-production was not a sudden or isolated 'event', it was part of a process, it involved a variety of strategies each in turn related to earlier ones. In South-west Asia one could go back 300,000 years and follow through the long inter-action between environmental change and cultural adaptation. Lack of information, and space, prevents such a leisurely perusal of the record. But one should at least go back 20,000 years and consider the evidence of climatic fluctuations from that time to about 7000 years ago.

20,000 b.p. (before present) is an arbitrary point in time, taken because it marks the maximum extension of the Würm glaciation over Europe. A time when the ice has pushed south to a line roughly from the Bristol channel to Berlin. This glacial maximum is sometimes known as the Upper Pleniglacial.

(1) The theoretical implications of the north european glacial sequence

In theory, the effect of the concentration of cold air over the European ice-sheets would be to shift the present-day pressure systems further southwards. The sub-tropical high pressure system that now dominates the Mediterranean would be replaced by the Atlantic rainstorm belt associated with cool, stormy conditions. There would be more rain or, at least, it would be more evenly distributed throughout the year. Temperatures would be lower. Thus – still in theory – glacial maxima over Europe should correlate with 'pluvial' regimes over the Mediterranean.

It is widely accepted that there were two major advances during the last Würm glaciation: the early Würm advance, also known as the Lower Pleniglacial, dating between 58,000 and 40,000 years ago, and a second, more important, Würm advance, the Upper Pleniglacial, dating between 29,000 and 20,000 years ago. Then followed the gradual establishment, as the ice retreated between 20,000 and 11,000 years ago, of sub-tropical conditions, with oscillations marking minor glacial advances.

There is in fact evidence that during the early advance pluvial conditions reigned over the Mediterranean. But there is no such evidence for the second advance despite its greater importance. One recent explanation for this inconsistency is that, regardless of what was happening in the Alps and further north, the Mediterranean only experienced one glacio-pluvial phase during the Würm glaciation (Vita-Finzi 1969c).

An assessment of the relative merits of mono-glacialism *v.* multi-glacialism is well beyond the scope of this book, but if such fundamental issues have not yet been resolved the interpretation of the already inadequate range of evidence must clearly be fraught with difficulty.

(2) CORRELATION OF CLIMATIC EVENTS IN SOUTH-WEST ASIA WITH THE EUROPEAN GLACIAL SEQUENCE

We can start by examining some of the attempts made to correlate the climatic sequence in South-west Asia with that further north. These have mainly been based on trying to synchronise relic shorelines (marine terraces) along the Mediterranean coast with glacial oscillations, for as the ice-sheets waxed and waned water was subtracted or added to the oceans. Thus when, 20,000 years ago, the ice gradually began to retreat, water locked in the ice-sheets was released and sea levels rose. When the ice-sheet occasionally stopped and then re-advanced, the sea should correspondingly have regressed.

It has proved possible to make correlations between shorelines and major glacial advances and retreats in many parts of the world. Studies of the continental shelf off the Atlantic coast of America suggest that the last glacial maximum was marked by a major regression to −130 m. below present sea-level. Only around 14,000 years ago did the sea-level begin to rise, rapidly until 7000 years ago and then more gradually (Milliman and Emery 1968). Van Andel and Veevers' work (1967, 100) on the Timor shelf off northeast Australia correlates reasonably well with these findings: a drop of 120 to 140 m. at the maximum of the last glaciation; a rapid rise from 18,000 b.p.; sea-levels at −60 m. at 11,000 b.p., at −30 m. at 9000 b.p. and the transgression slowing down drastically shortly afterwards.

But in the Mediterranean, although there is good evidence of marine transgressions and regressions, it has proved difficult to synchronise them with even major glacial fluctuations and quite impossible to find correlations with lesser oscillations. An ambitious study was carried out in the Ashdod region near Haifa in Israel where there is a huge coastal deposit, 150 to 200 m. thick, laid down by sea, river and wind action. Four major cycles of marine regression and transgression were elucidated. Only the fourth is of concern here. The end of the fourth regression is marked by terraces at −90 to −50 m. It is followed by a final transgression (m3) which includes several oscillations, one marked by terraces at −32 to −21 m., another, later, one by terraces at −7 to 2 m. The question is what these terraces represent. Using the multiglacial sequence, the first (−90 to −50 m.) regression was originally interpreted as corresponding to the early Würm advance (Lower Pleniglacial) and the second (−32 to −21 m.) to the second Würm advance (Upper Pleniglacial) *c.* 20,000 b.p. H. Wright (1960, 77) protested that this was inconceivable because the early, Lower Pleniglacial, advance was far less important than the later Upper Pleniglacial. Since then, with some juggling, the major regression is thought to correspond to the Upper Pleniglacial and later regressions to post-Upper Pleniglacial oscillations (Perrot 1968). There is clearly altogether too much room for manoeuvre!

If the major fluctuations cannot be synchronised, it is hardly surprising that minor oscillations are completely elusive. Many of the terraces found here and there along the Mediterranean coasts may mark such oscillations but many others may be the result of local earth-movements or shifts in river regimes.

Other attempts have been made to correlate relic shorelines of inland lakes with the glacial regimes, on the assumption that changes in lake levels correspond to fluctuations in rainfall or evaporation linked with glacial fluctuations. Certainly many lakes stood much higher 20,000 years ago than they do today. Lake Burdar in Anatolia reached a maximum height of +80 m. above the present level; lake Konya covered 2000 square miles; lake Urmia on the Turkish border, today only 17 m. deep, was about 87 m. deep and twice the present size. The Caspian Sea stood 30 m. higher (Butzer 1970, 53). But precise correlations with glacial fluctuations are thwarted by the distorting effect of local landslides, torrents or earthquakes. This is particularly true of the Dead Sea which lies within the Jordan rift valley and has been much modified by tectonic activity: lake Lisan rapidly dropped about 190 m. after 20,000 b.p., partly as the result of a considerable decrease in humidity but certainly also because of fairly violent tectonic activity (Farrand 1971).

It must be pointed out that even if we could correlate Mediterranean fluctuations with glacial advances and retreats these transgressions and regressions would give little indication of the prevailing climatic conditions: 'Whatever the climatic history of the Mediterranean lands, their shores will retain evidence of the full suite of fluctuations experienced by the oceans as a consequence of high latitude glaciation. . . . It is therefore possible to envisage the coexistence in the Mediterranean area of Quaternary transgressions and regressions with persisting "Tertiary" conditions, a situation analogous to the current disharmony between "interglacial" conditions in middle and low latitudes, and continued glaciation at high latitudes' (Vita-Finzi 1969c).

(3) THE SNOWLINES IN SOUTH-WEST ASIA

We cannot find neat correlations between glacial fluctuations over Europe and climatic developments in South-west Asia. Somewhat more substantial evidence is available on local glacial advances in the highlands of South-west Asia.

Relic glacial cirque formations have been found well below present-day levels. In the high ranges of north-east Iraq and neighbouring south-east Turkey, H. Wright (1960; 1961a, b) estimated that the snowline which today lies at about 3300 m. was once 1800 to 1200 m. lower. These are the highest ranges in the Tauros/Zagros arc and since they form the 'corner' of the arc they receive a very heavy rainfall. A reduction in temperature would have resulted in very considerable snowfall, and, particularly if the summer temperatures were reduced and prevented the snow from melting, the snowlines would certainly have extended far below those of the present-day. Even so the figures seem very high when compared to estimates of a drop of 800 to 600 m. in the Azerbaijan and the Elburz ranges not far away in the south Zagros region (Butzer 1971, 296). In Anatolia in the high plateaus of the interior the snowline seems to have been 1000 to 800 m. below the present level. In regions closer to the Mediterranean, on Mount Hermon, in the high Lebanon, the South Balkans, peninsular Italy, Iberia and Morocco, the figures are between 1000 and 1200 m. (Butzer 1971, 296).

Although the anomalies between the figures for the different inland regions have not yet been adequately explained, we may presume that the maximum dip in the snowlines occurred at roughly the same time and that it correlates with the maximum extent of the Würm glaciation (the Upper Pleniglacial) dating between 29,000 and 20,000 years ago. Unfortunately, there is no way of knowing when or how quickly the snowlines began to shift upwards. When did they reach present-day levels? The question obviously has a bearing on how much terrain was available to upland hunter-gatherers during the Late Pleistocene.

(4) THE PROBLEM OF TEMPERATURE V. RELATIVE HUMIDITY

Although the extent of the depression of the snowlines has been reasonably well established, it is extremely difficult to know what this represents in terms of changes in temperature or relative humidity. In very general terms it is reckoned that a depression of the snowline by 1000 m. gives a lapse rate, or temperature reduction, of between 5° and 7°C (H. Wright 1961). This estimate correlates reasonably well with the palaeotemperature measurements of deep sea cores from the east Mediterranean – one from between Crete and Cyprus, the other from west of Crete[1] – which indicate that the surface temperature of the Mediterranean sea between 30,000 and 12,000 years ago was about 5°C colder than today, with a seasonal range of 9 to 10°C. However, like fluctuations of sea-level, temperatures of sea water give little indication of the local climate, for 'sea temperatures are the result of a complicated process of absorbtion of heat, . . . its movement by convection currents and drift currents, and the giving up of heat somewhere else' (Raikes 1967, 104).

Butzer (1971, 296) suggested that temperatures during the Upper Pleniglacial might have been between 8° and 9.5°C lower around the Mediterranean and between 5.5° and 6.5°C lower in the interior, but qualified this by saying that the figures would depend on the relative humidity. And this, of course, is the crux of the matter. One cannot arrive at any accurate estimate of temperature if one does not take the relative humidity into account. For example, the higher snowline of the Anatolian highlands as compared to the coastal highlands, could be the result of relatively higher temperatures or of lower humidity.

Changes in humidity may result from a variety of conditions. There may be a straight change in the amount of precipitation, or simply a more equal annual distribution of rainfall. Or the rate of evaporation may alter because of a change in temperature. It is reckoned that if temperatures decrease by 6°C, evaporation is reduced by at least 25%. Thus the fact that Late Pleistocene lakes were far larger than today could either be due to a decrease in temperature (and therefore in evaporation) or to an enormous increase in precipitation. Moreover, there may be a greater retention of humidity because of more abundant vegetation covering. The latter in turn may be a reflection of a more equal distribution of

1 The first is based on the oxygen-isotope analysis of planktonic Forminifera (Emiliani 1970); the second includes a complete faunal analysis as well as an oxygen-isotope analysis (Vergnaud-Grazzini and Herman-Rosenberg cited in Farrand 1971).

rainfall, or of increased evaporation, or could simply be due to lack of interference by man.

It is therefore imperative to find evidence that will disentangle these interlocking factors of temperature and relative humidity. Below, the least satisfactory line of evidence, the use of changes in the macro-fauna is considered first, followed by geological, and finally, pollen evidence.

(5) MACRO-FAUNAL EVIDENCE

By 20,000 years ago the range of fauna in South-west Asia was already similar to the present. There were no dramatic extinctions to demonstrate changes in climate. The evidence is therefore mainly limited to examining alterations in the importance of different species. The approach is beset with problems. First of all, the larger animals are not very sensitive to minor climatic or environmental changes. Sheep will withstand a considerable climatic range as long as the terrain is rolling; goats are equally tolerant as long as the terrain is rugged (H. Wright 1968). Secondly, most of the evidence comes from occupation sites, and changes in species composition may simply reflect changes in hunting practices or food preferences. Thirdly, where a home-base rather than a temporary hunters' camp is involved the game may have been brought in from a variety of different terrains thus masking any slight shift in game territories.

Two examples illustrate the limitations of this approach. The first comes from the cave of Shanidar at 650 m. in the Zagros mountains of Iraq. Throughout the long cave sequence, from 40,000 b.p. onwards, the faunal assemblage remained much the same (Reed 1960). It included wild goat whose natural territory were rocky ridges; wild sheep at home on the treeless slopes; red deer, inhabitants of grassland or woodland; fallow deer and roe deer usually restricted to woodlands; and gazelle restricted to grassland (H. Wright 1961). Such an eclectic faunal assemblage masks any minor climatic/environmental shifts. It is only from the pollen analysis of an area not too distant that we can tell that there undoubtedly were climatic changes during this long time range (p. 78).

The second example comes from the Mount Carmel caves in Israel. Miss Bate, working in the 1930s, discovered that the proportion of gazelle to red deer bones found in different levels in the caves differed significantly (Garrod and Bate 1937, 143). She suggested that since gazelle preferred open country, a predominance of this species would indicate relatively dry conditions. Since red deer preferred woodland, a predominance of red deer would indicate wetter conditions. She synchronised a series of 'wet' maxima with the European glacial maxima.[2] But later, Hooijer (1961), studying the fauna from the contemporary strata of another coastal cave, Ksar 'Akil in Lebanon, found no such drastic fluctuations. Probably the Mount Carmel fluctuations were due to some very local phenomena: such as disease, hunters' bias, or slight changes in local environment.[3] Even the correlation between red deer and woodland is dubious: 'Red deer is a grazer, not a browser, so it prefers the open landscape' (H. Wright 1968).

(6) GEOLOGICAL EVIDENCE

The geological evidence is often far more convincing, though it has been handicapped by attempts to force it into a generalised climatic framework rather than simply accepting it as evidence of local conditions (Higgs and Vita-Finzi 1972).

On the coastal lowlands of the Levant there are great deposits of wind-blown soil. The great coastal accumulation at Ashdod, already mentioned, is largely composed of wind-blown soil and sand interspersed with riverine and marine sediment. Though the dating of the deposits is not very convincing (p. 70) some at least of the wind-blown sands date to the Upper Pleniglacial and later. Such deposits indicate that the local climate was semi-arid and the vegetation rather open – thus almost the opposite of the 'pluvial' conditions postulated for this time range.

Coastal alluvial deposits that inter-digitate with the sand-dunes date to a time when the dunes were exposed. The upper part of these alluvial gravels should belong to the Late Pleistocene and probably corresponds to the lower alluvial deposits bordering the wadis. All these alluviums contain re-deposited *terra rosa* which can be explained by intense seasonal rainfall. However, the steeper longitudinal profiles of the wadis suggest that the peak discharge was less than today and that over-all conditions were drier. Angular fragments are found in these deposits and probably indicate frost action, so conditions may also have been slightly cooler (Vita-Finzi and Higgs 1970).

2 Higgs (1961) working at Haua Fteah in Libya used wild cattle as a climatic indicator. High percentages of cattle bones were equated with warm, dry conditions; low percentages with cold, possibly wet conditions. This evidence tallied with the geological evidence which seemed to indicate cold, possibly wet conditions until 12,000 years ago, followed by a dry interlude (see p. 76). Higgs correlated this dry interlude with one of Miss Bate's gazelle maxima.

3 It has recently been pointed out that the creation of marshy conditions on the coastal plain of Palestine was mainly caused by the lithification of the coastal dunes into a relatively impervious calcarenite (Higgs and Vita-Finzi 1972).

Angular rock debris is, however, interpreted in different ways by different authorities. In Libya, loose scree slopes in northern Cyrenaica and a level of angular debris in the cave of Haua Fteah were thought to indicate cooler, *moister* interludes between 30,500 and 12,000 b.p. and after 9800 b.p. (Hey 1963; Higgs 1961). Farrand (1971) interprets angular rock debris in the caves of Jerf 'Ajla, Yabrud, el-Tabun, Qafzeh and Oumm-Qatafa in the same way, and a similar interpretation is offered for Ksar 'Akil in the Lebanon (H. Wright 1961b). In the last instance it was suggested that the cool, moist interlude dated to the tenth and ninth millennia b.c. and correlated with the final glacial oscillation, the Younger Dryas (Butzer 1971, 550).

There does not seem to be much synchronisation between the recorded fluctuations in the different areas.

At a local level the possibility of a cooler, moister interlude in the tenth and ninth millennia b.c. suggested for Ksar 'Akil would seem to tally with evidence from the Jordan valley. At this time range spring and alluvial deposits formed and there is evidence that Natufian hunter-gatherers occupied now-dry wadis in the Judean hills and in the Negev and Sinai deserts.

In sum, the geological evidence from the Levantine area would seem to suggest that in some areas conditions during parts of the Upper Pleniglacial period (29,000 to 20,000 years ago) and later (but how much?) were semi-arid. In the Late Pleistocene (after 20,000 b.p.) rainfall still remained less than today and took the form of torrential seasonal downpours, and temperatures were lower. In the early Post-Pleistocene (tenth and ninth millennia b.c.) conditions were still cool but perhaps moister.

On the other side of South-west Asia, in the uplands of Iran, Vita-Finzi (1969b) has examined the thick deposits known as the Tehran formation. These appear to have been laid down by powerful but short-lived flows, probably the result of intense but brief downpours. He therefore postulates a regime of low temperatures and an over-all decrease in precipitation, perhaps due to a reduction in the relative importance of cyclonic as opposed to convectional precipitation. This deposition probably ties in with the time of cool steppe conditions recorded at lake Zeribar in the Late Pleistocene, 20,000 to 12,000 b.c. (p. 78). The archaeological inclusions tend to confirm this date.

(7) PALEOLIMNOLOGICAL EVIDENCE

So far this laborious collection of bits and pieces of evidence illustrates primarily the inadequacy and ambiguity of much of the material. With some relief we can now concentrate on paleolimnological material – the evidence from lake or bog sediment – though even this line of evidence presents some problems.

It was mentioned in chapter 3 (p. 50) that conditions in bogs and marshes are excellent for organic preservation. As the sediments accumulate so layer after layer of organic material is laid down. Samples taken from a core drilled through the sediment can be analysed for diatoms, seeds, cladocera[4] and, most important, pollen. Absence or presence of species and fluctuations in the percentages through time will indicate changes in the environment which may reflect climatic fluctuations, or – particularly after the beginning of farming – the human effect upon the landscape.

The pollen spores will have blown in from a fairly wide area so the pollen spectrum will not reflect purely local conditions. Nor will all the contemporary vegetation be equally represented; some trees and plants will be under-represented, others over-represented. The reason for this is that different species produce different amounts of pollen and the pollen is dispersed in various ways.[5] Anomalies can be adjusted by cross-checking the modern pollen fall-out of the area against the existing vegetation (Wright, McAndrews and van Zeist 1967; Zeist, Timmers and Bottema 1968).

The accuracy of the pollen analysis will depend on such factors as size of sample, the way in which pollen in poor condition is identified and the techniques used to prepare the sample. A revealing case of how samples taken from the same section of the same cave, the Cueva del Toll in Spain, but collected and analysed by two different teams, can differ is reported by Butzer and Freeman (1968).

Bearing all these drawbacks in mind, it remains true that pollen analysis, sensitively handled, can throw a great deal of light on changes in environment and climate. One should not, however, generalise too widely from a particular core. Fortunately, although relatively few sediments have been tested in South-west Asia, they do come from a fair range of environments and altitudes.

---

4 Cladocera are crustaceans. In general, micro-fauna are far more sensitive climatic indicators than macro-fauna. Rodents, molluscs and insects have low ranges of tolerance. In South-west Asia very few micro-faunal studies have been attempted except as a by-line of lake sediment analysis. An exception is Tchernov's (1968) work on rodent population in the Levant.

5 For example, plantain (*Plantago*), sage-brush (*Artemisia*) and Chenopodiaceae are over-represented. Oak (*Quercus*) may leave almost ten times as much pollen as pistachio (*Pistacio*). Not only pistachio but also almond (*Amygdalus*), maple (*Acer*) and juniper (*Juniperus*) are much under-represented.

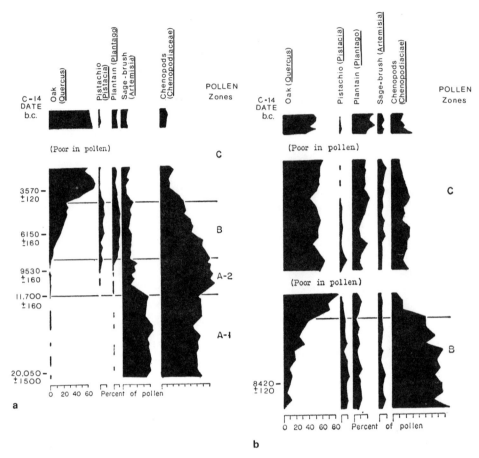

8 Selected pollen curves from **a** Lake Zeribar, western Iran **b** Lake Mirabad, south-western Iran.
(modified from van Zeist 1967; H. Wright 1968)

The first core to be analysed in detail was from lake Zeribar lying at 1300 m. in the Zagros mountains of western Iran. At present this area has 600 to 800 mm. of rainfall and lies within the oak forest belt which extends between 800 and 2000 m. (Zeist 1967). The bottom of the core dates to about 20,000 b.c.[6] The lowest zone, terminating c. 11,500 b.c., contains practically no tree pollen. 60% of the pollen is from chenopods and 40% from sage-brush, *Artemisia* (fig. 8). Both the cladocera and the water-plant remains are cool-temperate varieties (Megard 1967). In Late Pleistocene times this

6 There is a carbon-14 date from the bottom of this zone (A–1) of 20,050 ± 1500 b.c.(Y–1431) and one from near the top of 12,850 ± 300 b.c.(Y–1160).

78

area must have been cooler and drier than today and instead of oak-forest there was a cool steppe vegetation similar to that now found on the high plateau of north-west Iran.

Samples from two unpublished cores from Lalabad Springs and lake Nilofar, both in the Kermanshah valley of western Iran at a similar altitude to lake Zeribar, seem to indicate that cool steppe conditions predominated from at least 40,000 b.p. (H. Wright 1968).

The bottom part of the next zone at lake Zeribar, dating between 11,500[7] and 9000 b.c., shows a sharp drop in *Artemisia* (only 15%) and a rise in chenopods. This could be due to increasingly dry conditions reducing the *Artemisia* steppe to a desert or to changes in the lake level favouring a local expansion of chenopods. It is more likely to be the latter as the gradual appearance of tree pollen after 9000 b.c. conflicts with the idea of a desert steppe (Zeist 1967; 1969). The fact that there was no oak pollen before 9000 b.c. means that there was probably no oak within 75 km. of the lake – for oak pollen disseminates over about that distance. Since the modern oak belt is only 100 km. wide and lake Zeribar is 75 km. from the outer limit it is possible that the oak belt was squeezed out of existence (Wright, McAndrews and van Zeist 1967). Samples taken from lake Mirabad, at the foot of the Zagros mountains (800 m.) rather support this conclusion (fig. 8). At the base of this core, which dates to *c.* 8500 b.c.,[8] there is only a tiny amount of tree pollen (fig. 8). This may mean that until shortly before this date, the cold steppe extended right down to the lowest slopes.[9]

The vegetation begins to change around 9000 b.c.[10] In the lake Zeribar core tree pollen begins to appear; warm temperate cladocera became common and the cool temperate varieties fade out soon afterwards (Megard 1967). There may have been an over-

7 There is a carbon-14 date from the base of zone A-2 of 11,700 ± 160 b.c. (Y-1686) (fig. 8).
8 There is a carbon-14 date from near the base of zone B of 8,420 ± 120 b.c. (Y-1759) (fig. 8).
9 The lack of tree pollen is also recorded from the cave of Shanidar in Iraq (already mentioned for its stubbornly unchanging macro-fauna). The samples from the pre-24,000 b.c. level contain mainly herbaceous pollen with just a little tree pollen. There follows a rather mysterious stratigraphical hiatus from 24,000 to 10,000 b.c. after which there is even less tree pollen (Leroi-Gourhan 1969). This evidence has to be treated with caution. Samples from cave sediments are often less complete than those from lakes and marshes and they may be contaminated by human occupation. Moreover, the Shanidar material has never been properly published: 'the preliminary pollen counts reporting palm and fir at Shanidar, never elaborated, confirmed or published in any detail, unfortunately continue to be quoted seriously' (H. Wright 1968).
10 There is a carbon-14 date from lake Zeribar, half-way through zone B, of 9530 ± 160 b.c. (Z-1687).

all increase in temperature and precipitation (though still less than today) and perhaps also the rainfall began to be concentrated in the winter months. Between 9000 and 8000 b.c. there seems to be a gradual transition from cool steppe to warm oak-pistachio or almond-pistachio savanna and this then predominates between 8000 and 4000 b.c. First plantain (*Plantago*) invades, then slowly the tree pollen increases until by 4000 b.c. it reaches *c.* 40% of the total. Oak (*Quercus*) pollen is abundant but there is also 10% pistachio and since pistachio and almond pollen are always greatly under-represented the vegetation may be closer to a pistachio-almond savanna than to an oak-pistachio savanna (Megard 1967). The climate must have been drier than at present, although, taking into account the carbonate content and the cladoceran fossils, it was not warmer.

The lake Mirabad core shows a similar development into almond-pistachio or oak-pistachio savanna, with somewhat more oak, about the same amount of plantain and rather less *Artemisia*. Only after 4000 b.c. do the samples from Zeribar and Mirabad show that conditions were sufficiently moist for the development of the modern oak forest.

How valid is this picture of environmental change for areas beyond the Zagros mountains?

Samples from a core taken in the Ghab valley of north-west Syria, at a much lower elevation, just below 300 m., suggest a somewhat similar pattern though with less severe conditions (fig. 9). Between 37,000 and 25,000 years ago conditions were dry and relatively cold. The surrounding mountains were virtually treeless except for stands of cedar at high elevations. But then, between 23,000 and about 14,000 b.c., at a time when the Zagros region was apparently experiencing cool, dry conditions and a cool steppe vegetation, this area shows a decrease in steppe flora, both *Chenopodiaceae* and *Artemisia*, and an increase in tree pollen including a sudden peak in oak (the latter, however, is only represented in one spectrum and could be accidental). Only between 14,000 and 9000 b.c. do steppe conditions again prevail, suggesting a cool, dry climate, and then, around 9000 b.c., at about the same time that warmer conditions are signalled by oak-pistachio colonisation in the Zagros, a similar colonisation occurs in north-west Syria. But while present-day conditions did not apparently become established in the Iranian mountains until 4000 b.c., they were established in north-west Syria by 8000 b.c. (Niklewski and van Zeist 1970).

The climatic/vegetation sequence from the Ghab in north-west Syria correlates reasonably well with others from Greece and Italy,

calculated ages b.p.	local zonation	GHAB VALLEY — east flank Djebel Alaouite	GHAB VALLEY — Djebel Zawiyé	TENAGHI PHILIPPON (GREECE)	local zonation	(calculated ages) b.p.
0						
					Z 5	
5000	Z 3	forest	steppe forest	forest	Z 1-4	
	Z 2					
10000 / C 14: 10080	Z 1	steppe → forest	steppe → steppe forest	steppe → forest	Y	10300
	X 5	steppe	steppe	steppe	X 5	14600
15000	Y 4 / 3	steppe and forest				16000
20000	Y 2		steppe	steppe with pine stands	X 3,4	
	Y 1	forest and steppe				
25000	X 3	steppe				22500
30000	X 2	forest and steppe	steppe	alternately steppe and steppe with pine stands	X 1,2 P 5,6,7	
35000	X 1	steppe and forest	steppe	steppe	P 4	33000
	W 2	forest	steppe forest			37000
40000	W 1	forest and steppe	steppe	alternately steppe and steppe with pine stands	P 1,2,3	
45000 / C 14: 45650	V	steppe and forest	steppe	steppe	V 3	49000
	U 3	forest	steppe forest	steppe with pine stands	V 1,2	
	U 2					
	U 1		steppe			
	T 2		steppe forest			
	T 1	forest		forest	U	
			open forest			
C 14: 47000	S	forest and steppe				
	S		steppe	steppe	T	
		steppe and forest				
	R					

9 Tentative correlation of the vegetation history in north-western Syria and north-eastern Greece.
(Niklewski and van Zeist 1970)

though the advent of cool, dry conditions and associated steppe vegetation seems to occur at slightly different times. Since altitude, aspect and other local phenomena will have played some part it would in fact be curious if synchronisation were perfect. In fig. 9 the Ghab sequence is compared with a very detailed sequence from Tenaghi Philippon in Macedonia, which lies only 40 m. above sea-level. Here steppe conditions were established long before 48,000 b.c. Until 12,000 b.c.[11] there was an alternation between steppe and steppe with pine. After 12,000 b.c., thus somewhat earlier than in north-west Syria, there is a gradual increase in woodland, and the colonisation by trees such as hop hornbeam (*Ostryra*), hazel (*Corylus*), elm (*Ulmus*), ash (*Fraxinus*) and pistachio (*Pistacia*) suggests a marked increase in humidity and probably in temperature (Wijmstra 1969; Zeist 1971).

A core from Ioannina in north-west Greece shows a transition to steppe at a time intermediate between the Ghab and Tenaghi Philippon samples. Here, between 40,000 years ago and 20,000 b.c.,[12] there is at first evidence of woodland with firs (*Abies*), hornbeam (*Carpinus betulus*) and beech (*Fagus*), and then oak (*Quercus*) predominates. Only between 20,000 and 8250 b.c.[13] do the herbaceous pollen values shoot up, indicating drier, cooler conditions (Bottema 1967). Towards the end of this phase there is an increase in pine and fir and then after 8250 b.c. there is a decrease in *Artemisia* and an increase in oak.

Samples from northern and central Italy from the Late Pleistocene time range show a great predominance of herbaceous pollen (Bonatti 1966). A sample from a core taken from a crater lake near Rome at 200 m. altitude, shows that between 23,000 and 13,000 b.c. there was a cold *Artemisia* steppe followed by an increase in grassland between 13,000 and 10,000 b.c. and then colonisation by hazel, oak and fir.

Before one accepts these various pollen cores as illustrating a widespread climatic-vegetational sequence, one further core has to be considered which fits the pattern less neatly. This is the long core from lake Huleh in the Jordan valley, supplemented by shorter cores from the same area and from lake Kinneret lying 20 km. further south. The Huleh basin is 70 m. above sea-level while lake Kinneret lies 210 m. below sea-level. Horowitz (1971) has

11 There is a carbon-14 date for zone X2/X3 (9.50–10 m.) (fig. 9) of 20,690 ±165 b.c. (GrN 1467a); for zone Y (6.25 m.) 12,650 ±200 b.c. (GrN 4183); and for zone Zl (4.30 m.) 5900 ± 50 b.c. (GrN 4182) (Wijmstra 1969).
12 A carbon-14 date for zone 11b is 38,050 ± 1000 b.c. (GrN 4793).
13 A carbon-14 date for the upper end of zone 111 is 8250 ± 90 b.c. (GrN 4875).

suggested that he has a climatic/vegetational sequence going back to before 60,000 b.p. showing an almost perfect correlation with the European glacial sequence. Thus, for example, between 30,000 and 20,000 b.c., at the time of the maximum glacial extent (Upper Pleniglacial), pluvial conditions, cool and humid, reigned with much tree, particularly oak (*Quercus ithaburensis*) and also considerable open-field vegetation.[14] The lake was large and marsh vegetation was therefore reduced. Then between 20,000 and 14,000 b.c.,[15] at a time of glacial recession, the lake shrank, the marsh increased, conditions were warm and humid and maquis rather than woodland predominated with a decrease in oak and an increase in olive (*Olea europaea*), pistachio (*Pistacia*) and pine (*Pinus halepensis*). Subsequently, between 14,000 and 9500 b.c., correlating with a minor glacial advance, conditions became cooler and more humid with a great deal of oak and open-field vegetation. The lake again increased. Finally, from 9500 to 3000 b.c., prevailing conditions were warmer and moister than today. Horowitz states firmly: 'Pluvial phases can be correlated with European glacial phases and the same is true for the interstadials and interpluvials. Even the minor fluctuations during the Holocene have their parallels in European sediments.'

It is hard to understand why this strong correlation is found in Jordan and not, for example, in Greece – which lies closer to the ice-sheets. Though conditions in the Jordan valley were obviously less rigorous than in many other parts of South-west Asia it seems doubtful whether the climatic/vegetational changes really merit such labels as 'pluvial' or 'interstadial'. Many authorities would question Horowitz' assumption that an oak maximum is indicative of cool, humid, 'pluvial' conditions. Nor is the precise correlation with the European sequence acceptable when one notes that the long core has only one carbon-14 date. The only other carbon-14 dates, from a shallow core, are post 3000 b.c.[16]

Having now assembled all the various types of evidence, is it possible to make any generalisations? Certainly two statements are warranted. First, there is no evidence of drastic change, no violent desiccation as postulated by Childe (chapter 2, p. 24). Secondly, there were climatic/environmental changes, certainly until 8000

14 This apparent anomaly is explained in terms of local topography and water balance in the Huleh basin (Horowitz 1971).
15 There is a carbon-14 date of 16,850 ± 195 b.c. (Hv 1725).
16 There is a carbon-14 date from a depth of 11.5 m. in a borehole U.P.15 from lake Huleh of 2,615 ± 75 b.c. (Hv 1724) and from a depth of 4.5 m. of 315 ± 110 a.d. (Hv 1723).

or 7000 b.c. and in some areas, for example, the Zagros mountains, until much later. These changes may have operated at a local or regional level, or as part of a more widespread phenomenon, and they may have played some role in the transition to food production, affecting the inter-related system of patterns of exploitation, mobility and social organisation. We may suspect that the recession of the lakes and the exposure of tracts of fertile alluvial soil had some significance. We may also expect that slight environmental changes may have altered the status of present-day marginal areas. More directly, the availability and frequence of various plants and animals is likely to have affected how, where and when experimentation with herding and cultivation occurred.

On the whole the evidence, both geological and paleolimnological, suggests that despite the fact that at the time of the maximum Würm extent the snowlines were lower close to the Mediterranean coast than in the interior, conditions ameliorated more rapidly in the Levant than further to the east. Thus in the Zagros, probably even at quite low elevations (lake Mirabad), cool steppe conditions are found from 20,000 to 9000 b.c. while in the Levant woodland was fairly extensive between 20,000 and 14,000 b.c. and samples from the Ghab core suggest that steppe conditions only prevailed between 14,000 and 9000 b.c. By 8000 b.c. woodland may have already reached the present-day extent in the Levant while further east it took another 4000 years. Van Zeist (1971) has suggested that these contrasts might indicate that conditions favouring a more intensive exploitation were found in the west both prior to 14,000 b.c. and after 9000 or 8000 b.c., while further east such conditions emerged only later. Certainly there is more evidence of settled hunter-gatherer communities based on intensive exploitation in the Levant than further east. It must be admitted however that we do not know how far the distribution of wild winter cereals correlates with woodland colonisation. It may well be that such cereals were available in the Zagros long before the oak-pistachio covering was established. Nor do we know how far, if at all, animal distributions were affected (chapter 5, p. 93).

MESO-AMERICA

The ice-sheets over North America extended south of the Great Lakes – in latitude even further than those over Europe. The last glacial phase, the Wisconsin, runs parallel with the Würm in

Europe. Advances and retreats are similar though not identical (compare Butzer 1971, 274 and 354).

Meso-America and South-west Asia lie at roughly comparable distances – about 20° of latitude – south of the ice-sheets.

There was human occupation in both North and South America by 20,000 b.c and there are occasional hints that it goes back even earlier. But the great majority of the sites post-date 9000 b.c. There is no reason therefore to examine the climatic/vegetational sequence prior to 20,000 b.c.

The evidence from Meso-America is meagre. There are only a couple of deep pollen cores taken near Mexico City and another – still to be published in detail – from lake Gatún in the Canal zone of Panama. The Mexico City cores have been interpreted in a series of articles by Clisby and Sears (1955a, b). They suggest that the 33 to 22 m. section of the core contains pollen spectra indicative of moist conditions corresponding to the last glacial maximum. This is then followed by a long, vacillating pattern corresponding to the final retreat.

Evidence from New Mexico and Texas may also have some relevance. These regions lie north of Mexico and were closer to the ice-sheet. They are still more desert-like than the semi-arid uplands of north and central Mexico where early plant cultivation occurred. Conditions are therefore not directly comparable and the evidence only provides a rather general guide-line. In New Mexico and Texas the snowline was depressed by about 1300 m. (Leopold 1951). It is thought that minimum winter temperatures were not greatly altered but that the summers were considerably cooler. Today summer temperatures are around 26.5°C (80°F); with a lapse rate of 7.5°C they may have been about 16°C (61.3°F). The annual mean temperature may have been lowered by about 3°C (9.2°F) to about 16.5°C (50.4°F) (Reeves 1965). These calculations do not take into account the possible effects of changes in relative humidity. But there seems to be little evidence of increased precipitation; a rise in lake levels on the llana Estacado of north Texas is thought to be the result of a decrease in evaporation and an increase in run-off, rather than an increase in precipitation (Reeves 1965).

These findings are compatible with the macro- and micro-faunal evidence from the Tehuacán valley in central Mexico – one of the areas of early plant cultivation. The macro-faunal evidence is more satisfactory than that from South-west Asia since prior to 7000 b.c. the valley was inhabited by animals that are now either extinct in the western hemisphere or range further north in cooler and often drier regions. Species that disappeared or moved north-wards include the horse, antelope, large jack rabbit, large fox, small ground squirrel or chipmunk, gopher and quail – except for the Bobwhite quail which survived in the area (Flannery 1968). There had been mammoth in the Central Valley of Mexico but these seem to have disappeared before 10,000 b.c.

There is also micro-faunal evidence from the valley. Rodents, insects and molluscs are sensitive climatic /vegetational indicators because of their low tolerance range. They are less likely to be affected by human activity than larger animals although shell-fish and snails may be collected by men and therefore may not be indigenous to the site at which they are found. In the Tehuacán valley much of the evidence on the rodent population of the cave sites comes from the examination of owl pellets. Owls using the caves sallied forth to catch small rodents. Being eclectic in their tastes they sampled a reasonable cross-section of the rodent popula-tion. The fleshy parts of the rodents were dissolved in the stomach acids, the fur formed a cocoon round the clean skeleton and the whole was neatly regurgitated while the owl roosted (Flannery 1967). The rodent remains thus preserved show a sharp break around 7000 b.c. Before this date there were a great many deer mice but no kangaroo rats. Afterwards the position was reversed. Today the kangaroo rat is ubiquitous in the area.

Both macro- and micro-faunal evidence indicates that prior to 7000 b.c. conditions in the valley were cooler and drier. There was open grassland dotted with mesquite in the alluvial bottoms and prickly pears growing up the hillslopes (MacNeish 1967a).

In contrast, earlier, less detailed evidence from Tamaulipas in north-east Mexico was interpreted as indicating that conditions prior to 7000 b.c. were not only cooler but considerably wetter. The great number of red tropical deer was considered significant (MacNeish 1958, 197). But perhaps, rather than increased precipita-tion, it was a case of decreased evaporation and increased run-off.

After 7000 b.c. temperatures rose. Precipitation may have decreased, or more probably, higher temperatures resulted in greater evaporation. In the Tehuacán valley MacNeish (1971) postulates a diminution of grassland steppes, an expansion of thorn forest onto the alluvial slopes and an expansion of cactus onto the travertine slopes. The environment took on its present aspect. In Tamaulipas, between 7000 and 5000 b.c., red tropical deer were still slightly more prevalent than white-tail deer, but after 5000 b.c. the white-tail deer associated with drier conditions predominate (MacNeish 1958, 193).

PERU

Though Peru lay far to the south of the great ice-sheets, there were local glaciers in the high ranges. In northern Peru there are numerous relic cirques at elevations between 3300 and 3800 m. In the central area (between latitudes 8° and 15°) glaciers coalesced at elevations varying between 3500 and 4000 m. There were smaller piedmont glaciers in the Cordillera Oriental from north of Cuzco to the eastern shore of lake Titicaca. Probably the snowline during the Wisconsin maximum was about 1200 to 1300 m. lower than today (Hester 1966). Some of the upland lakes were far more extensive. Lake Titicaca, for example, is only a remnant of the much larger Pleistocene lake Ballivián (Willey 1971, 33).

So far, little work has been published on the correlation, if any, between fluctuations in the Andean glaciers and the glacial sequence over North America. When the soil and pollen analyses from Ayacucho are completed they may clarify the picture. MacNeish, in a preliminary report (1971), believes that if the Ayacucho evidence is representative of the Andean sequence it indicates that 'the South American glacial advances and retreats do not coincide with those of the Wisconsin glaciation in North America'; in which case the need for studies on local rather than widespread environmental developments again becomes apparent.

Although the lowland coastal deserts of Peru are not a primary centre of plant cultivation they are an early centre and are mentioned in chapter 7 (p. 192). There is evidence from this area that the Late Pleistocene sea-levels were between 66 and 133 m. lower than today. In the early Post-Pleistocene, between 9000 and 8000 b.c., parts of the northern coast, now true desert, were grassy savanna with stands of trees supporting herds of mastodon, horses and camelids. Lanning (1967a, 45) equates this moist, cool interlude with the Valders glacial re-advance over North America (the equivalent of the Younger Dryas in Europe). Gradually conditions became increasingly arid and a contraction of the inland fog meadows – the *lomas* – in the fourth millennium b.c. has been cited as evidence of further desiccation (Lanning 1965). However, there is some dispute over this interpretation. Parsons (1970) suggests that the more extensive *lomas* are cyclical phenomena associated with the occasional southerly extension of the warm El Niño coastal current and the resultant sharp increase in precipitation.

The evidence from Meso-America and Peru is insufficient for even the sort of tentative conclusions suggested for South-west Asia.

In sum, information on climatic and environmental change is inadequate. Although there were changes of local, regional and continental character we may reasonably doubt that food-production was simply the outcome of 'a historical imperative dictated by the converging effects of the physical environmental change on (man) ... and on his sources of food' (Raikes 1967, 135). But we may accept that environmental change played some part in many subsistence adaptations, including the move to food-production. 'Changes in the ecosystem became interconnected with changes in subsistence; with changes in subsistence patterns there were alterations in the ecosystem' (MacNeish 1971). We may suspect that their importance was more marked in some regions than in others.

5 The Distribution of Potential Domesticates

In 1807 Alexander von Humboldt stated that the origin of cultivated plants was 'un secret impénétrable'. Ever since, people have been trying to find the key. One approach has been to concentrate on the problem of the distribution of the wild progenitors. The idea behind this is simple. Cultivation can only occur where potential cultigens are available. If the distribution of the relevant wild species can be discovered then potential areas of early cultivation can be delimited. The same holds true for animal domestication.

But – and each of these early chapters seems to begin with a series of 'but's' – it is less simple than it sounds.

WHAT ARE POTENTIAL DOMESTICATES?

Vast numbers of plants and animals are potential domesticates. We tend to think in terms of plants and animals that are important in modern-day economies. But there must have been trial-and-error, and what became important was not necessarily originally so. For example in Meso-America amaranth was, to begin with, more important than maize. The related plant, quinoa, is unimportant today but once had great ritual significance (Sauer 1963a). In the Mississippi valley not only amaranth but also giant ragweed (*Ambrosia trifida* L.), lamb's-quarters (*Chenopodium* sp.), sunflower (*Helianthus annuus* L.), and marsh elder or half-breed weed (*Iva xanthifolia* [Fresen.], *Nutt.*) may all have been cultivated[1] – some at a very early date (Fowler 1971). Early cultigens need not have been food crops; in many societies plants were used as containers or ornaments, or for dyes, medicines, fibres, stimulants or poisons (Harris 1967).

The range of potential animal domesticates is equally wide. Gazelle may have been herded in early Post-Pleistocene times in

---

1 Though the noted increase in size could also be the result of selective gathering.

the Levant. Mesopotamian seals of the fourth and third millennia b.c. show gazelle and oryx antelope as part of the temple herds. Other Mesopotamian seals dating *c.* 2500 b.c. show fallow deer in enclosures (Isaac 1970, 100). Other species may have been loose-herded. At the present time both musk-ox and moose come into contact with their herders only at certain times of the year (Wilkinson 1972). Such practices would be hard to verify in the archaeological record.[2]

So the number of potential distributions that could be considered is very large.

What are nuclear centres?

It has often been unquestioningly accepted that domestication is likely to have begun where there was a great *range* of potential domesticates – thus the search could be reduced to a few 'nuclear areas'. But this may be an illusion. Harlan has recently suggested that there may be centres and non-centres – nuclear areas and diffuse areas. The non-centres are ones where over a wide region 'different crops were introduced into cultivation in different areas at different times' (Harlan 1972). South-west Asia, north China and Meso-America may be centres; Africa, South-east Asia (and the South Pacific) and South America may be non-centres. It must be admitted that the non-centres are primarily root-crop areas about which there is scant information and where the importance of diffu-sion rather than independent experimentation has still to be evaluated (Appendix A). But though it is too early to assess the validity of the concept, it provides a warning against unthinkingly concentrating only on nuclear areas.

Even within an accepted nuclear area one has to proceed cautiously. Was the potential variability initially exploited? Could not just one or two plants or animals have been domesticated and then, later, the range have been extended? Helbaek (1959a, b) proposed that the early farmers in South-west Asia cultivated a combination of barley, emmer and einkorn wheat (as well as pulses). Since the wild emmer has a rather restricted distribution he concluded that cultivation must have begun within a fairly circumscribed area. But sites have been found where emmer was apparently not culti-vated (Tepe Guran, Tepe Sabz, Mureybit and Mersin) and it seems quite probable that einkorn wheat was domesticated inde-

2 Wilkinson (1972) has a fine list of animals in close relationship with man in many parts of the world at different times.

pendently of emmer (J. Renfrew 1969; Harlan 1967). One has always to bear in mind that the reasons behind the initial experimentation varied from site to site, from area to area, and that the generalisations are at most only rough approximations to reality.

But let us accept that there are nuclear centres and that of the areas we are dealing with both South-west Asia and Meso-America fall into this category. In order to delimit the potential 'centres' more precisely we want to know what was available in the early Post-Pleistocene when early experimentation occurred. We are not interested in what is available today. But the evidence on past distributions is totally inadequate, for it is virtually limited to material from archaeological sites and pollen cores. Investigators have therefore been forced to work with modern distributions.

THE RELEVANCE OF PRESENT-DAY CENTRES OF DIVERSITY

Many investigators, using such material, still adhere to some well-worn (sometimes out-worn) propositions formulated by Nikolai Ivanovich Vavilov in the 1920s and 1930s.[3] One proposition was that cultivated plant species (and their parasites and enemies) showed centres of diversity. Another was that this diversity was the result of a very long process of cultivation and therefore indicated centres of origin of domestication. Centres of diversity thus became synonymous with centres of origin. Vavilov and his workers collected vast numbers of plants from more than twenty-five countries; wheat alone was represented by 26,000 strains. Using this material Vavilov was able to demonstrate, for example, that while cultivated wheat species in Europe showed relatively little diversity, those in South-west Asia, Ethiopia, Afghanistan and the Mediterranean showed great diversity. He went on to demonstrate that the centres of diversity of different crops often overlapped. Thus in South-west Asia wheat, barley, rye, lentil, flax, vines, figs and pistachio were all equally varied, whilst in the Andes the crops were potatoes, tomatoes, tobacco and lima beans. In 1926 he proposed six world centres of plant cultivation, in 1935 he increased this to eight, with further subdivisions (Vavilov 1954, 21). Since then the tendency has been for 'lumping' rather than 'splitting' so that, for example, Turkey, Syria, Palestine,

3 His was not the first attempt to define centres of origin. There had been De Candolle's *Géographie Botanique Raisonnée* in 1855 and *Origines des Plantes Cultivées* in 1882, with Darwin's *Variation of Animal and Plant under Domestication* sandwiched between in 1868, but these were all fairly theoretical approaches (Darlington 1963, 134).

Transcaucasia, Iran and Afghanistan form one centre rather than two or three.

But it is becoming clear that one cannot automatically correlate diversity and origins. Helbaek (1960) states categorically 'varietal multiplicity in a species has, fundamentally, no dependence on a very long time factor'. Ethiopia, for example, despite its diversity of cultivated crops has none of the wild relatives and so can hardly be an originating centre. Diversity is frequently found in areas which combine a wide range of ecological niches with partial isolation (Zohary 1970a). Vavilov was aware of this fact but simply subsumed it under general conditions leading to both diversity *and* origin: 'The diversity of conditions, ranging from desert to oasis, and from soils devoid of humus to soils of the alpine and sub-alpine zones rich in this substance – have favoured the origin and concentration in these countries of an exceptional specific diversity of vegetation' (Vavilov 1926, 243).

The problems associated with using plant diversity as an indicator of origin are compounded by the fact that both cultivated and wild species often have a diffuse origin, for as a species enlarges its geographical range it changes, evolves and picks up additional germ plasm (introgression) from its relatives (Harlan 1970). Moreover, man-made selections 'permitted still wider use of the crop and more infiltration of strange germ plasm and still more cycles of induced variability. When varieties from different nuclear areas came together, still more variability and still wider adaptation became possible' (Harlan 1961).[4] So sunflowers, *Helianthus annuus* L., spread across North America in the last one or two hundred years in the wake of the plough, ' "Donations" of genes from *different* species, situated in *different* locations and adapted to *different* environments allowed *Helianthus annuus* to expand rapidly over the entire area' (Zohary 1970a). In Meso-America primitive maize crossed with tripsacum and teosinte giving a great boost in variability; so much so that having absorbed the heredities of its relatives it apparently swamped its wild progenitor out of existence. We have already seen how in South-west Asia hexaploid wheats have no wild ancestor but are the result of a cross between emmer wheat and a goat-grass, perhaps *Aegilops squarrosa* (chapter 3, p. 59). Darlington (1963, 136) concludes: 'Species in cultivation no less than in nature arise and develop by utterly different processes . . . the results likewise are

---

4 Again, Vavilov recognised this, without perhaps following up the implications: 'Cases are known in which the present large number of varieties comprising a species is the result of a union of two or more species or their hybridisation' (Vavilov 1951, 18).

utterly diverse in their coherence or lack of it.' Some species have a single or sudden origin, while for others 'the origin is no origin at all but a gradual transformation, extending over wide areas and long periods and shifting its focus in the course of time'. How then can one talk of domesticated species originating in specific nuclear centres? What originated was a primitive domesticate that may not even exist today.

In sum, one will never arrive at a precise delimitation of 'centres of origin'. It is much less confusing if one gets rid of this concept and instead considers nuclear areas of initial domestication and centres of diversity as two different things (Harlan 1970).

THE VALIDITY OF PRESENT-DAY DISTRIBUTIONS AS INDICATORS OF THE PAST

If diversity of cultivated species is not an index of origin, how can the nuclear areas be defined? Recent work had concentrated on assessing, through genetic affinities,[5] the probable wild progenitors of domesticated plants and animals, and then tramping the hills to find the 'wild' distributions. Zohary (1970a) has optimistically stated that in South-west Asia wild wheat and barley distributions are well known and 'most of the elements for such an assessment are also available for rye, oats, lentils, chickpeas, broad beans, vines, olives, figs and pistachios'. Harlan (1970), his partner in many projects, says pessimistically, 'we have only the sketchiest knowledge of the distribution and ecological behaviour of the wild species (of wheat)'. Assessments of the present state of knowledge obviously differs, but even if the information were available this use of present-day wild distributions raises a further series of questions. Indeed, most investigators carefully insert some caveat that the 'wild' distributions must, for one reason or another, be used with some caution. However, caveat made, they then proceed to use them to make fairly sweeping predictions. Modern distributions do almost certainly have some significance, but 'the one reason or another' needs to be carefully set out.

The most important question is whether the present distributions are the same as those pertaining when early farming began. We have already examined the climatic evidence (chapter 4) and found

5 Cytology is the study of chromosomes. These are the thread-like objects which bear the genes and are found in the nuclei of the cells of all higher organisms. Each species usually has a fixed number of chromosomes. By comparing number, size, form and behaviour of the chromosomes of cultivated and wild species one gets a fairly good idea of their relationship (Hawkes 1967).

that, however inadequately documented, there were changes. In parts of South-west Asia there was a shift at the end of the Pleistocene, around 9000 b.c., from cold steppe vegetation to an oak–pistachio covering. Present-day climatic conditions probably stabilised around 7000 b.c. (Raikes 1967, 110). The earliest evidence of herding and cultivation dates to about this time, or even somewhat earlier. We cannot therefore take it for granted that conditions were precisely as today. Indeed, there may be some correlation between changes in vegetation and shifts in the subsistence patterns. Unfortunately, we do not know how far the distributions of important potential domesticates were affected by Late Pleistocene and Post-Pleistocene changes. It may be that some were not directly affected; sheep and goat, for example, are more affected by the type of terrain than by the vegetation or climatic regime. Wild einkorn and emmer thrive as a natural component of both park-forest and steppe-like formations (Zohary 1970b). But some distributions may have been less extensive prior to the stabilisation of present-day conditions. Van Zeist (1969) has suggested that cereal distribution may have been much more limited.

Accepting that prior to 7000 b.c. conditions may have been rather different, this would only affect a few, very early sites. The majority of sites date sometime later. If present-day conditions had stabilised, then modern distributions should be relevant. None the less, slight environmental change during the last 9000 years will make precise delimitation impossible. This lack of precision will particularly affect the study of the environmental potential of sites which today appear to be very marginal.

Many small-scale changes in plant distribution have been caused by man. For example, in the oak–pistachio belt, both the oak and the pistachio have virtually disappeared under the onslaught of grazing animals. We do not know what effect the over-grazing has had on wild grass distribution. It was suggested in chapter 4 (p. 66) that the plain of Konya in Anatolia presented a very different aspect in the seventh millennium b.c. It was then probably an area of good grassland, perhaps with wild cereal stands. But arable farming reduced the vegetation covering, which in turn reduced the water retention. The great herds of cattle could no longer be supported and they were replaced by sheep and goat with the attendant ill-effects of over-grazing. Fairly recently irrigation led to an increase in salinity and this too has affected the plant covering. Clearly present-day distributions will not correspond with those pertaining when the great township of Çatal Hüyük flourished (Cohen 1969, 1970).

Ploughing also affects plant distributions, for grasses like barley and einkorn with a natural 'weedy' tendency thrive on disturbed habitats and will colonise the waysides and field boundaries. Harlan and Zohary (1966) suggest that in Afghanistan much of the barley is segetal, i.e. a secondary colonisation, but that some 'seems' to be growing in primary habitats and may be a specific steppe race associated with the open grasslands. The 'wild' barley reported from Cyprus, Crete, western Anatolia, northern Iran and southern U.S.S.R. all 'seems' to occur in secondary disturbed habitats. There is clearly often some doubt as to whether distributions are primary or secondary.

Local changes in distribution may also result from local changes in hydrology. Beidha in southern Jordan, *c.* 6800 b.c., was probably situated in a valley filled with fertile alluvium which retained a considerable amount of water run-off from the surrounding bare rocks. Flash-floods and lack of terracing led to the almost complete erosion of the alluvium and today it takes considerable imagination to understand why the site was initially occupied. Five kilometres away, on the escarpment, rainfall is sufficient to allow the growth of wild cereals (Raikes 1967, 173). The fact that none are found today does not alter the possibility that they may have been present 9000 years ago.

Two final examples of the problem of exact distribution delimitation. One-seeded einkorn, *Triticum boeoticum* ssp. *aegilopoides*, is today restricted to western Anatolia and the south Balkans, but it is found on early farming sites much further to the east, at Çayönü in south-east Turkey, Jarmo in Iraq and Ali Kosh in Iran (J. Renfrew 1969, Zeist 1972). At Çayönü there is mainly domesticated one-seeded einkorn, plus a little wild one-seeded einkorn, and a few possible two-seeded specimens. Van Zeist (1972) proposed that since Çayönü lay outside the (modern!) range of one-seeded einkorn the grain must have been imported, along with the stray wild grain, and that since virtually no two-seeded einkorn is found, although the site is within the (modern!) range of two-seeded einkorn, the local population was not indulging in wild plant gathering.[6] Given all the potential causes of slight alterations in the wild distribution in the past nine thousand years, such precise predictions seem unwarranted.

The second example underlines this point. *Aegilops squarrosa*, or an ancestral form of *Aegilops squarrosa*, is generally thought to

6 It is not clear whether the emmer from the lowest levels is wild or domesticated. Van Zeist, in keeping with the above assessment, suggested that though morphologically 'wild' it was in process of cultivation.

have been a component of the hexaploid wheats (p. 59). Its distribution centre is close to the Caspian Sea and Zohary (1971) suggested
that the cross between domesticated emmer and the wild grass
occurred somewhere in this region. However, the earliest examples
of domesticated hexaploids are found far to the west, at Knossos
on Crete and at Tell Ramad in Syria (H. Jarman 1972).

Although the foregoing arguments have concentrated on plant
distributions they are equally applicable to animal distributions.
The problems have been succinctly summed up in a recent paper
by Jarman and Wilkinson (1972). A 'wild' population may in fact
be feral, i.e. 'escapees' from domesticated stock. 'Wild' distributions
may have been so affected by selective pressures during the last few
millennia that they no longer correspond to Late Pleistocene or
early Post-Pleistocene distributions and may only represent a
fraction of the former distribution, having been displaced or become
extinct over much of the former range.

So far we have indulged in destruction. Can anything be retrieved? Despite all the problems, it still seems true that there are
nuclear areas of initial domestication. That in these areas a variety
of plants, and sometimes animals, were domesticated, and that, by
and large, vegetation zones may have been relatively stable since
7000 b.c., though many individual distributions have since been
altered. It should be possible to accept with caution well-documented
distributions and to use them to make certain generalisations about
the approximate areas in which the various plants and animals might
initially have been brought into domestication. The evidence must
not be pushed too far.

Below, the distributions of certain of the plants and animals
associated with early farming in South-west Asia and the Aegean
are set out. The evidence of New World distributions is so scrappy
that it is dealt with in Appendix B.

SOME PLANT AND ANIMAL DISTRIBUTIONS IN SOUTH-WEST ASIA AND
THE AEGEAN

(a) Winter cereals

The main crops grown by the early farmers of South-west Asia
were winter cereals and pulses. There is little detailed information
on the pulses – though both lentils and field-peas are apparently
not indigenous to Anatolia (Helbaek 1970).

The early cultivators concentrated on three types of winter
cereal: barley, einkorn wheat and emmer wheat. A little later

a fourth type, hexaploid wheat, was grown. In broad terms these winter cereals flourish in the sub-tropics, between 25°N and 45°N, in areas where high rainfall variability is often combined with rainfall minima just sufficient to prevent complete destruction by drought. The minimum mean rainfall is *c*. 300 to 500 mm. though this is somewhat modified by latitude (closer to the Equator where temperatures are higher, evaporation is greater) and by soil-types, aspect, etc. (Raikes 1967, 134, 123). The rain falls mainly in the winter months; summers are dry and hot.

These wild cereals have a 'weedy' tendency, they need much soil nitrogen and so flourish on 'open' soils where there is not too much competition (Hawkes 1969). Indeed, it has often been proposed that when men began to create 'disturbed' environments – grazing-lands, middens and trackways – these 'weedy' crops moved in. Man found them useful, harvested them, extended the 'disturbed' area by clearing, hoeing, etc. and eventually the weed became a crop. This 'dump heap' theory has been criticised for not taking into account that weeds have evolved just as much as crops; 'the sequence is more likely to be from wild plant adapted to naturally disturbed habitats to a crop-weed complex', i.e. both crop and weed-companion derive from the same wild progenitor (Harlan and de Wet 1965; Harlan 1970). In some cases the weeds later became crops in their own right. Both oats and rye seem to have been introduced into Europe as weeds in barley and wheat crops, but then in colder, less favourable climes they were taken into cultivation,

The wild cereals particularly favour 'open' soils on basaltic and limestone formations, where they may form the dominant plants. Stands can be very extensive, very dense and very high yielding. It is reckoned that today, in a good year, wild emmer near the Sea of Galilee yields 50 to 80 kg. per 1000 square metres which compares favourably with 50 to 150 kg. for locally-grown durum and barley (Zohary 1969).

But barley and the different wheat races do not have precisely the same distributions. Wild barley, *Hordeum spontaneum* Koch., progenitor of domesticated *Hordeum distichum* L. and probably *Hordeum vulgare* var. *nudum* (see chapter 3, p. 54) has the widest distribution – from Afghanistan and probably still further east in the Hindu-Kush and Tibet, to Soviet Central Asia and westwards to the East Mediterranean (fig. 10). It does not tolerate extreme cold and so is rarely found above 1500 m., but does tolerate considerable drought and so extends into the warm steppes and desert fringes. 'It grows in the mountain forest, on the coastal plain,

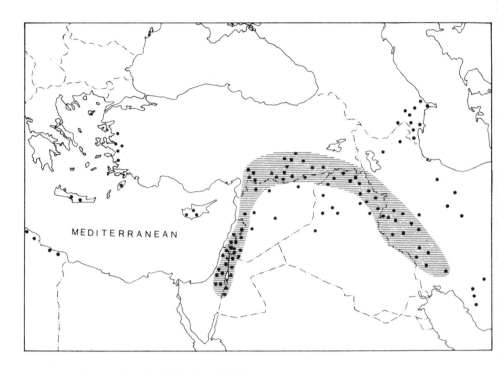

10   Distribution of wild barley, *Hordeum spontaneum*. Dots represent known sites.
Areas in which primary habitats occur are shaded.
(Zohary 1969)

in the shade of rock outcrops in semi-desert areas and as a weed in
the fields of every conceivable crop' (Helbaek 1960).

Several races have been distinguished – some are adapted to
primary habitats, others are very weedy and probably spread in the
wake of farming. There is a small-seeded race found at elevations
between 500 and 1500 m. on the hillslopes off the Tauros range
in south-eastern Turkey and along the Zagros range in Iraq and
Iran. It is thought that the stands found close to the upper margins
are segetal, but lower down stands in 'rather primary habitats'
form a component of the open woodland (*Quercus brantii*) (Harlan
and Zohary 1966).

In contrast to this race there is a more vigorous type found in
the catchment area of the upper Jordan valley, in south-west Syria,
north-west Jordan and northern Israel. This barley has large seeds
and long awns and is found in primary stands as a component of the
park-forest (*Quercus ithaburensis*). Towards the north it grades into
the Turkish–Iraqi race mentioned above. Towards the south and
east, at lower elevations, it tends to hybridise with a third race, a

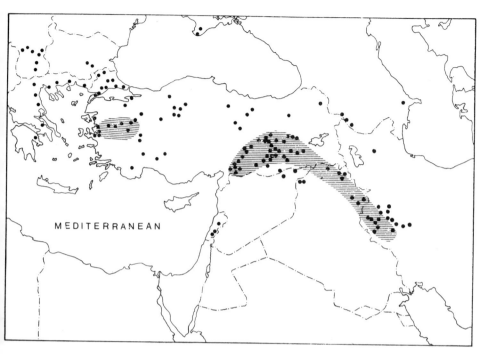

11   Distribution of wild einkorn, *Triticum boeoticum*. Dots represent known sites. Areas in which primary habitats occur are shaded. (Zohary 1969)

small, slender, very 'grassy' wadi race found at low elevation, — 350 m. to + 600 m., from the Negev and Sinai northwards to the Turkish border and eastwards to Afghanistan.

These three South-west Asian races of barley are fairly well documented, but information is less precise to the east and west. Barley from North Africa has been reported as a component of the open woodlands and scrub of Cyrenaica. Most of the examples from Crete, Cyprus, western Anatolia, western Iran and southern U.S.S.R. are thought to be segetal; so too are those from the east – from Tashkent and Quetta. But others from Afghanistan may be a primary form – a component of the steppes. Harlan and Zohary (1966) sum up: 'the wild barley is too widespread, and sometimes too conspicuously weedy to do more than indicate the general perimeter of the most likely region of early domestication.'

Wild einkorn wheat, *Triticum boeoticum* Boiss., has a distribution which is more limited than barley but wider than emmer. It is found from Transcaucasia right across northern Iraq, Syria, Turkey and into the Balkans. The centre of distribution seems to

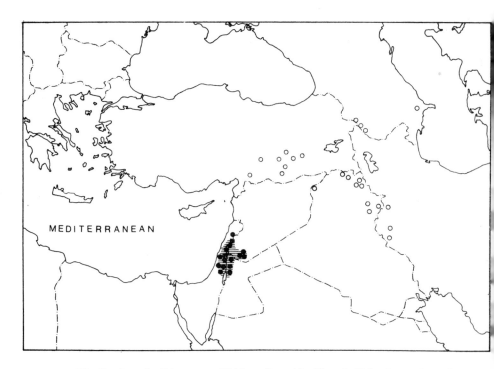

12 Distribution of wild emmer, *Triticum dicoccoides*. Dots in Palestine and south Syria represent known sites of *Triticum dicoccoides*. Hollow dots represent *Triticum araraticum*. The map is incomplete for *Triticum dicoccoides* has now been found in Turkey and Iran and probably Iraq.
(Zohary 1969)

lie in a belt from Syria through southern Turkey to northern Iraq and adjacent Iran (fig. 11). It is more tolerant of cold than barley, so grows at altitudes up to 2000 m., but less tolerant of drought, so rarely exists below 600 m. Like barley it is tolerant of a wide range of habitats, from the low foothills of the Euphrates with little rainfall and high temperatures, to the high plateaus and mountain ridges of Anatolia with a cool, continental climate. It forms a natural component of both herbaceous park forest and of steppe-like formations (Zohary 1970b).

Two main races can be distinguished: a small one-seeded race, *Triticum boeoticum* ssp. *aegilopoides*, now found only in western Anatolia and the south Balkans, and a larger, generally two-seeded type, *Triticum boeoticum* ssp. *thaoudar*, found in south-east Turkey, Iraq and Iran. In central Anatolia and Transcaucasia all intergradations are present (Harlan and Zohary 1966).

Domesticated emmer, *Triticum dicoccum* Schübl., derives from wild emmer, *Triticum dicoccoides* Korn. The latter, in turn, is the result of introgression between wild einkorn, *Triticum boeoticum* Boiss., and a species of goat-grass, probably the ancestor of the present-day *Aegilops speltoides*.

This goat-grass has a more restricted distribution than wild einkorn, though it too forms a natural component of herbaceous formations. It is not found in northern Iran or Transcaucasia but does grow around the East Mediterranean. Its distribution centre lies through southern Turkey, northern Syria and northern Iraq. It spreads over the Anatolian plateau, as far west as Thrace, and as far south as Central Israel (Zohary 1970b).

The distribution of wild emmer does not match up with the overlap zone of einkorn and *Aegilops speltoides*, but why should it? Emmer is less tolerant than either, so the initial hybrids would only have survived in favourable habitats. It needs warmer conditions than einkorn and so only overlaps the southern and eastern fringes of the einkorn distribution, at altitudes usually between 750 and 1000 m. – although it has been found at — 100 m. in the Sea of Galilee basin and at 1400 m. on Mount Hermon. It has no great weedy tendency and so would not have spread as a segetal component. Two races of emmer are known from South-west Asia. *Triticum dicoccoides* is a robust, large-seeded form with heavy awns, wide

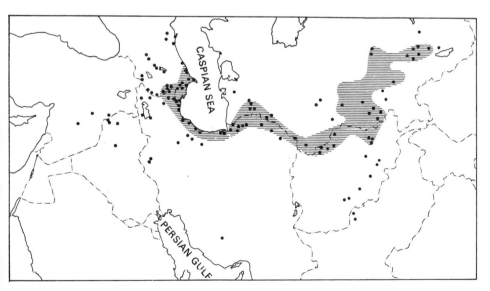

13   Distribution of wild goat-grass, *Aegilops Sqarrosa*. Dots represent known sites. Areas in which primary habitats occur are shaded.
(Zohary 1969)

leaves and thick stems. It is found in the upper Jordan valley – in Israel, southern Syria and Transjordan (fig. 12) (Harlan and Zohary 1966). It can be a component of either steppe formation or park-forest. Until recently there seemed to be a gap in the distribution between this race and the more easterly one, *Triticum araraticum*, but now scattered finds of *Triticum dicoccoides* have been reported from southern Turkey and western Iran and it may also occur in northern Iraq (Zohary 1971).[7]

The second race, *Triticum araraticum*, is a much smaller form, not much larger than wild einkorn. Though it overlaps with *Triticum dicoccoides* its centre of distribution lies further to the east. It is found in Soviet Armenia and Georgia, as well as Turkey, Iran and Iraq (fig. 12). It is never really abundant, occurring in isolated patches or thin scatters in the lower oak-woodland. It never forms the dominant species of the grassland flora (Harlan and Zohary 1966). Among modern cultivated crops this wild form has only one close cultivated relative, *Triticum timopheevi*, found in Georgia, U.S.S.R. *Triticum dicoccoides* would seem to be the progenitor of all the other present-day South-west Asian domesticated forms (Zohary 1970b). This, of course, does not rule out the possibility that there were early cultivated forms related to *Triticum araraticum*, which, being less effective, were later swamped by the cultivated descendents of *Triticum dicoccoides*.

Finally, the distribution of another goat-grass needs to be mentioned. *Aegilops squarrosa*, or an ancestor thereof, seems to have played a part in the origin of the hexaploid wheats (p. 59). *Aegilops squarrosa* is a tolerant plant, found in deserts, steppe and temperate forest. It can occur in primary or segetal situations. It has a rather easterly centre of distribution, in the South Caspian area, but also extends into Iran, adjacent Transcaucasia and Transcaspia, and is found westwards to eastern Turkey and western Iraq and eastwards to Pakistan and Kashmir (fig. 13) (Zohary 1970b).

(b) *Potential animal domesticates*

The distribution of potential animal domesticates is more problematic.

Sheep and goat – possibly preceded by gazelle – seem to be the earliest domesticates in South-west Asia, appearing in the

---

7 Though the two races are very similar morphologically, they differ in chromosome pairings and hybrids are sterile. However, a cytogenetically bridging form has now been discovered, interfertile with both (Rao and Smith cited by Dagan and Zohary 1970).

archaeological record sometimes in the ninth millennium b.c. The distributions are difficult to ascertain. The first problem, already mentioned in chapter 3 (p. 43), is how to tell them apart. Quite recently a most heretical view was put forward, that the two species did not become distinct prior to the Late Pleistocene. Payne (1968) suggested that until then there was a single capra-ovine stock and that towards the end of the Pleistocene isolated populations in North Africa, India and East Asia became separated from those of Europe, South-west Asia and Western Asia. Some-where within this last grouping the modern genera, *Capra* and *Ovis* emerged, either from an isolated pocket of caprine stock or as a genetic freak suddenly producing an isolated gene pool, or even as the result of human selection. The fact that there are apparently no well-documented cases of wild sheep prior to 9000 b.c. seems to favour this thesis.

This theory, however, has been firmly squashed on several grounds. The functional complex of male agonistic behaviour and cranial morphology in sheep and goat are so different that it is thought that they must have separated out several million years ago (Reed and Schaffer 1972b). There are also very considerable biological distinctions: the haemoglobin A and B structures reflect multiple differences between the two species; at least four mutations are involved in the gene for the haemoglobin B chain alone. The im-munoglobins show equally important antigenic differences. Not only are there considerable differences in haemoglobin structure between the two species, but also between domesticated and wild sheep (both the wild Argali, *Ovis ammon*, and the wild mouflon, *Ovis musimon*). This rather negates the argument that sheep could result from human selection and that all so-called 'wild' sheep are, in reality, feral (Curtain 1971). Finally, chromosome pairings are quite different: domesticated sheep have 54, while domesticated goat have 60 (Curtain 1971). Payne's case does not sound too convincing, though the lack of Pleistocene sheep still needs an explanation.

Accepting the more orthodox view that sheep and goat separated out at some distant time in the past, there is very little evidence of early Post-Pleistocene wild stock in Europe. At most there were pockets around the Mediterranean: sheep or goat have been reported from Upper Palaeolithic contexts in the Kastritsa cave, Epirus, Greece (Renfrew 1972, 269) and in Mesolithic contexts from Châteauneuf-les-Martigues in southern France (Escalon de Fonton 1966). At the latter site there is some possibility of an independent attempt at domestication in the seventh millennium

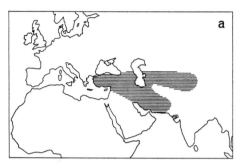
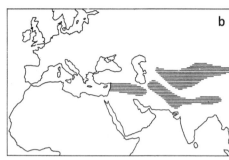

14   Generalised distribution of wild goat   Generalised distribution of wild sheep

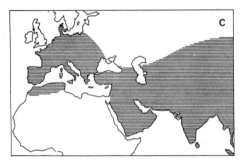
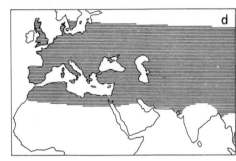

Generalised distribution of wild pig   Generalised distribution of wild cattle
                                              (Piggott 1965)

b.c. But far the greater part of the distribution is concentrated in South-west Asia and further to the east. Although the potential area for domestication is more limited than for dog, cattle or pig, it is still very considerable. Sheep and goat are tolerant beasts. Wild sheep need rolling meadows, but where these are available, survive at sea level around the Caspian and at 2700 m. in the Zagros mountains. Goats, given rugged terrain, are found at sea level on the Persian Gulf, at 180 m. in the sandstone hills of south-west Iran and at 3000 m. in the Zagros mountains (Flannery 1965).

Again following the orthodox view, domesticated sheep, *Ovis aries*, are descended from the wild Urial or Asiatic mouflon, *Ovis orientalis*, which is found in Cyprus, Anatolia, the Zagros mountains, Afghanistan, Baluchistan, Kashmir and the Punjab. The distribution extends northwards to Transcaucasia and south and west into Russian Turkestan (fig. 14b).

The goat, *Capra hircus*, is descended from the bezoar, *Capra hircus aegagrus*, found in Asia Minor, the Zagros mountains, the Elburz mountains and the Caucasus (fig. 14a) (Hole, Flannery and Neely

1969, 266). Payne (1968) extends this distribution to include a slight overspill into north-east Africa.

The wild aurochs, *Bos primigenius*, ancestor of the cow, *Bos taurus*, has such a wide distribution that no potential 'centre' can be demarcated. It apparently once roamed from north-west Europe to Russia, through South-west and East Asia and through North Africa (fig. 14d) (Grigson 1969). The extent of the eastern and southern range is unclear because of the possibility that the Indian wild cow, *Bos indicus*, spread beyond the sub-continent. It is also very difficult to distinguish between *Bos primigenius*, bison (*Bison bonasus*) and water buffalo (Jarman 1969). But at least in South-west Asia, there is no evidence of bison south of the Caucasus though there is the possibility of water buffalo in the Lebanon (Hole, Flannery and Neely 1969, 298).

Cattle do not seem to have been among the first animal domesticates; so far the earliest finds date to the mid-seventh millennium b.c. So far also, domesticated cattle have only been found at sites where domesticated sheep or goat are present. This is perhaps not surprising – to initiate animal herding by penning wild aurochs, weighing a ton apiece and having a horn span of three feet, would seem a bold venture. In reality it is not perhaps as difficult as it looks – it has been found that musk-ox calves, if caught when four to six months old, are relatively easily man-handled (Wilkinson 1972).

Even if cattle herding was originally associated with sheep or goat rearing, this does not mean that the first attempts were necessarily restricted to the more confined natural habitat of sheep or goat. For example, early farmers could have arrived in Europe, bringing with them the knowledge of breeding and domesticated sheep and goat, and then attempted to domesticate the local aurochs. The evidence for domesticated cattle in Greece is as early as that from South-west Asia. Against this reconstruction of events is the fact that both at Knossos on Crete and at Nea Nicomedeia in Macedonia the domesticated cattle are small. If the local wild aurochs were being domesticated one would expect a greater range in size. Only later, when farming spread to south-east and Central Europe is there a wide range in size and good evidence for local breeding (Bökönyi 1971a).

Pigs, *Sus scrofa*, like cattle, could have been domesticated over a very wide area (fig. 14c). However, with the possible very dubious exception of the Tas Ayir and Zamil Koba cave sites in the South Crimean mountains, there is no indication that pigs were independently domesticated in Europe (Tringham 1969). In South-west

Asia there is no evidence of domestication until about 7000 b.c. Part of the explanation for the delay may be that unlike the ruminants, pigs have little ability to break down foodstuffs such as dry grass, leaves, twigs, etc., and they therefore compete directly for food with man. Moreover, 'to cycle grain through a pig before consumption by man is to lose more than three-fourths of the potential energy originally present in the grain' (Reed 1969).

Finally the wolf, considered to be the progenitor of the dog, *Canis familiaris*, is again widespread throughout Europe and South-west Asia and independent domestication is likely to have occurred over and over again, particularly as the dog is just as useful to hunters as to herders and the taming of wolf pups up to six or seven weeks is extremely easy (Clutton-Brock 1969a; Reed 1969). This postulated diffuse origin is underlined by finds of domesticated dog at Star Carr in England *c.* 7500 b.c. and at Cayönü in south-eastern Turkey and Jarmo in Iraq at about 7000 b.c.

The assumption, mentioned on p. 90, that barley and emmer were originally cultivated together is often linked with the further assumption that sheep and goat husbandry went hand-in-hand with cereal farming. This would mean that the area in which the initial experimentation began in South-west Asia could be reduced to the lowest common denominator which – in terms of wild distributions – is emmer. It is true that so far most excavated sites do show a mixed economy, but this is a somewhat circular form of proof, for the search has concentrated on the zone where all the wild distributions overlap. The possibility of independent sheep- or goat-herding settlements, or even cattle- or pig-herding, and the possibility that einkorn or barley may have been domesticated without emmer must certainly be borne in mind. One can accept that there is an important centre in South-west Asia where many potential domesticates co-exist, but to confine the search to this centre may distort the attempt to understand the processes involved in the gradual shift to food-production.

6   South-west Asia

PROBLEMS OF DELIMITATION OF THE SOUTH-WEST ASIAN CENTRE

Food-production, both plant cultivation and animal domestication, began early in South-west Asia and, as far as can be established, represents an indigenous development. This chapter is concerned with the archaeological evidence for the transition to food-production. It concentrates primarily on the Mediterranean and Warm Temperate zones within South-west Asia (fig. 7) although in all probability the original 'centre' was more extensive.

It is legitimate to exclude Egypt. Clark (1971) suggested that there may have been early attempts to cultivate local grasses and perhaps herd local animals such as cattle, oryx and gazelle, but the evidence is insubstantial. There is a hiatus in the archaeological record between 15,000 and 5000 b.c. and so far at least the transition to food-production in Egypt appears to be linked with the introduction of emmer, barley, sheep and goats from the Levant.

It is also reasonable to exclude much of Europe. Certain animals may have been loose herded but this did not lead to a basic modification of the hunter-gatherer way of life.[1]

The exclusion or inclusion of the Aegean (more precisely the European part of the Aegean) is more problematic. There is good evidence that by 6000 b.c. there were farming communities on Crete, in Greece and probably Macedonia.[2] On the Greek mainland (at Argissa, Sesklo, Souphli, Achilleion, Ghediki and Nea

---

[1] At Châteauneuf-les-Martigues in the Bouches-du-Rhône, southern France, sheep may have been herded in the seventh millennium b.c. – although the suggestion is based solely on an increase in the number of caprine bones, not on changes in the age/sex structure or the morphology (Fonton 1966). Evidence for the manipulation of deer herds in Europe is discussed by Jarman (1972b). Tringham (1969) mentions rather doubtfully the possibility of independent pig domestication at Soroki in the Bug-Dniester basin of Russian Moldavia in the late sixth millennium b.c. In the same article she demolishes the rest of the 'evidence' for independent domestication around the Crimea.

[2] The carbon-14 dates for Nea Nikomedeia range from 6230 ± 150 b.c. to 5330 ± 75 b.c. On cultural grounds it is more likely to have been occupied around the mid-sixth millennium b.c.

Nicomedeia) emmer, einkorn and barley were cultivated (J. Renfrew 1966; Zeist and Bottema 1971; Renfrew 1972, 271). At Knossos on Crete the more advanced hexaploid wheat was also grown (Evans 1971). All the communities kept herds of sheep and goat and some kept a few cattle and pig[3] (Higgs 1962; Jarman and Jarman 1968). It is this early appearance of domesticated cattle and pig – as early as in South-west Asia – that has led some authorities to suggest that the Aegean should be included within the initiating 'centre' (Butzer 1971, 564). But available evidence does not support such a view.

Although it is impossible to define the distribution of potential domesticates precisely, there is little reason to suspect that wild emmer flourished on the Greek mainland or on Crete. Wild einkorn and barley were at most sparsely represented in the Balkans. Enclaves of sheep or goat existed around the Aegean and Mediterranean shores but were not an important component of the fauna. Only wild boar and aurochs were well represented, although on Crete, where domesticated cattle bones were found at Knossos in the earliest occupation level, there is no evidence of indigenous aurochs.

If the aurochs had been locally domesticated – on Crete or the mainland – one would expect to find a considerable variation in animal size, ranging from the large aurochs to the much smaller domesticated breed.[4] Instead, only bones of small animals are found.

In fact the evidence fits a different hypothesis far better. The fairly abrupt appearance of farming communities; the invariable appearance of emmer, sheep and goat as the most important elements of the economy; the small size of the cattle and the indubitable cultural links with Anatolia all suggest colonisation rather than local development. The colonists probably came from western Anatolia and it seems likely that cattle were domesticated early in this region. Unfortunately this is archaeologically *terra incognita*.

Any enlargement of the South-west Asian centre should probably be towards the east. Evidence from the Caspian and Turkmenia hints of early domestication but lacks precision and is not easy to interpret.

In some Caspian caves high percentages of gazelle are reported.

---

3 At Argissa 84% of the total fauna were domesticated sheep or goat, 10% were domesticated pig, 5% domesticated cattle; at Nea Nikomedeia the percentages were 66:15:13 and at Knossos 74.7:18.4:6.5 (Renfrew 1972, 271).

4 At a later date, in Hungary, where local aurochs were brought into captivity, a considerable range of animal size is found (Bökönyi 1971a).

However at the Belt cave where they constitute 62% of the fauna *c.* 6500 b.c., the predominance of male animals and the lack of juveniles suggests a hunting bias (or perhaps insufficient faunal sampling) rather than herding (Legge 1972).

In some of the east Caspian caves cattle and goats are thought to have been domesticated before the seventh millennium b.c. (goat at Dam-Dam-Chashma and, further south, at Gari-Kamarband). But there are no carbon-14 dates for these sites and the evidence is not conclusive (Masson and Sarianidi 1972, 29). On the west Caspian shore, at the Hotu cave *c.* 6000 b.c., sheep or goat made up over half (56%) of the faunal assemblage. At the Belt cave, in the same area, an abrupt increase of sheep or goat (84%) at the expense of gazelle is carbon-14 dated to 5300 b.c.[5] It is assumed, though not proven, that these high percentages indicate domestication. The Hotu assemblage was aceramic while soft pottery was found at the Belt cave.

Not only is the evidence of domestication around the Caspian inadequately documented but the connections with areas to the west, for example the Zagros region (where goat/sheep domestication was probably under way by the ninth millennium b.c.) remain ambiguous. It would seem that some of the Caspian chipped stone industries (including those from sites with possible domestication) closely resemble the Zagros Zarzian, whilst others show little connection (McBurney 1968; Masson and Sarianidi 1972, 28).

In southern Turkmenia there seems to be a rather abrupt transition to food-production associated with the Djeitun culture (Masson and Sarianidi 1972, 33). There are no carbon-14 dates for the early Djeitun. A late phase has a date of 5050 ± 110 b.c. Two-row barley (*Hordeum distichum*) and wheat (including club wheat, *Triticum compactum*) were grown; sheep and goat and, in the late phase, cattle were herded.

The Djeitun culture has much in common with the Jarmoan culture found further to the west in the Zagros and Tauros regions. The Jarmoan culture is primarily an aceramic culture. Pottery only appears in the later settlements, such as Upper Jarmo and Tepe Guran. The Djeitun communities, on the other hand, were from the first pottery-using and the pottery is apparently comparable to the late Jarmoan. The importance and direction of the cultural contacts and their role in the spread of food-production are unclear. The Djeitun and Jarmoan cultures may represent more or less independent parallel developments. Early transitional stages of the Djeitun

5 The carbon-14 date for the 'gazelle-Mesolithic' at the Belt cave was 6620 ±380 b.c.; for the 'Soft-Ware Neolithic', 5330 ± 260 b.c. (McBurney 1968).

may still be found. Or the Jarmoan may have played a significant part in the formation of the Djeitun culture.

For want of detailed information from these more easterly regions this chapter is confined to South-west Asia.

Even within South-west Asia the search may have to be extended beyond the Mediterranean and Warm Temperate zones. These are the areas in which the distributions of many potential domesticates (both plants and animals) overlap (chapter 5) and attention has therefore focused on them. But, in the first place, the zones and the distributions were not necessarily always the same as today. Secondly, initial experimentation need not have been restricted to the areas where the wild progenitors were available. There may have been more reason to experiment in adjacent areas in an attempt to extend the range of valuable plant and animal resources (Hole and Flannery 1967). In this respect the northern part of the Assyrian downlands may be important.

Thirdly, even if early experimentation occurred within areas where potential domesticates were available it was probably not confined to the overlap zone. It is true that mixed farming quickly came to predominate in South-west Asia but initially there must have been many experiments with only one or two species. Einkorn and barley may have been cultivated beyond the range of wild emmer; sheep and goat may have been herded in areas where no wild cereals grew. Communication, via herders moving up and down the valley systems with their flocks, or via trade routes (for obsidian, shells, pigments, etc.) would quickly have brought about a dissemination of information, stock or seed and facilitated the development of mixed economies.

In sum, the area considered in this chapter is probably too restricted. But since we cannot analyse information that has not been collected we are forced to concentrate on those parts of South-west Asia that have been covered by surveys and excavations.

THE TERRAIN

The terrain needs to be examined in a little detail. The Mediterranean zone has already been briefly defined in chapter 4 (p. 67 and fig. 7). The western section of the arc comprises the western slopes of the Judean and Samarian hills, Mount Carmel, the Galilean mountains, the upper Jordan valley, the lower slopes of the Lebanon range and the hills of the Syrian coast. It also includes the low-lying coastal plain, though this was often too hot and humid for early settlement (Perrot 1962b). The top of the arc is formed by the southern slopes and intermontane valleys of the Tauros mountains. The western flanks of the Zagros mountains form the eastern section. In both the Tauros and the Zagros regions the lower ridges rise in a series of tiers from about 600 m. to 1350 m.

The rainbearing winds coming off the Mediterranean sea water the western slopes of the Mediterranean ranges and filter over the low Syrian saddle to reach the Tauros and Zagros slopes. By about 7000 b.c., when the climate had more or less stabilised, the hillsides at altitudes between 600–800 m. and 2000–2300 m. were covered with open stands of oak, juniper, hawthorn, pistachio and wild pear (Zeist, Timmers and Bottema 1968). Since then, with deforestation, over-grazing and soil erosion, most of the fertile red loams (*terra rosa*) have been washed away and only scrub, heather, pistachio and stunted evergreen oaks remain. Sometimes not even these – only rough grass and thorn bushes (Butzer 1970, 41).

Such hill and valley systems provide very varied terrain. Wild goat would keep mainly to the steeper cliffs and ridges, sheep to the gentler slopes, gazelle, aurochs and onager to the valley floors and red deer to the gallery forests along the river courses (G. Wright 1971). The vegetation alters with altitude and aspect and in certain niches wild stands of grain flourish, sometimes spreading over thousands of hectares. There are also many caves suitable for human occupation, often situated at the junction of two or more microenvironments with easy access to a wide variety of plants and animals.

To the north and east of this zone rise the high mountains (fig. 7). Steppe vegetation (*Artemisia herba-alba*) begins at about 2000 m. and the snowline lies between 3300 and 4800 m. (Butzer 1970, 49).

To the north-west, the Anatolian plateau rises to about 1000 m. In the intermontane basins, such as Konya and Burdar, domestication occurred at an early date. These basins had been filled with large lakes during the Pleistocene and, in the Post-Pleistocene, as the lakes contracted, great sheets of fertile alluvium were exposed (chapter 4, p. 71). These basins lie within the Warm Temperate zone and in the early Post-Pleistocene were probably covered with grasslands and stands of deciduous or mixed forest. Here again large tracts have been rendered arid and sometimes saline through deforestation, over-grazing and the side-effects of irrigation (Cohen 1970). The basins would have been the natural habitat of cattle and probably goat, einkorn and barley. It is not certain whether there were indigenous sheep or emmer.

To the south of the Mediterranean zone lie the semi-arid grasslands with less than 300 mm. of rain (fig. 7). These include the eastern slopes of the Mediterranean hills which form a rain-shadow area, the more fertile piedmont area which fringes the top of the arc from Aleppo in the west to Kirkuk in the east, and a smaller southerly extension, the plain of Khuzistan. The last two are downland areas which could be dry-farmed and although at present they lie just outside the natural habitat of sheep, goat and wild grains, farming communities were established very early on. Southwards the downlands deteriorate into real steppe-land, including the barren Jazireh region of Syria.

South again, beyond the early farming settlements, lie the alluvial plains of Mesopotamia, and then the land rises once more to the Arabian desert.

CULTURAL DEVELOPMENTS

Human occupation in South-west Asia goes back *c.* 300,000 years, to a time long before the emergence of *Homo sapiens*.

For many hundreds of thousands of years the archaeological evidence is meagre. It is not until *c.* 75,000 years ago that it becomes possible to build a more coherent picture of cultural developments. By this time groups equipped with a fairly crude kit of core-bifaces and flake tools (Middle and Late Acheulian tradition[6]) inhabited the Mediterranean coast, the Syrian steppe and the intermontane basins of the Levant. They hunted such animals as elephants, hippopotami and rhinoceri, all of which have long since disappeared from the area (Perrot 1968).

(1) MOUSTERIAN

By about 40,000 b.c. Neanderthal man, *Homo sapiens neanderthalensis*, had emerged. The chipped stone assemblages slowly became more refined, with a shift away from core tools towards tools made on flakes. This is known as the Mousterian tradition and variants are found in both the eastern and western parts of South-west Asia (fig. 15, fig. 16). Particularly in the west the Mousterian assemblages show considerable variety. Cores were often carefully prepared prior to striking off the flakes. This is known as the Levallois technique and the assemblages are termed Levallois-Mousterian.

It appears that gradually Mousterian or Levallois-Mousterian groups began to operate a slightly more specialised economy. In the

---

6 The cultures derive their names from the French sequence. The South-west Asian assemblages are similar but not identical.

LEVANT			ZAGROS		
Levallois–Mousterian			**Mousterian**		
Ras al-Kelb (Lebanon)	>50,050	(GrN 2556)	Shanidar D	48,650 ± 3000 (GrN 1495)	
Ksâr 'Akil (Lebanon)	41,800 ± 1500 (GrN 2579)		(north-west Iran)	44,950 ± 150 (GrN 2527)	
Jerf Ajlah (Syria)	41,050 ± 2000 (NZ 76)		Kunji	>38,050	(SI-247)
Kebareh (Israel)	39,050 ± 1000 (GrN 2561)		(south-west Iran)	>38,050	(SI-248)
	33,350 ± 500 (GrN 2551)		Hazar Merd (Iraq)	>21,000	(C 818)
Tabūn (Israel) D	33,450 ± 900 (GrN 2170)				
C	38,950 ± 1000 (GrN 2729)				
B	37,750 ± 800 (GrN 2534)				
Rosh Ein Mor, Negev (Israel)	>37,000	(Tx-1119)			
Jabrud 6 (Syria)	23,900 ± 410 (GrN 4404)				
Kebaran			**Baradostian**		
Ksâr 'Akil (Lebanon)	26,890 ± 380 (GrN 2195)		Yafteh	38,910 ± 3000 (SI-333)	
Nahal Zin, Negev (Israel)	13,870 ± 1730 (Tx-1121)		(south-west Iran)	>38,050	(SI-335)
Ein Guev	13,750 ± 415 (GrN 5576)			36,050 + 3400 (GX-709) − 7500	
				>34,050	(GX-708)
				>33,650	(GX-706)
				32,850 + 2900 (GX-711) − 4500	
				32,350 + 2100 (GX-707) − 3500	
				30,550 + 2400 (GX-710) − 3400	
				29,810 ± 3000 (SI-334)	
				27,460 ± 1150 (SI-332)	
				19,050 ± 800 (SI-336)	
			Shanidar C	33,490 ± 600 (GrN 2016)	
			(north-west Iran)	32,590 ± 500 (GrN 1494)	
				>32,050	(W-180)
				31,950 ± 900 (GrN 1830)	
				31,350 ± 1000 (W-650)	
				27,550 ± 1500 (W-178)	
				26,750 ± 1500 (W-654)	
			Zarzian		
			Shanidar B2 (north-west Iran)	10,050 ± 400 (W-179)	
Natufian			**Karim Shahir**		
Es-Sultan (Jericho)	9,216 ± 107 (P-376)		Zawi Chemi Shanidar	8,640 ± 300 (W-681)	
	8,840 ± 180 (GL-70)		(north-west Iran)		
Mureybit* I† (Syria)	8,640 ± 140 (LV-607)		Shanidar B1	8,650 ± 300 (W-667)	
			(north-west Iran)		
			Ganj Dareh Tepe basal	8,450 ± 150 (Gak-807)	
			(Iran) D	7,018 ± 100 (P-1484)	
			C	7,289 ± 196 (P-1485)	

* The basal level of the original excavation by Van Loon at Mureybit was termed phase I. Since then further excavation has uncovered an under-lying Natufian level. This was also called phase I (Gilot and Cauvin 1973). To avoid confusion this has been emendated on this chart to phase I†.

15 Carbon-14 dates for hunter-gatherer and herding cultures in South-west Asia. All expressed b.c. and according to the Libby half-life of 5570 ± 30.

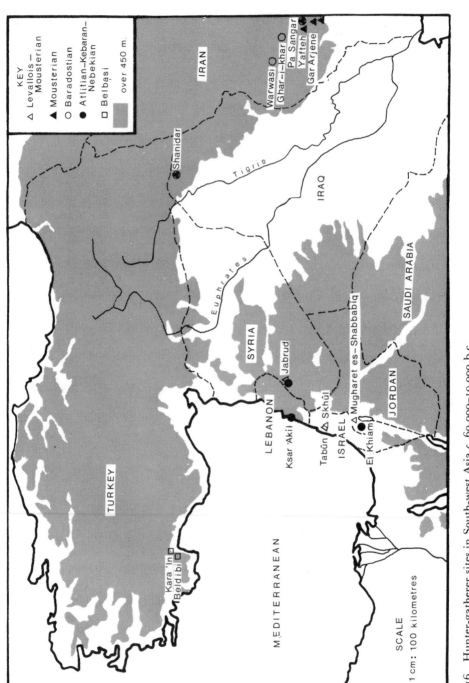

16   Hunter-gatherer sites in South-west Asia c. 60,000–10,000 b.c.

KEY

△ Levallois–
   Mousterian
▲ Mousterian
○ Baradostian
● Atlitian–Kebaran–
   Nebekian
☐ Belbaşi

over 450 m.

IRAN

Warwasi ○
Ghar-i-khar ○
Pa Sangar
Yafteh ●
Gar Arjene ▲

Shanidar ●

Tigris

IRAQ

Euphrates

SAUDI ARABIA

SYRIA

Jabrud ●

Mugharet es–Shabbabiq △

JORDAN

LEBANON

Ksar 'Akil ●

Tabūn △ Skhūl

ISRAEL

El Khiam △ ●

TURKEY

Kara 'In ☐
Beldibi ☐

MEDITERRANEAN

SCALE
1 cm: 100 kilometres

early Levallois-Mousterian levels in the Tabūn cave on Mount Carmel (Israel) there is a wide range of fauna and little evidence of any hunting preference. In the late Levallois-Mousterian levels aurochs assume a considerable importance. This trend becomes still more pronounced in an even later Levallois-Mousterian level in the nearby cave of Skhūl (S. Binford 1968a). In the east, evidence from Shanidar cave and from caves in the Khorramabad valley (south-west Iran) shows a similar emphasis on large game. Almost 90% of the bones are from ungulates (thus probably 99% of the meat supply). At Shanidar 75.1% of the bones are from wild goats, 20.4% from wild sheep and 4.4% from red deer (Perkins 1964).[7] There seems to be little evidence of wild-plant gathering, fishing or small-game hunting.

If this trend is correct, and not too heavily biased by imperfect preservation (or excavation) it would suggest that while Mousterian groups were becoming more skilled in hunting techniques they were exploiting only a small fraction of the available resources (Hole and Flannery 1967).

Mousterian sites also begin to show some functional differentiation. In a preliminary survey of the Khorramabad valley at least two types of site were noted: seasonal base-camps and temporary butchering sites. Base-camps, such as Ghamari, Kunji and Yafteh, were usually cave-sites situated at the junction between valley floor and limestone cliff with wide views over the valley. They yielded large spreads of ashes, men's and women's equipment, heavy concentrations of chipping debris and finished artefacts, and a wide variety of animal bones, including complete skeletons of wild goat and sheep and selected cuts of aurochs, red deer and onager. These larger animals were perhaps cut up at the temporary butchering sites and only the more important cuts were 'schlepped' back to base.

The butchering sites, such as Gar Arjeneh and Pa Sangar, have much smaller concentrations of material; only men's tools, and often only the remains of one animal per occupation.

In the Levant a similar dichotomy has been remarked: at the cave of Mugharat es-Shubbabiq (Israel) there was evidence of intensive occupation, while at the cave of Jabrud (Syria) there were many temporary occupations. The first may have been a base-

7 42.9% of the sheep were immature animals. Using immaturity as a criterion of domestication such a figure would be sufficient to warrant labelling these animals as domesticated. Nobody does – which is either a mistake, or, more probably, is justified on the grounds that a single criterion is insufficient proof of domestication (chapter 3, p. 47).

camp, the second a temporary hunting and butchering site (S. Binford 1968a).

One should note that the satisfactory unanimity in the evidence from east and west is somewhat blighted by Hole's (1971) comment that 'in both cases we began by making similar assumptions about the kind of things we should find and it is not surprising that we found them'. (More such honesty and we shall have to start excavating and analysing all over again!)

Throughout this early period there is no evidence of human occupation in southern Anatolia or in the Tauros intermontane valleys. In the latter region it is probably due to lack of field-work, in the former it may be that climatic conditions were too severe (Cohen 1969).

(2) BARADOSTIAN/AURIGNACIAN

By about 35,000 b.c., the beginning of the Late Pleistocene, *Homo sapiens* seems to have displaced or evolved out of *Homo sapiens neanderthalensis* throughout South-west Asia. By this time too the rhinoceri and hippopotami have disappeared.

The chipped-stone industry is now predominantly made on blades. It belongs to the Aurignacian-type tradition.

There is a greater degree of cultural diversity. In the east, in Iraq, the local variant is known as the Baradostian. It is marked by an increase in the range of chipped-stone tools. There are small, slender points, bladelets, small rather rough core-scrapers and a few blade-scrapers. The presence of a great many burins – tools with narrow chisel-like points – may indicate an increase in wooden and bone equipment (Garrod and Clark 1965; Hole and Flannery 1967).

There is not much evidence on the Baradostian subsistence base but both at Shanidar and further south in the Khorramabad valley the emphasis still seems to be on large game. For example at Shanidar (level C) wild goat make up 59.5% of the total bone assemblage, and wild sheep 38.5% (Perkins 1964). The human population seems to have been rather thinly scattered and not many sites are known (fig. 16).

Both at Shanidar and at the Yafteh cave in south-west Iran the Baradostian occupation ends between 26,000 and 23,000 b.c.[8] But at other sites such as Warwasi, Ghar-i-Khar and Pa Sangar, all in Iran, it probably continued much longer, perhaps until *c.* 10,000

8 The carbon-14 dates from Yafteh in Iran, averaging around 30,000 b.c., are all from the early Baradostian deposits. It is thought that the later occupations may have continued until about 23,000 b.c.

b.c. and then developed into the Zarzian culture (Braidwood, Howe and Reed 1961; Young and Smith 1966; Hole and Flannery 1967).

There is rather sketchy evidence for the contemporary Aurignacian-type variants in the west, in the Mount Carmel caves, the Judean desert and the Lebanon range. A considerable number of sites have been found and there may have been an increase in population. Alternatively, there may simply have been an increase in functionally distinct sites. There are a greater number of open-air sites although caves continue to be occupied. Indeed some of the caves, such as El Khiam in Jordan, Jabrud in Syria and Ksâr 'Akil in the Lebanon contain very thick deposits.

As in the west, the range of equipment increases. There is more worked bone and in the final phase (known as the Kebaran in the south, and the Nebekian in Syria) composite tools are found – one or more microliths set in bone or wooden mounts (Perrot 1962).

Unfortunately economic data for the various Aurignacian-type cultures is inadequate. It has been postulated that some of the later groups began to practise a broader-based economy. The wider range of tools could indicate more varied hunting, gathering and food-preparing patterns. Some of the microliths in the western assemblages and the slender points in the Baradostian could have been used to tip arrows, and the use of the bow-and-arrow would have made small game hunting much easier (Hole and Flannery 1967; G. Wright 1971).

Further north, information from Anatolia is negligible. So far the only early material comes from caves on the south-central coast near Antalya. Here the Belbaşi group, which is apparently contemporary with late Aurignacian-type groups further south, is associated with the only cave engravings known in South-west Asia. They have been found in the caves of Kara 'In, Öküzini and Beldibi (Mellaart 1965, 17).[9]

(3) ZARZIAN

Between 11,000 and 8000 b.c. the ice-sheets over Northern Europe began to recede. In areas directly affected the climate and environment altered quite radically and there was a marked economic shift to a more intensive use of a greater number of food resources. But South-west Asia lay some distance from the ice-sheets, climatic and cultural changes were less dramatic and it is hard to know how far they were connected (chapter 4, p. 65).

9 Further to the east, engravings in the cave of Palani near Adiyaman may also be of this date (Anati 1968).

In the Zagros region the Zarzian culture emerges. The cave of Shanidar, deserted for about 16,000 years, was re-occupied around 10,000 b.c. (fig. 15). A Zarzian group established a base-camp which was occupied for long periods, year after year. Flannery (1972) postulates that such a base-camp could have been occupied by fifteen to forty people: perhaps six to eight males, each with one to three females plus children. This has yet to be proven. There is more substantial evidence that the cave occupants were beginning to utilise the valley resources more intensively. Although wild goat still accounted for 60% of the animal bones and red deer for another 20%, the remaining 20% show a much wider range of game than in the earlier cultures (Butzer 1964, 425). There are bones of fallow and roe deer, boar, wolf, jackal, fox, brown bear, marten and beaver. Little gerbils were caught and land tortoises, river clams and great quantities of land snails were collected. Fishing was a minor activity. The importance of plant-gathering in the over-all economy cannot be assessed but numerous wild cereal grains have been found in pits within the cave and the discolouration of the pit soils could be due to plant decomposition (R. S. Solecki 1963; Leroi Gourhan 1969).

There may be a correlation between the increasingly wide range of hunting (and gathering?) activities and the variety of chipped-stone artefacts found in the cave. There are blunt-back blades, round and steep scrapers, many notched blades and many microliths, including shouldered arrowpoints and a variety of geometric forms.

Evidence of a broad spectrum economy is found at other sites, both cave sites (Palegawra in the Tainai Chai valley in Iraq) and open-air sites (Turkaka and Kowri-Khan in Iraq). The game species vary, undoubtedly reflecting local availability. Sites on, or overlooking, the valley floors have higher frequencies of onager bones, while sites on the ridges have more goat or sheep (Braidwood 1962). Adaptability, and perhaps a degree of isolation, is reflected in the variety of local assemblages. Assemblages in the drainage of the two Zabs in Iraq are somewhat different from those in the Kermanshah valley in Iran and different again from those in the Khorramabad valley of south-west Iran (Braidwood and Howe 1960; Hole and Flannery 1967).

It is not clear whether there was any increase in population. In the Upper Zab valleys and in the Kermanshah valley there are eleven Zarzian sites compared to three Baradostian. But in the Khorramabad valley the position is reversed, with six Baradostian and only two Zarzian (Hole and Flannery 1967).

(4) KARIM SHAHIR

The Zarzian culture probably lasted about a thousand years. Around 9000 b.c. there is a fairly sharp cultural transition – a little too sharp; intermediate sites will probably still be found[10] – and the Karim Shahir culture emerges (fig. 15). And now, for the first time, there is some, rather tentative, indication of herding (fig. 20).

Tens of thousands of bones were excavated at the open-air site of Tepe Asiab, high up in the Kermanshah valley at an elevation of 1400 m. (fig. 17). They are still being analysed but Bökönyi (1972) has stated that there are bones of domesticated goats. He also mentions that a great many horn cores were found, suggesting selective male slaughter.

A second site with possible evidence of herding is Zawi Chemi Shanidar in Iraq. This open-air site covers about 275 m. by 215 m. and lies close to the greater Zab river, four miles from Shanidar cave (fig. 17). Here again great quantities of bones and also a mass of snail shells were found. In the lower Karim Shahir levels about two-thirds of the bones (65.9%) were from wild sheep, most of the rest being red deer (24.5%) and wild goat (9.6%). In the upper Karim Shahir levels sheep increased to 81% of the total, with goat 10.1% and red deer 8.9% (Perkins 1964). In the lower level 44.3% of the sheep were immature, in the upper level 54.2%; immature goats remained stable at 25%. Perkins (1964) suggested that the increase in the number of immature sheep in the upper level signified the onset of domestication, but this assumption of a change in the economic base is hardly warranted by the figures. Rather it would seem that sheep were being manipulated, perhaps herded, in both levels. Apparently there were no morphological changes and no mention is made of changes in sex ratios. It has already been pointed out (chapter 3, p. 46) that to use only one criterion – in this case age-structure – to infer domestication is not at all satisfactory.

This becomes very apparent when one examines the faunal evidence from the cave of Shanidar. We have seen (p. 115) that already in the Mousterian level 42.9% of the sheep were immature. This has always been regarded as aberrant rather than as evidence of domestication. The figures settle below 25% in the following Baradostian phase, then in the Karim Shahir phase (B I) over half (54.9%) of the sheep bones and 42.9% of the goat bones are from

---

10 One of the reasons why there is a considerable number of loose ends in the Zagros material is that since the early 1950s, when Braidwood worked in Iraq, the political situation has become more difficult and therefore no further excavations have been possible.

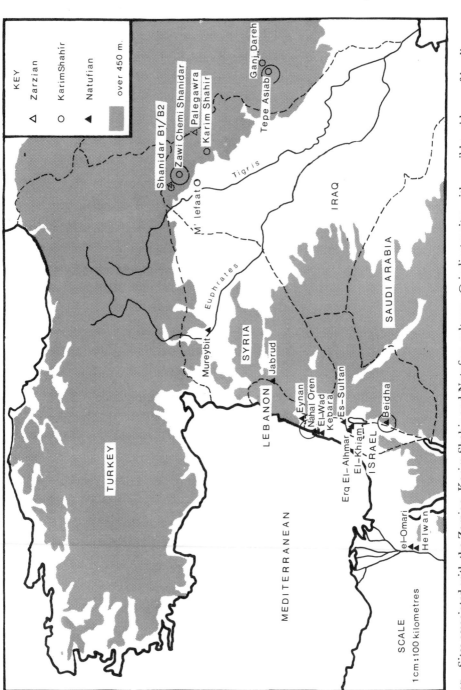

17 Sites associated with the Zarzian, Karim Shahir and Natufian cultures. ⊙ indicates sites with possible evidence of herding.

immature animals. Should these figures also be considered aberrant, or were sheep or goat, or both, being manipulated?

At other sites where the faunal assemblage has been studied in less detail there is no way of knowing whether some animals were being herded. For example, it is clear that a wide range of game was hunted at the type-site of Karim Shahir, including sheep and/or goat, pig, cattle, deer, gazelle, wolf, marten, fox and bird. Were some of these species being herded? Is it significant that some of the earliest clay animals – too amorphous for recognition – found in South-west Asia come from this site? And that other little animal figures, equally undistinguished, are found at Ganj Dareh Tepe where goat may have been domesticated (P. Smith 1968; 1970)?

As well as possible herding and the continuation of a wide range of game hunting, there may also have been an increased reliance on plant resources. But the evidence for this is all indirect and is of very varying quality.

Some of the changes in the equipment could be associated with increasingly efficient plant gathering and processing techniques (chapter 3, p. 34). In general the Karim Shahir chipped-stone industry is a small blade industry, not particularly refined. But at many sites blades with 'sickle-gloss' are found. This silica sheen is often construed as evidence that grasses were cut. However, when Harlan tried to replicate this gloss by cutting grasses he was unsuccessful. It may be that it results from reed cutting – in which case it proves nothing about the increased importance of edible plants (Braidwood 1962). The numerous serrated and notched blades may have been part of the plant processing equipment; pierced stone balls found at Karim Shahir, Zawi Chemi and M'lefaat may be digging-stick weights; the axes with chipped or polished bits found in the upper Karim Shahir levels at Zawi Chemi and at Karim Shahir, Gird Chai and M'lefaat might have been used for root grubbing or hoeing. Or they may all have served some quite different function. An examination of the wear patterns might be informative.

Perhaps more convincing is the first appearance of heavy ground-stone equipment. At Zawi Chemi, for example, there are large trough querns, many grinding stones and some pestles. It is probable that some at least were used for grinding cereals or pounding acorns or nuts. (Others may have been used for grinding pigments – red ochre was found on two skeletons from Tepe Asiab.) There is also an increase in the number of pits, possibly used for storing plant foods.

Although taken item by item none of these changes are conclusive proof of a more intensive utilisation of plant resources, taken together they do suggest a trend in that direction. The evidence is still insufficiently detailed to sustain more elaborate reconstructions – such as the one recently attempted by Smith and Young (1972). They postulated that cultivation had begun and suggested that long fallow systems can be distinguished by the presence of digging-stick weights (pierced stone balls) and forest clearing equipment ('axes'), and short fallow systems by chipped and ground-stone hoes (necessary for breaking up grass sod where insufficient time has lapsed for forest regeneration). Not only is the 'evidence' tenuous but *both* types of equipment are found at Karim Shahir, Zawi Chemi and M'lefaat!

There are changes in settlement patterns, though how far or in what way these indicate changes in the economic base is hard to establish. There is certainly an increase in the number of sites. There are more Karim Shahir sites between 9000 and 7000 b.c. than the sum total of all the earlier sites in the region from 35,000 b.c. onwards (G. Wright 1971, based on unpublished material). It would be interesting to know how far this is a reflection of an increase in population, how far it reflects functionally distinct sites (base-camps, butchering sites, etc.), or how far it is caused by an increase in the number of temporary settlements associated with a more intensive seasonal round of resource exploitation.

There is a move away from caves to open-air sites; most of the caves and rock shelters that Braidwood explored had no Karim Shahir material, and even the cave of Shanidar had only a thin level. This might be a response to climatic or environmental changes or to shifts in the subsistence patterns.

Sites are found in a great variety of micro-environments. Maybe there was a scheduled seasonal round geared to the exploitation of different resources ripening at different times of year. Or maybe there were functionally-distinct sites with inter-locking economies. We have seen that Tepe Asiab may have been a high-pasture goat herders' camp. The age structure of the animals suggests that it was mainly occupied between February and April and occasionally between August and April (Bökönyi 1971). Was such a group an independent unit moving up and down the hillsides? Or was there a base-camp at a lower elevation, and was the herding-camp part of a pattern of transhumance practised by part of the community?

Generally speaking, the structures found at the Karim Shahir sites do not seem to indicate any great permanence of settlement. At Tepe Asiab the only structure excavated was a large shallow ovoid basin, perhaps 10 m. in diameter, which might have been a pit-house (Braidwood, Howe and Reed 1961). Close-set stone scatters on the terrace of Karim Shahir may have been part of house structures, for some contained stone-lined pits with traces of fire (Braidwood and Howe 1962).[11] M'lefaat in northern Iraq had pit-houses with stone walls and paved floors, one of which had been renewed several times (G. Wright 1971),[12] and at Zawi Chemi Shanidar there seems to be the remains of a circular stone wall, 4 m. in diameter which had been re-built three times. It may have been a hut, though there was no hearth inside (Solecki 1964). Re-occupation of this site would probably account for the numerous burials. There were 28, of which 26 were grouped together and were associated with a platform of stones and an arc-like alignment of flat stones (R. S. Solecki 1963).

Only one site shows more permanent architecture. This is Ganj Dareh Tepe, a small mound in the high eastern part of the plain of Kermanshah, 1350 m. above sea level and an inhospitable place (figs. 17, 15). In the lowest level (E), 1 m. thick, there were no structures, but in the next level (D), well preserved by a conflagration, there were a series of very small abutting rectangular cubicles and a few round structures. They were made of mud-brick, coated inside and out with mud-plaster. There were no hearths and the cubicles were too small to have served as living quarters. This was probably a storage area and indeed small domed bins were found in many cubicles and also some clay containers. In level B there were larger rectangular rooms with hearths (P. Smith 1970a).

This site has another feature that distinguishes it from the rest of the Karim Shahir sites. A few coarse sherds and a large intact vessel, all of chaff-tempered ware, were found in level D, carbon-14 dated to 7000 b.c. – thus a couple of millennia earlier than pottery found elsewhere in South-west Asia (P. Smith 1968). It may be that they had simply been sun-dried and got 'baked' in the conflagration. If so, we catch a glimpse of a whole range of equipment that the archaeologist usually has no knowledge of.

Adding together all these bits of information in an attempt to reconstruct the subsistence base is a fairly disheartening process. It must by now be clear how hypothetical such reconstructions are, how easily the available material can be interpreted in a variety of ways and how very great is the need for more problem-orientated research.

11 However, previously the excavators had noted that 'there were no vestiges of any discernible structure or other formal architecture' (Braidwood and Howe 1960, 52).
12 Again, Braidwood and Howe's original description (1960, 51) was more cautious.

Before leaving the Karim Shahir culture, two further trends must be mentioned. One is that there is a slight increase in the number of non-utilitarian objects: animal, and occasionally human, clay models, beads, pendants, rings and bracelets made from a wide variety of stones. Particularly at Zawi Chemi Shanidar, some of the numerous bone objects have carved designs, usually simple notchings and incisions, sometimes a little more representational (Solecki 1964).

The second, more important, is that there are hints of the beginning of wider contacts. A few pieces of obsidian at Zawi Chemi Shanidar and Shanidar cave mean contact, even if at second-hand, with lake Van, 225 kilometres away in Anatolia. The bitumen holding a flint blade in a bone mount found at Shanidar cave must have come from the south, over 160 kilometres away (R. S. Solecki 1963) and a small piece of copper at Shanidar, which had been made into a perforated pendant or bead, may have come from the Ergani lodes in eastern Anatolia. Though very minor, these finds are significant, for it is through such contacts that the knowledge of plant and animal manipulation could have spread.

The Karim Shahir culture ended around 7000 b.c. Meanwhile contemporary groups in the Levant were also beginning to experiment with animal manipulation.

(5) NATUFIAN

In the west the Natufian culture is roughly contemporary with the Karim Shahir, beginning around 10,000 b.c.

Natufian sites are rarely found more than 40 kilometres from the coast, in a region that extends from south-west Syria, through the Lebanon and into Palestine. An exception is the recently excavated site of Mureybit, far to the east on the Euphrates in Syria (Gilot and Cauvin 1973).[13] Within this narrow elongated strip, sites are found in a wide variety of setting, in and beyond the present-day Mediterranean zone. The Natufians re-occupied caves and terraces in the Judean and Carmel mountains, such as el Wad, Kebara, el-Khiam and Jabrud. They settled in the upper Jordan valley, for example at Eynan, and further south at es-Sultan – today a desert oasis. South again, they camped at Beidha in what is now a semi-arid wadi and there are even surface traces in the Negev and Sinai deserts. Many of these dramatically arid sites were almost certainly less marginal twelve thousand years ago (chapter 4, p. 76).

13 Some authors would include the Egyptian sites of Helwan and el-Omari within this culture; Perrot (1968) disputes this.

The Natufian culture is not only more widespread than any of the earlier Levantine cultures but there are more sites and often heavier concentrations of material. All this seems to indicate an increase in population.

Natufian sites show considerable diversity. So, rather than offer generalisations which require instant emendation, four of the more important sites will be compared.

El Wad (Mugharet-el-Wad) is one of the Mount Carmel caves to the south of Haifa. It is 45 m. above sea level on the southward side of a small wadi, well placed to utilise a wide variety of micro-environments.

It is one of the few settlements where site-catchment analysis has been attempted (chapter 2, p. 31). Vita-Finzi and Higgs (1970) consider that resource exploitation would have been limited to the terrain within two hours walking distance of the site and suggest that the el Wad group operated within a radius of about 5 kilometres. In terms of the present-day environment this includes nearly 50 % marsh, 33 % grazing land, 7 % dunes and 12 % arable land. In winter, game resources are scarce but in the dry summer months the game is attracted by the water-reserves in the swamps. The cave may only have been occupied in summer and in winter the group could have moved inland to sites such as Rakafet and Hayonim (Vita-Finzi and Higgs 1970). The only problem with this reconstruction is that it projects present-day conditions back twelve thousand years and this may be misleading.

The Natufian occupation level was up to 3 m. thick and extended on to the terrace in front of the cave. There were great quantities of stone chipping waste and tools. The chipped-stone industry was primarily on blades, evolving out of the earlier traditions, but there were also some fairly heavy tools including large scrapers and rough picks. There were blades with sickle gloss and great numbers of microliths – far more than at other Natufian sites. Some were fixed into slotted bone mounts which were sometimes embellished with fine naturalistic carvings. Other microliths, particularly crescentic ones, often with blunted backs, may have been used as projectile points (Garrod and Clark 1965). There were also bone fish gorges.

Out on the terrace, limestone mortars and basalt pestles were set close to ash lens, and storage pits were cut down into the bedrock. There was also an area of close-set paving.

The range of equipment and facilities suggests a broad-spectrum economy. The fish-hooks substantiate fishing; the grinding stones, storage facilities and perhaps the sickle gloss blades suggest that plant resources were fairly intensively used. The lamentable state of the teeth of the skeletons found in the cave, many with a great number of pre-molar abscesses, may also indicate a plant diet with a liberal admixture of grit[14] (Butzer 1964, 432). As well as plant gathering and fishing, this Natufian group hunted an impressive range of game. Gazelle was by far the most important animal, but there were other ungulates such as fallow deer, wild goat, aurochs, onager and boar, and also musteline, wild cat, leopard, probably Syrian bear, marten, badger, wolf, red fox, spotted hyena, coney, gerbil, hare, squirrel, vole, rat, mole and two species of hedgehog (Butzer 1964, 432).

Many of the other coastal caves such as Erq el-Alhmar and Kebara[15] had mortars and fishing equipment. At Kebara gazelle were again the main meat source. Superficially such sites seem to have been quite similar to el Wad (G. Wright 1971).

But one cave, only 2 or 3 kilometres from el Wad seems to have been different. This is Nahal Oren (Wadi Fallah), also on the edge of the coastal plain, where over 6 m. of deposit is being excavated. This covers occupations by Aurignacian-type groups through to Pre-Pottery Neolothic B. The Natufian level alone is 1 m. thick.

At this site there seems to be a more specialised economy, with a much stronger bias in favour of hunting rather than plant gathering. There are no mortars,[16] no storage pits. The only installations were a stone-walled enclosure – or perhaps a double terrace – outside the cave, superseded, a little later, by a stone-walled oval hut structure (Stekelis and Yizraely 1963; Perrot 1968). Even using a flotation machine an average of only 6 seeds per cubic metre were retrieved, compared to an average of 1000 bones. Of the animal bones, gazelle predominates, making up just over 75% of the total, followed by aurochs, fallow deer, very little roe deer and occasional boar. And at this site there is good evidence that the gazelle were either herded or at least hunted so selectively that it amounts to definite manipulation. 54% of the gazelle bones were from animals of less than one year, compared with the average 25% for a 'wild' population (Legge 1972b).

Some 250 kilometres to the south, at Beidha in Jordan, there again

14 As at Shanidar in the Zagros, the Natufian occupants buried their dead in the cave. Some of the early graves were communal, with three to seven tightly-flexed inhumations, both adults and children, packed into a pit in a fairly haphazard way. Does such a unit represent a family grave? Sometimes one of the burials within the communal grave is distinguished by the addition of a head-band, necklace and bracelets.

15 There was a particularly well-developed bone industry at this site, including two fine naturalistically carved handles.

16 Limestone mortars with holes pierced in them were found in association with fifty burials, but these burials may be intrusive from the overlying Pre-Pottery Neolithic A level (Perrot 1968).

seems to be evidence of animal manipulation (figs. 17, 20). This is an open-air site in a dry wadi with only 200 mm. of rain. It is hemmed in by steep sandstone cliffs. The nearest spring entails a 5 kilometre walk and a 200 m. climb. However, in the early Post-Pleistocene precipitation may have been a bit higher, perhaps up to 400 mm., and the valley would have been somewhat more hospitable (Raikes 1966). Even so, wind-blown sand already posed a problem in Natufian times.

The initial settlement was a small Natufian encampment. The excavators found part of a large pebble-paved pit and a large circular hearth. The camp seems to have been abandoned because of encroaching sand but from time to time Natufian groups returned and at a somewhat higher level part of a pit-house floor was found (Kirkbride 1968). From our point of view, the important aspect of these Natufian occupations is that 76% of the animal bones are of goat and three-quarters of these are immature. This would seem to be a clear case of manipulation, though, as at Zawi Chemi Shanidar in the Zagros, there is no evidence of morphological change (Perkins 1966). In comparison only a few gazelle bones are present, and of these only 30% are immature (Legge 1972b).

Eynan ('Ain Mallaha) in the upper Jordan valley is a very different type of site: much more permanent and far larger (Perrot 1962a; 1966). It lies close to lake Huleh (though the exact extent of the lake in early Post-Pleistocene times is not known), on the edge of the oak–pistachio zone within which dense, extensive stands of wild cereal flourish. Such wild stands can yield 500 to 800 kilograms per hectare in a good year and the American archaeologist, Harlan, who tried harvesting the wheat with a stone-bladed sickle, managed to collect a kilo of clean grain in an hour. He reckoned that a family of experienced plant collectors could collect a metric ton during the three weeks that the grain was ripe and would then have enough to last a whole year.[17] He even found that he did almost as well by hand as with a stone-bladed or steel-bladed sickle (though to the detriment of his hands!). Also, the wild wheat has almost 10% more protein than modern bread-wheat (Harlan 1967). Alas, there are no plant remains from Eynan so we cannot tell whether the inhabitants gorged themselves on good protein-full wild wheat. But there are a large number of basalt mortars, some decorated, and pestles which could have been used to process the grain. There are also blades with sickle gloss – though these may have been used to cut reeds from the

---

17 The experiment was actually undertaken in the Diyarbakir province of south-east Turkey but the results are equally valid for the Jordan valley.

lake-side. In addition there are large numbers of bell-shaped, plaster-lined pits in the central open area in the village.

The inhabitants fished and hunted, though there are relatively few microliths and no projectile points.[18] Of the animal bones, 44.6% are from gazelle, 33.4% from deer and 14.2% from boar. At this site there seems to be no evidence of herding activity. Instead, the singular dearth of immature gazelle and boar suggests a particular hunting bias (Ducos 1969).

Without recourse to food-production, local wild resources were sufficiently plentiful and stable to permit the establishment of a fairly large permanent settlement. It covered about 2000 square metres and there were three building phases, each with about 50 circular stone-built pit-houses clumped around a central area.[19] In the basal level they averaged 8 m. in diameter, then in level II, they decreased to 5 m. and in level I they further decreased to between 4 and 3.5 m. Each house had one hearth, querns and mortars were set in the floor and there were burials below the floors and in pits. The population at any one time may have been between two and three hundred (Perrot 1966).

A final Natufian site must be mentioned, though the material is not very illuminating. It constitutes the basal level of the great tell of es-Sultan (Jericho). This tell rises over 17 m. on a desolate, arid, high terrace of the river Jordan, 200 m. below sea-level. The eastern slopes of the Judean hills rise beyond to 1000 m. The tell was almost continuously occupied from about 9000 b.c. to 1560 b.c. and for much of this long time span the inhabitants only survived because of the proximity of a spring. As Wheeler (1956) says, this spring 'is said to produce a thousand gallons of water a minute . . . For a very great distance, save for the muddy rivulet of Jordan, it is the only usable water. It symbolised life in that sullen valley.' However, just as at Beidha, conditions may have been somewhat less extreme in the tenth millennium b.c. It is even possible that lake Huleh was still much larger than today and that Jericho was not too far distant (G. Wright 1971).

At the very base of this tell the excavator, Kathleen Kenyon, found a rectangular platform surrounded by stone walls. The platform surface seems to have been kept very clean. Set in one of the walls were two pierced stones. They were too close together to be

18 Microliths made up 13% of the stone assemblage, and of these only 5% were geometric. Compare this with el Wad (levels B1/2) where 79% – 86% were microliths and of these 59% were geometric (Cauvin 1966).
19 Ein Guev on the eastern side of lake Tiberius may have been a similar settlement; a circular pit-house was found.

door sockets and the excavator thought that they might have held totem poles and that this structure was perhaps a small Natufian shrine built by the first settlers. A more prosaic explanation is that the pierced stones were pierced mortars similar to those associated with burials at Nahal Oren (Perrot 1968).[20]

The Natufian level is up to 4 m. thick in places and there are slight humps which could be the remains of very flimsy structures. There is very little evidence for the subsistence base: no plant or animal remains, no mortars, pestles or storage pits. Nothing to indicate a particular concentration on plant gathering. There is a single geometric microlith and a single harpoon which, interestingly, is too large for the present-day minuscule fish of the oasis.

There is evidence of some sort of trade. The considerable amount of obsidian ultimately derives from Anatolia, 700 kilometres away (Kenyon 1969).

In sum, the Natufian culture, between 10,000 and 8000 b.c., shows a great deal of variety. Some groups intensively exploited a wide range of resources. Others had more specialised economies. There is no clear evidence of plant manipulation, but certainly at Nahal Oren and at Beidha there was animal manipulation. At many sites the settlement was sufficiently permanent to warrant some building activity. Terraces in front of caves were regularised with pavings. Open sites had house structures – slight at es-Sultan, more substantial at Eynan. If the basal structure at es-Sultan is indeed a shrine then it represents an early, more organised expression of non-utilitarian concepts.

(6) Pre-Pottery Neolithic A

The Natufian develops into the cumbersomely named Pre-Pottery Neolithic A culture (P.P.N.-A). Only a few sites have been excavated (fig. 19) but it seems clear that once again there were considerable regional differences. Many of the coastal groups continued to practise an economy in which hunting, and sometimes herding, remained of prime importance while certain inland groups began to experiment with cereal cultivation.

It is not surprising that a coastal community such as the one at Nahal Oren made no move towards plant cultivation for there was probably little suitable arable land. Here and at el-Khiam in the Judean desert gazelle remained of paramount importance and the

20 It is curious that at both Nahal Oren and es-Sultan the only examples of mortars are these pierced ones.

age structure of the animals suggests considerable manipulation (fig. 20). At Nahal Oren 50.3% of the gazelle in the P.P.N. levels were immature (Legge 1972b). Well-made arrowheads were added to the hunting equipment.

Although there is no reason to suspect that crops were grown at Nahal Oren, there is a greater range of plant-processing equipment including mortars and limestone bowls. There are heavy bifacial tools such as picks, tranchets and axes. Small amounts of obsidian indicate trade contacts. It is possible that the community remained at Nahal Oren for the greater part of the year; they certainly built more permanent structures. The uneven natural terrace outside the cave was levelled to form a series of artificial terraces on which 14 round houses were constructed, often with adjoining walls. These houses were 2 to 5 m. in diameter and each had a central stone-lined hearth (Stekelis and Yizraely 1963).[21]

Evidence of cereal cultivation is limited to two inland P.P.N.-A sites (fig. 19).

The first, tell es-Sultan (Jericho), can hardly have been a typical early farming settlement. The arid terrace is unlikely to have been a natural habitat for wild cereals. There are, however, wild stands of barley at lower elevations on the Jordan valley floor and also close by in the Judean hills. Experimentation could have occurred in these environments and the cultivated grain found at es-Sultan could have been obtained by barter. There may have been no cultivation at the oasis. Or, once obtained, the cultivated grain could have been sown locally. Alternatively, wild grain could have been obtained by barter or foraging and the inhabitants then experimented with cultivation. But unless conditions were very different from today only a tiny amount could have been grown without some form of irrigation. Could the inhabitants have instigated a simple irrigation system? In view of the architectural sophistication of the settlement there is no reason why not.

There is no way of knowing to what extent the community depended on cultivated crops. Or, for that matter, on wild plant foods. A total absence of querns and mortars could signify that seeds, whether wild or cultivated, were of little importance. Or simply that some other preparation process was used (a reminder of the limitations of such indirect evidence). The plant sample is restricted to a few carbonised fragments and mud-brick impressions. In all there are 2 grains of emmer wheat (*Triticum dicoccum*), 6

---

21 Abu Suwan near Jerash on the Transjordanian plateau is very similar to Nahal Oren.

grains of very primitive hulled two-row barley (*Hordeum distichum*), some fig pips and a piece of twisted awn possibly of wild oat (*Avena sp.*) (fig. 20) (J. Renfrew 1969).

The faunal evidence is much more extensive. There are bones of aurochs, goat, boar and a great many gazelle. They are all apparently wild (Kenyon 1969) – although closer analysis of the age-structure might reverse this opinion. It used to be thought that there were domesticated dogs, but Clutton-Brock's study (1969) of the bones indicates that they conform to those of the modern-day wild pariah dog, Arabian wolf or jackal. Arrowheads are rare.

The fact that these people had access to cultivated crops does not explain why, from a modest Natufian substratum, without any temporal hiatus, the settlement exploded into something that can quite reasonably be called a township (Childe 1957b). It spread out over 4 hectares, covering a much wider area than the Natufian settlement. It is estimated that the population was between 2000 and 3000 people (Kenyon 1969).

They lived in well-built, mud-brick round houses, 4 to 5 m. in diameter, with sunken floors, usually one room but sometimes two or even three. The bricks were very uniform and had a flat base and curved upper surface (hog-back). There were many intramural burials and sometimes separate groups of skulls.

Not only was the settlement very large but it appears to have had massive fortifications. Some time after the first houses were built a great stone wall was constructed, 1.75 m. wide and still 3.6 m. high in places. Beyond it was a wide ditch, while on the inner side was a huge circular tower, 8.5 m. high with an internal staircase. Curvilinear, well-plastered structures were built up against the north flank of the tower. These may have been water tanks fed by a water channel from the top of the tower. Other structures were added to the south side of the tower. Pains were taken to keep the walls and tower in good order. As layer after layer of occupational debris accumulated against the wall it was heightened and a mud-brick superstructure was added. The tower girth was enlarged by an additional metre all round and the flanking rooms were re-built. Curiously, these additions made it impossible to enter the tower.

The P.P.N.-A settlement was long-lived. In some parts of the site 25 occupation levels were found, in others 23, in others 8 or 5.

The carbon-14 dates for es-Sultan range between 8340 and 7630 b.c. (fig. 18). When the dates were first published, they were greeted with considerable disbelief; it was thought to be quite impossible that such an important settlement could exist so early and so close to the transition from a hunter-gatherer to a food-producing way of

LEVANT			ZAGROS-TAUROS			
Pre-Pottery Neolithic A			Jarmo		9290 ± 300 (W-657)	
Es-Sultan		8350 ± 200 (BM 106)	(Iraq)		9250 ± 200 (W-665)	
		8350 ± 500 (BM 250)			8525 ± 165 (H 551/491)	
		8300 ± 200 (BM 105)			7090 ± 250 (W-607)	
		7825 ± 110 (P-378)			6880 ± 200 (W-651)	
		7705 ± 85 (P-379)			6000 ± 200 (W-652)	
		7632 ± 86 (P-377)			5800 ± 250 (W-608)	
		7440 ± 150 (BM 251)			4757 ± 320 (C-113)	
		7370 ± 150 (BM 252)			4745 ± 360 (C-743)	
		6945 ± 150 (GL-43)			4700 ± 170 (F-44)	
					4620 ± 165 (F-45)	
Beidha	VI	6990 ± 160 (K-1086)			3316 ± 450 (C-744)	
(Jordan)	VI	6765 ± 100 (P-1378)	Ali Kosh (Iran)			
	VI	6760 ± 130 (K-1082)	Bus Mordeh ph:		7950 ± 200 (UCLA 750D)	
	VI	6595 ± 100 (P-1379)	,,		5720 ± 170 (I-1489)	
	VI/V	6690 ± 50 (GrN 5063)	,,		5430 ± 180 (I-1496)	
	IV	7178 ± 103 (P-1380)	Ali Kosh ph:		6900 ± 210 (Shell 1174)	
	IV	6860 ± 50 (GrN 5136)	,,		6475 ± 180 (Humble 0-1833)	
	IV	6840 ± 200 (BM 111)	,,		6475 ± 180 (Humble 0-1816)	
	IV	6815 ± 102 (P-1381)	,,		6460 ± 200 (Shell 1246)	
	IV	6780 ± 160 (K-1084)	,,		6300 ± 175 (Humble 0-1845)	
	IV	6690 ± 160 (K-1083)	,,		6150 ± 170 (I-1491)	
			,,		5820 ± 330 (Humble 0-1848)	
			,,		5790 ± 600 (I-207)	
Pre-Pottery Neolithic B			Çayönü	4/5	7570 ± 100 (GrN 4458)	
Mureybit	I	8640 ± 170 (LV 605)*	(Turkey)	4/5	7250 ± 60 (GrN 4459)	
(Syria)	I	8510 ± 200 (LV 606)*		4/5	6840 ± 250 (M-1609)	
	I	8142 ± 118 (P-1216)		4/5	6620 ± 250 (M-1610)	
	I	8056 ± 96 (P-1215)				
	I	7780 ± 140 (LV 604)*	Tepe Guran		6400 ± 200 (Copenhagen)	
	II	8265 ± 117 (P-1217)	(Iran)			
	X/XI	8018 ± 115 (P-1220)	Bouqras	I	6290 ± 100 (GrN 4852)	
	XVI	7954 ± 114 (P-1222)	(Syria)	I	6190 ± 60 (GrN 4818)	
	XVI	7542 ± 122 (P-1224)		II	6010 ± (GrN 4819)	
Es-Sultan		7220 ± 200 (BM 115)	Tepe Sarab	5	6006 ± 98 (P-466)	
		7006 ± 103 (P-382)	(Iran)	4	5655 ± 96 (P-465)	
		6720 ± 150 (GrN 963/GL 41)		1	5694 ± 89 (P-467)	
		6708 ± 101 (P-381)				
		6660 ± 75 (P-380)				
		6250 ± 200 (GL 28)				
		5850 ± 160 (GrN 942/GL 38)				
Munhata	IVB or V	7210 ± 500 (M-1793)	**ANATOLIA**			
(Israel)			Asikli Hüyük		7008 ± 130 (P-1240)	
Beidha	II	7080 ± 50 (GrN 5062)	(central Anatolia)		6857 ± 128 (P-1238)	
(Jordan)	II	6942 ± 115 (P-1382)			6843 ± 127 (P-1241)	
	II	6600 ± 160 (K-1085)			6828 ± 128 (P-1242)	
Ras Shamra basal		6414 ± 101 (P-460)			6661 ± 108 (P-1239)	
(Syria) basal		6192 ± 100 (P-459)	Hacilar	V	6750 ± 180 (BM 127)	
Ramad		6250 ± 80 (GrN 4428)	(south-west Anatolia)			
(Syria)		6140 ± 50 (GrN 4821)	Suberde	II (lower)	6326 ± 300 (P-1387)	
Nahal Divshon		6220 ± 180 (Tx 1123)	(central	,,	6299 ± 91 (P-1391)	
(Negev, Israel)			Anatolia)	,,	6226 ± 79 (P-1388)	
Mersin basal		6000 ± 250 (W 617)		,,	5634 ± 85 (P-1389)	
(Turkey)				II (upper)	6045 ± 76 (P-1386)	
				,,	5958 ± 88 (P-1385)	
			Çatal Hüyük East XII		5807 ± 92 (P-1374)	
* Gilot's and Cauvin's (1973) phase II for Mureybit appears to be the same as Van Loon's phase I. Their phase II has therefore been emendated to phase I on this chart. It is not clear whether all the P.P.N. levels are P.P.N.-B or whether some of the earlier ones are P.P.N.-A. (p. 139).			(central	X	6142 ± 98 (P-782)	
			Anatolia)	X	6086 ± 104 (P-1370)	
				X	5987 ± 109 (P-1369)	
				X	5965 ± 85 (P-1372)	
				X	5894 ± 102 (P-1371)	

18 Carbon-14 dates for early food-producing cultures in South-west Asia. All expressed b.c. and according to the Libby half-life of 5570 ± 30.

life (Braidwood 1957). Since then the dates have been accepted, partly because another great township, only a little later in date, has been uncovered at Çatal Hüyük in Anatolia. But the acceptance still leaves unexplained how such a settlement, based on a primitive economy, in an inhospitable environment, was able to develop. Could it have been a great trading centre? It is strategically placed between the Judean hill country and the semi-desert, with good connections to the north via the Jordan valley and in a position to tap the resources of the Dead Sea. There is certainly evidence of some trade: obsidian which came from Kayseri in Anatolia, nephrite and other greenstones apparently also from Anatolia. These are not enough to suggest extensive trade, but perhaps many perishable commodities were exchanged, such as bitumen, salt and sulphur. Anati (1962) points out that with the increasing importance of plant foodstuffs, there might be a greater demand for salt and, in historic times, the Dead Sea was always the principal source for the surrounding areas. Bitumen would be important for mounting flints and daubing baskets, sulphur for fire-lighting and perhaps medicinal purposes. Both were available in the Dead Sea area and indeed a few blocks of sulphur were found in the P.P.N. levels at es-Sultan. The evidence is inconclusive but we shall see later (p. 158) that trade undoubtedly played a role in the growth and development of Çatal Hüyük in Anatolia.

The second site with cultivated cereal remains is Beidha in Jordan. This site, like es-Sultan, is at present marginal both in terms of dry farming and of the natural range of wild cereals. It has only 200 mm. of rainfall. But it has already been suggested (p. 84) that conditions were somewhat different in the early Post-Pleistocene. Not only was precipitation probably greater but the more extensive vegetation would have helped retain moisture and the villagers would also have benefited from the water run-off from the cliffs. The presence of barley and emmer, wild aurochs and onager bones at the site certainly seems to indicate less desolate conditions. Even so, the P.P.N.-A villagers, like the Natufians before them, had problems stabilising the shifting sands below the settlement. As far as the range of wild cereals is concerned, it may be that either the somewhat different environmental conditions affected the distribution patterns or, as postulated for es-Sultan, grain may have been transplanted from its natural habitat. Raikes (1967, 148) points out that conditions on the escarpment, 5 kilometres from the settlement, would have been suitable for wild cereals. Alternatively, it was not grown in the vicinity but was gained by barter.

Much of the grain found at Beidha was barley (*Hordeum spon-*

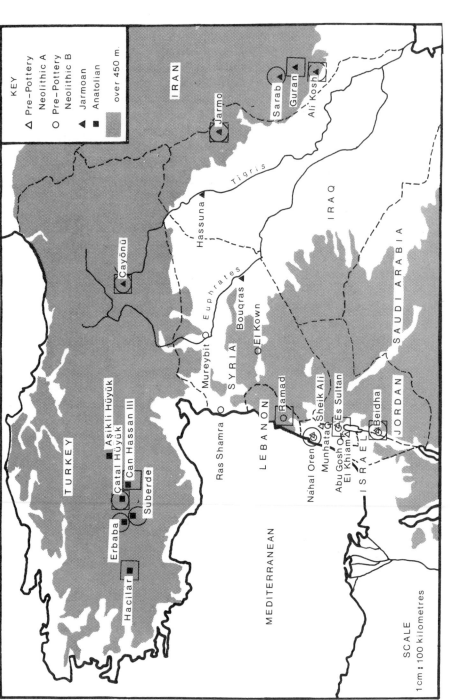

19 Sites associated with the Pre-Pottery Neolithic A and B, Jarmoan and Anatolian cultures. ○ indicates sites with evidence of herding
    □ indicates sites with evidence of cereal cultivation.

taneum) (fig. 20). It is morphologically transitional between the wild and cultivated forms, with brittle rachis like the wild form but larger grain size. Emmer (*Triticum dicoccum*) was less important. Though morphologically distinct from the wild form there was still a wide range of grain size. The villagers also collected large numbers of pistachio nuts, as well as field peas, two kinds of wild lentil, vetch (*Vicia narbonensis*), medic (*Medicago* sp.), cock's comb (*Onobrychis crista-galli*) and crop weeds such as goat-face grass (*Aegilops* sp.), rye-grass (*Lolium* sp.) and wild oats (*Avena ludoviciana*) (Helbaek 1966b).

Domesticated goat provided most of the meat supply, accounting for 86.5% of the bone sample (fig. 20). The rest of the sample included a wide variety of game including aurochs, ibex, bezoar, gazelle, boar, hare, jackal, hyrax and horse or onager (Perkins 1966; Kirkbride 1968).

The P.P.N.-A levels (VII to IV) at Beidha date between 6900 and 6700 b.c. (fig. 18). They lie directly above the earlier Natufian encampments. The total size of the village is unknown because much has been eroded away. The first P.P.N.-A occupation was perhaps temporary, only sandy clay floors and post-holes were found with exterior hearths. Then in level VI a series of small, circular pit-house complexes were built, little honeycombs of adjoining rooms made of stones with inset wooden posts and interior lime plastering. Each complex seems to have been surrounded by its own encircling wall beyond which lay the court-yard with the hearths. The interstices between the rooms and the wall may have been used for storage. There was also a terrace wall probably built to retain the dunes. In level V one begins to find free-standing, single-roomed houses of which one is sub-rectangular. And by the next level the pit-houses, both circular and sub-rectangular, are all single-roomed and free-standing, with some rather grand ones, 5 × 6 m. in size. These are centrally placed within the settlement and have white plastered floors and walls and large hearths with raised and plastered sills and inset stone bowls (Kirkbride 1968).

(7) Pre-Pottery Neolithic B

The origins of the following P.P.N.-B culture and the relationship between the P.P.N.-A and B are not easy to grasp. At es-Sultan and Beidha the P.P.N.-B begins around 7000 b.c. (fig. 18). But at es-Sultan there is a hiatus between the P.P.N.-A and B occupation levels while at Beidha and at Nahal Oren the break is much less sharp. At Mureybit, on the Euphrates near Aleppo in southern

	wild 2-row barley	hulled 2-row barley	naked 2-row barley	hulled 6-row barley	naked 6-row barley	wild einkorn	einkorn	wild emmer	emmer	bread wheat/club wheat	pea	lentil	vetch	flax	gazelle	sheep	goat	cattle	pig	dog
ANATOLIA																				
Çatal Hüyük VI	√			√			√		√	√	√		√							
Çatal Hüyük X																?	?	√		√
Suberde																?	?			
Can Hasan III						√	√		√			√	√			?	?	?	?	
Hacilar aceramic	√			√			?		√		√	√								√
ZAGROS/TAUROS REGION																				
Ali Kosh, Ali Kosh phase		√	√						√			√				√	√			
Ali Kosh, Bus Mordeh phase	√			√	√	√			√							?	√			
Cayönü						√	√	√	√		√	√	√	√		√	√		√	√
Tepe Sarab																√	√			
Tepe Guran	√	√																		
Jarmo	√					√	√	√	√		√	√	√			?	√			?
LEVANT																				
Ramad P.P.N.-B.		√					√	√	√		√									
Mureybit P.P.N.-B.	√					√														
Beidha P.P.N.-B.																				
Es-Sultan P.P.N.-B.		√					√		√		√	√	√			?				
Be. iha P.P.N.-A.	√								√				√				√			
Es-Sultan P.P.N.-A.		√							√											
Nahal Oren P.P.N.-A.															?					
8000 b.c.																				
LEVANT																				
Nahal Oren															?					
Beidha																	√			
ZAGROS REGION																				
Tepe Asiab																	√			
Zawi Chemi Shanidar																?				
Shanidar BI																?	?			
Ganj Dareh Tepe																?				

9000 b.c.

20 Chart showing domesticated plants (and some related wild species) and domesticated animals at individual South-west Asian sites.

Syria the 'break', if it exists, is virtually indiscernible. The excavator, van Loon (1966a, b; 1968) placed all the levels, from I to XVI, within the P.P.N.-B, while Perrot (1968) suggested that the early levels (I–VIII) were P.P.N.-A and the later levels (IX to XVI) were P.P.N.-B. Important features such as the 'parching' pits straddle the transition between the two cultures. If we follow van Loon the P.P.N.-B would, according to the carbon-14 dates, go back as early as 8500 b.c. Even if we accept Perrot it would still begin a thousand years earlier than at es-Sultan and Beidha (fig. 18).

Many authorities favour the view that the P.P.N.-B is an intrusive culture from the north, from northern Syria or the mountains of eastern Anatolia or the headwater region of the Euphrates (Perrot 1962b; Kirkbride 1966). Since these are all archaeologically *terra incognita* such a provenance remains safely untestable.

Although much of the chipped-stone industry is in line with the earlier tradition, there are some innovations: much fine, flat, pressure flaking; many barbed-and-tanged or leaf-shaped projectile points and long denticulated 'sickle' blades (fig. 21). Many of the artefacts are made from a fine mauve-coloured flint and the discovery of the source of this flint might help to clarify the cultural origins. There is also a new form of quern with a double hollow and one open end.

Another frequently cited innovation is the appearance of rectangular houses with plastered floors. But though there is a trend towards rectangular houses (Flannery 1972) the transition is not sharp, nor necessarily associated with the beginning of the P.P.N.-B culture. Some, for example at Beidha, are already found in P.P.N.-A contexts. Others appear gradually: at Mureybit there is a gradual evolution from round to rectangular house types, with both represented in some levels. At Munhata (Israel) the trend is reversed; the early P.P.N.-B rectangular house gives way to the round house.

It may be that in some instances the P.P.N.-B represents an infiltration of new influences, in others an infiltration of new groups. Further work on the origin of such influences or groups might throw important light on the transition to food-production for with the P.P.N.-B culture cereal cultivation becomes more widespread.

By about 7000 b.c. settled communities become more frequent in the Levant and are found for the first time in southern Syria. Many of these permanent or semi-permanent communities subsisted on hunting and gathering activities. Others supplemented these activities with herding or cereal cultivation. It would seem that stability based on a hunter-gatherer economy, sometimes combined with herding, was associated with naturally 'optimal' areas where a wide range of wild resources was available within a restricted area, while in more marginal areas stability was achieved by a greater reliance on food-production and, in particular, cereal cultivation.

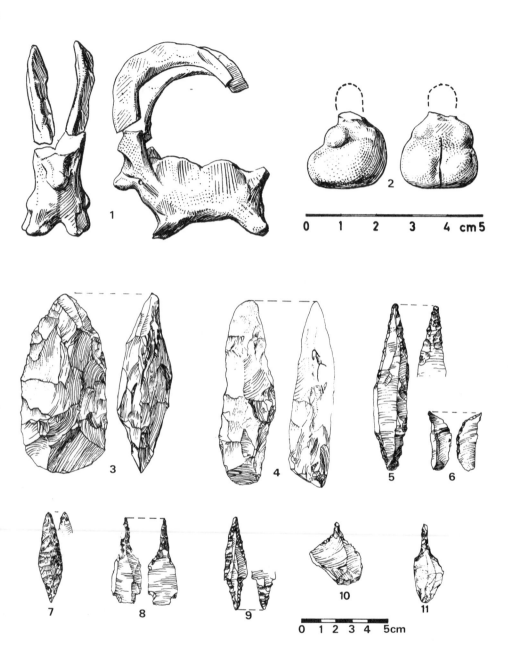

21   Artefacts from Beidha. 1: baked clay ibex, level VI (P.P.N.–A). 2: clay
figurine, level II (P.P.N.–B). (1 and 2 to same scale.) 3–11: flint artefacts, levels
II and III (P.P.N.–B). (3–11 to same scale.)
(after Kirkbride 1966)

Although it is rarely possible to reconstruct the precise subsistence base of the individual communities, one can catch a glimpse of the variety.

At Nahal Oren on the coast, gazelle were still the main meat source and made up 90% of the bone sample. The P.P.N.-B group constructed small rectangular houses with paved floors out on the terrace.

At Munhata (Israel) in the fertile upper Jordan valley where stands of wild grain were prolific, a settled community relied primarily on wild resources. There is no evidence of crop cultivation and only rather tentative evidence of sheep and goat herding. Sheep or goat account for 54.4% of the bone sample, followed by gazelle with 34% (Ducos 1969). The age-structure of the sheep/goat sample from the earliest levels (V and VI) are somewhat abnormal, with two maxima between 1 and 2 and between 2 and 4 years old. They are not, however, statistically significant.

At this settlement the earliest structures, in level VI, were insubstantial huts. In the next level there was a large enclosure (300 m. square) of mud-bricks on stone foundations, and traces of pavings. Then in level IV, more substantial rectangular houses with mud-plastered floors appeared and finally, in level III there was a switch to more or less circular structures including a large paved courtyard 15 m. in diameter surrounded by small rooms (photograph I). In this level there was also a large rectangular paved area.

Although the chipped-stone industry remained basically the same throughout, there were a great number of barbed projectile points and also many sickle-blades in level V, while the amount of ground-stone equipment – querns, grinding stones and pestles – increased in level IV. These changes may correlate with economic developments (photograph II). Perhaps plant gathering became more important and plant processing more efficient (Perrot 1967).

At Mureybit on the Euphrates not only the cultural affiliations but also the economic base is ambiguous. Considerable quantities of plant remains were found. All were apparently wild. They included much two-seeded einkorn (*Triticum boeoticum* ssp. *thaoudar*), small amounts of wild barley (*Hordeum spontaneum*), wild lentils and two seeds of bitter vetch (van Zeist 1970). Processing equipment included querns, mortars and grinding stones. A whole series of fine, regular pits 80 cm. in diameter and 70 cm. deep were excavated, particularly in the middle levels of the site (VII to XII). The pits were lined with red clay which had been renewed many times and were filled with ash and rounded river pebbles. They may have been used to parch grain – a cache of about a thousand seeds was found close to one pit. Parching would make the glumes more brittle and thus make threshing easier. Even so, the wild grain would not be much good for bread-making and it was probably made into some sort of gruel (Harlan 1967).

The enigma at Mureybit is not that it seems to have been a permanent community based on wild resources – this would be perfectly feasible – but that wild einkorn, which makes up the bulk of the plant remains, is not today found anywhere in the vicinity. Even making allowances for changes in wild distribution it seems unlikely that it grew locally in the eighth millennium b.c. It is not so much a matter of rainfall, for although the present-day 250 mm. is about the minimum necessary for wild einkorn, it may have been greater. More important is the elevation of the site. Mureybit is 284 m. above sea-level; wild einkorn usually grows at elevations between 600 and 2000 m. The nearest present-day wild stands are 100 to 150 kilometres to the north in the Tauros foot-hills. There are various ways by which it could have reached the site. It could have been gained by barter. This seems fairly unlikely, although a little obsidian, found from level VIII onwards, indicates some contact with the north. The community could have spent three weeks of the year in the Tauros foot-hills harvesting the wild cereal. Or, as G. Wright (1971) suggests, it could have been transplanted and cultivated beyond its natural habitat. Perhaps domestication had not been under way long enough for morphological changes to occur.

In an area rich in wild game the villagers hunted onager, aurochs and gazelle in about equal proportions and, more rarely, Mesopotamian fallow deer, boar and wolf (Ducos 1969). There is no evidence of herding. At first they used concave-based projectile points, later fine, tanged points like those found further to the west. Hunting the large aurochs must have been fairly spectacular sport and, either as trophies or for ritual reasons, the horns were sometimes stuck into the house walls.

The early P.P.N. houses at this site were round, up to 4 m. in diameter and had paved floors. Later, from the tenth level upwards, there were roughly rectangular structures built of shaped chunks of limestone, coated with thick red clay mortar. One of these houses, although only 3.5 m. square, was further divided up into four tiny rooms (van Loon 1966a, b; 1968; Gilot and Cauvin 1973).

In the dry steppe country to the west of the Euphrates, El Kown (Syria) seems to be contemporary with Mureybit and so far at least there is no evidence of cultivation or herding (Dornemann 1969). Similar communities are likely to be found in the Upper Tigris valley, utilising the even richer wild resources of that area.

I Munhata. Southern part of the site showing round and rectangular house structures.
(*reproduced by courtesy of J. Perrot*)

So far we have considered settlements dependent on herding, settlements dependent on wild resources, and Mureybit, which can be interpreted in different ways. At other sites, all marginal to the natural habitat zones, cereal farming is definitely attested. Beidha at one end of the P.P.N.-B province, and Ramad at the other may serve as examples.

The P.P.N.-A settlement at Beidha was overlaid by three P.P.N.-B occupation levels. There seems to have been little change in the economic base (p. 133) but the form, and perhaps function, of the settlement alters. Although the top-most P.P.N.-B level (I) has been much eroded and the bottom level (III) much destroyed by over-lying buildings, there seems to be continuity, at least between levels III and II. They comprise one or more complexes consisting of a fine, large room surrounded by work-shop units (fig. 22). The large room in level II was 9 × 7 m. and had a raised hearth, a large, roughly square, highly-polished stone seat or table and a 'ritual'

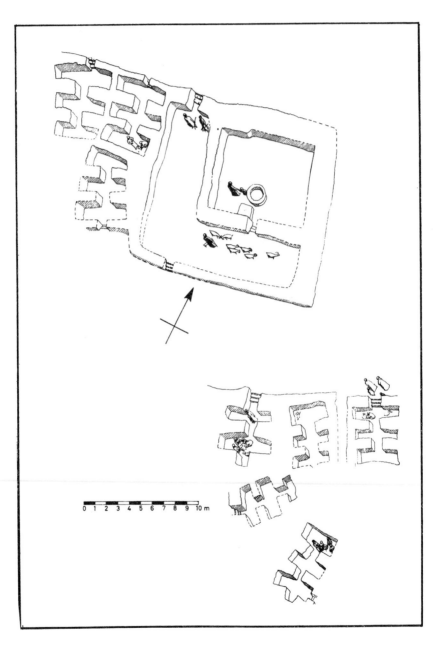

22   Partial reconstruction of Beidha, level II, Pre-Pottery Neolithic B.
(Kirkbride 1966)

II Munhata. Basalt quern and grinding stone.
(*reproduced by courtesy of J. Perrot*)

stone-lined pit. The floor and at least part of the walls were coated
with several layers of fine lime plaster, cream coloured except for
a red band running round the edge of the room along the lower
part of the wall and round the hearth and the pit. Beyond this
room lay an open courtyard and then the tightly-packed workshop
units, separated by narrow lanes. These units were long, rectangular
buildings with an ante-chamber at one short end, a long corridor
and three cubicles on either side, each roughly 1 × 2 m. Massive
separating buttresses may have supported an upper storey – perhaps
used for living quarters. The units show a certain degree of specialisation, some more than others; one (in level II) was a general
emporium with grinding-stones, pestles, bone tool-making equipment and bead-making equipment, another (in the same level)
had only bone tools and beads, while another (level III) was a
butcher's shop (Kirkbride 1968).

Perhaps Beidha was a regional bazaar, forerunner of Petra,
controlling trade routes from the desert to the Mediterranean coast
at Gaza and from the Red Sea to the Jordan valley and Jericho
(es-Sultan). Many Red Sea cowries and mother-of-pearl were excavated as well as local haematite and malachite, limestone from the
Nubian hills, calcite from the Nubian sandstones and a very small
amount of obsidian: two pieces from Nigde in Anatolia and one from
lake Van (Kirkbride 1968; Mellaart 1965, 44).

At Beidha, as at es-Sultan, there were burials without skulls; but there was also, 45 m. to the east of the village, a separate ritual area with three adjacent curvilinear buildings. The earliest may already date to the P.P.N.-A culture. The central one is the most elaborate with a paved floor, a central monolith and a series of stone settings.

On the map (fig. 19) Beidha appears as an isolated southern outpost, but a preliminary survey has shown that there is one P.P.N. site four hours' walk to the north, at Shaqaret M'Said, and another four hours to the south, at Adh Dhaman (Kirkbride 1966).

Tell Ramad lies far to the north at the foot of Mount Hermon in southern Syria (fig. 19). In an area where today there is only 250 mm. of rain per year, the seventh millennium villagers grew emmer (*Triticum dicoccum*) and smaller amounts of einkorn (*Triticum monococcum*), club-wheat (*Triticum compactum*), barley (*Hordeum distichum*) and lentils (*Lens culinaris*). Although no percentages have been published it is clear that these were only part of a very wide range of plant resources, for they also collected edible wild grasses such as bromus, and wild vetch, almonds (*Amygdalus*), pistachio (*Pistacia*) and hawthorn (*Crataegus*). Although they hunted, mainly gazelle and deer, they apparently made no attempt to herd animals. House structures seem to have been very flimsy; nothing remains of the Pre-Pottery village except some round plastered hearths (Contenson and Liere 1966b; Contenson 1966; 1971).

At this site the chipped-stone industry is in part similar to the Levantine small blade tradition, with much abrupt retouch, rather long 'sickle' blades and notched arrowheads. But there are also innovations: blades with flat, invasive retouch, rectangular 'sickle' blade elements and tanged arrowheads (Contenson 1971).

A small sounding of the basal level of Ras Shamra on the north Syrian coast uncovered remains of a plaster floor and similar 'intrusive' chipped-stone elements.

Within the P.P.N.-B province only one large settlement is found. Tell es-Sultan, re-occupied by the P.P.N.-B people, was even larger than its P.P.N.-A predecessor and again had layer upon layer of occupation debris, with, in some places, 26 levels. The earlier round house tradition is now replaced by fine rectangular mud-brick houses set round open courtyards. The mud-bricks are of a different shape from the earlier ones. They look rather like flattened cigars and have herring-bone patterns impressed in the tops to act as keys. House floors are carefully plastered, red, pink, cream or white. There are neat, rectangular, plastered hearths sunk into the house floors and more hearths as well as ovens out in the yards. Certain buildings may have been shrines; one large room, 6 × 4 m., with curved annexes and a central basin has been interpreted in this way. Though other P.P.N.-B groups practised skull cults the tell es-Sultan people elaborated the ritual. In one room there were the remains of forty burials, frequently headless, below the floor, and ten skulls on the floor. In some cases the facial features had been finely remodelled in plaster and the eyes had been set with shells. There were also fragments of life-size, fairly schematic figures.

There is a wider range of plants than in the P.P.N.-A levels: emmer (*Triticum dicoccum*) and two-row barley (*Hordeum distichum*) of a less-primitive type than before, einkorn (*Triticum monococcum*) which is apparently not indigenous to the surrounding area, and several pulses (*Pisum* cf. *sativum, Lens culinaris, Vicia faba*) (J. Renfrew 1969). There are fine, long, open-ended querns. Domesticated sheep are reported but the evidence is tenuous (Reed 1969).

Before proceeding further we may note that many of the seventh millennium Levantine developments are paralleled in other parts of South-west Asia – in the Zagros and Tauros foot-hills, in the piedmont area and in the Anatolian basins.

First of all there is a general increase in the number of sites. This may partly reflect functional differentiation or an increasing seasonal mobility with associated encampments but it probably also indicates an increase in population.

Secondly, settlements are frequently in new locations, often strategically placed to utilise areas with high water-tables. This may well reflect the needs of primitive crop cultivation and would have been a means of providing some security against fluctuations in rainfall and the possibility of drought (Hole and Flannery 1967).

Thirdly, there is considerable contact between areas, and the diffusion of farming techniques and the transfer of plants and animals beyond their natural habitat zones must be related, at least in part, to the increasingly substantial trade network. Although much of the trade may have been in perishable commodities some idea of the extent of the network is demonstrated by the distribution of obsidian. This black volcanic glass is not only imperishable but can be analysed for trace-elements and thus traced back to source. South-west Asian obsidian comes from flows in two regions of Anatolia, one in the central area near Acigöl and Çiftlik, the other from around lake Van at Nemrut Daǧ, Bingol. A third flow is as yet unlocated. Small amounts were already being imported in the ninth millennium b.c. to both Natufian and Karim Shahir communities but it was in the seventh millennium that this trade became important, reaching to Beidha (Jordan) in the south-west and to Ali Kosh (Iran) in the south-east. All the obsidian found at the Zagros sites comes from lake Van, most of the obsidian at the Levantine sites comes from central Anatolia though a little also comes from lake Van (fig. 23) (Renfrew, Dixon and Cann 1966; Dixon, Cann and Renfrew 1968).

Obsidian, and other trade items, were probably obtained in a variety of ways. Jane Jacobs (1969, 28) suggested that people came directly to the source to obtain obsidian supplies. This may be true for groups living at no great distance, but probably beyond a circumscribed area obsidian was bartered from village to village (Renfrew 1972, 465). Whether directly or indirectly obtained, obsidian formed between 80% and 90% of the chipped-stone industry at sites within a 200 to 300 kilometre radius of the source. Beyond this the percentage fell off exponentially (Renfrew 1972, 465). At Jarmo, 425 kilometres from lake Van, 45.5% of the industry was on obsidian; at Ali Kosh, 900 kilometres away, only 1 to 2.5%.

Trade was not the only means by which contact and exchange were established. There would have been seasonal movements, either by groups exploiting wild resources in different environmental niches, or as part of a transhumant pattern involving the movement of flocks of sheep and goat to fresh pastures up and down the valley systems. Temporary-looking settlements in the Zagros, such as Tepe Sarab and Tepe Guran, may have been seasonally occupied. Such movements would have allowed contact between groups exploiting different environments and may well have led to an exchange of both information and commodities (Flannery 1965; Hole, Flannery and Neely 1969, 349).

A final point is that such contacts did not result in economic or cultural uniformity. We have seen that in the P.P.N.-B province some communities grew crops, some herded, some did both and some did neither. A similar variety will be found in other contemporary cultures. There are different regional chipped-stone traditions and different ground stone equipment. Although for most of the seventh millennium we are still dealing with aceramic communities, some groups made fine stone bowls. Some sites have many clay figures of animals and humans, others have none. The architecture varies, though as time goes on there is a greater tendency to build small rectangular houses.

(8) JARMOAN

Having examined Levantine developments in the seventh millennium b.c. and then generalised about some of the more important trends found throughout South-west Asia, we turn to the east, to

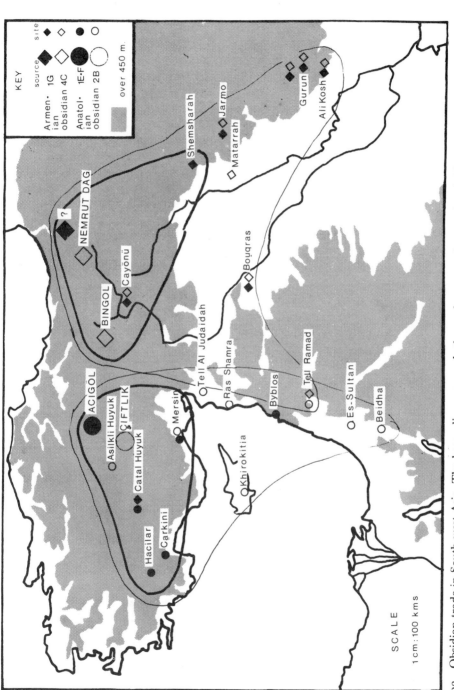

KEY

source	site			
	◆	◇	●	○
Armen-ian obsidian 1G 4C	◆	◇		
Anatol-ian obsidian 1E-F 2B			●	○

over 450 m.

Asilkli Huyuk

ACIGÖL

ÇIFTLIK

Çatal Huyuk

Hacilar

Çarkini

Khirokitia

Mersin

BINGOL

NEMRUT DAG

?

Çayönü

Shemsharah

Matarrah

Jarmo

Gurun

Ali Kosh

Bouqras

Tell Al Judaidah

Ras Shamra

Byblos

Tell Ramad

Es-Sultan

Beidha

SCALE

1 cm : 100 kms

23 Obsidian trade in South-west Asia. The heavy line surrounds the nuclear area close to the obsidian sources. The lighter line indicates the wider trade area. (adapted from Dixon, Cann and Renfrew 1968)

developments in the Zagros and Tauros hills and in the fringing piedmont.

The Jarmoan culture is contemporary with the P.P.N.-B and shows a similar diversity in site location and economic strategy. Unlike the western culture there is no evidence of any settlement larger than a village, but this is not conclusive. The basal levels of some of the great piedmont tells, often strategically placed at nodal trading points, remain to be investigated.

To give some idea of the range of environmental setting, economy and village structure we can look first at some of the settlements in the foot-hill zone and then at various piedmont sites.

Jarmo, the type-site site for the culture, is situated on a bluff above a small stream in an area where all the wild cereals are available and where about 650 mm. of rain falls each year. It was a modest settlement. There were probably never more than 25 houses and of those several were probably for storage and animal shelters. They were rectangular structures of sun-dried brick laid on stone foundations and sub-divided into several very small rooms. Floors were frequently covered with reed matting and there were large baked clay ovens, perhaps for parching grain, as well as storage pits dug in the floors. Houses and adjoining courtyards were frequently repaired and re-built with about 16 distinct occupation levels (Braidwood and Howe 1960, 40).

The economy was broad-based. The villagers grew a small amount of emmer (*Triticum dicoccum*) and einkorn (*Triticum monococcum*). They collected or grew field peas, lentils and blue vetchling and they herded goats and perhaps sheep. Domesticated goat was the main source of meat. Domesticated pig appears in the upper levels and although there are little clay models that look like dogs with curly tails, the relatively rare bones cannot be distinguished from wolf (Reed 1961; 1969). Hunting and gathering were still very important. They hunted a wide range of game (red fox, wolf, gazelle, aurochs, red and roe deer, wild goat and sheep, boar and perhaps onager), collected great quantities of snails and many acorns and pistachio nuts, as well as much wild two-row barley (*Hordeum spontaneum*) and wild, one-seeded einkorn (*Triticum boeoticum* ssp. *aegilopoides*).

The equipment at Jarmo shows strong links with the preceding Karim Shahir tradition but has a more extensive range. There are microliths – some geometric – fine stone bowls, a few large celts, occasional large pierced stones and many clay figurines, both animal and human. There are impressions of woven baskets and rugs. And in the final levels, probably dating to the end of the seventh millennium, pottery is found.

Trade contacts are documented by large quantities of obsidian originating from lake Van in the north, used mainly for microliths, and by shells from the Persian coast.

A preliminary survey indicated several rather similar sites in the vicinity (Ali Agha, Kani Sur, Khor Namik and Kharaba Qara Chiwak), and Braidwood suggests that the population density may have been close to the modern figure of about 11 per square kilometre, with villages of 140 to 160 inhabitants.

Two sites excavated further to the south, Tepe Sarab and Tepe Guran, both in Iran, look far less permanent than Jarmo. At Tepe Sarab, high in the hills at an elevation of 1260 m., pottery similar to the upper levels at Jarmo was found. Sheep and goat were herded. There was no grinding equipment and no obvious houses, simply ash lenses. This could represent a small, semi-nomadic herding community or else a high-pasture station used by herders from a more settled community.

No information on the bone remains from the aceramic levels of Tepe Guran have been published. There was cultivated barley (*Hordeum distichum*), and the remains of very insubstantial dwellings, marked only by the dark soil contours of rectangular or slightly curvilinear walls (Meldgaard, Mortenson and Thrane 1963).

Cayönü, in the Tauros foot-hills of Turkey is similar to Jarmo, though architecturally more advanced. There are five aceramic levels. The site is still being excavated and the information is a bit piece-meal. Faunal studies have not been completed but it seems that the early settlers relied on hunting for their meat supply. Game included aurochs, pig, deer, goat and sheep. In phases I and II only the dog was domesticated. Later, however, in phases IV and V, sheep, goat and pig began to be herded. The domesticated pig is the earliest known in South-west Asia. Even in these phases deer and aurochs hunting remained important (Braidwood, Çambel *et al.* 1971).

Although only a relatively small amount of organic material was preserved it seems to show an increasing reliance on cultivated crops. Domesticated one-seeded einkorn (*Triticum monococcum*) was grown from the first phase onwards, domesticated emmer appears in the later part of the second phase and supplants the wild emmer (*Triticum dicoccoides*) found in the first phase and the early part of the second. Peas were perhaps wild at first, but by the upper levels the domesticated field pea (*Pisum sativum* var. *arvense*) is present. Lentils are found and at least by phases IV and V are domesticated *Lens culinaris*. Bitter vetch (*Vicia ervilia*) and chick-pea (*Cicer*) may have been grown or gathered wild. Flax (*Linum* cf. Bienne) was probably wild. Large amounts of pistachio (*Pistacia atlantica*), lesser amounts of almonds (*Amygdalus* sp.), tiny amounts of wild einkorn (one-seeded *Triticum boeoticum* ssp. *aegilopoides* and possibly two-seeded *Triticum boeoticum* ssp. *thaoudar*), hackberries and acorns were gathered (Zeist 1972). Already in phases I and II there was a considerable range of grinding equipment as well as ground stone celts and blades with sickle-gloss (Braidwood, Çambel *et al.* 1971).

Çayönü displayed an unexpected wealth of structural features: pit ovens and small fragments of wall in the earliest phase; elaborate stone foundations to take wood and plaster floors in phase II; a large structure (9 × 10 m.) with a cement floor inlaid with coloured, ground and polished chips and an open area with two free-standing stones in phase III; much sun-dried mud-brick and what appears to be the foundations of a workshop complex in phase IV. The latter is a structure 5 × 8 m. with six or seven small rectangular rooms with functionally distinctive tools.

Another unexpected discovery is that the villagers brought in small quantities of native copper from the Maden lodes in the hills about 20 kilometres away and either hot- or cold-hammered it[22] (Braidwood, Çambel and Watson 1969; Braidwood, Çambel *et al.* 1971). There were also obsidian artefacts; the amount of obsidian increased in importance during the first four phases and then fell off sharply in the fifth (Redman 1973).

Moving southwards down on to the piedmont and beyond the range of the wild cereals we find other sites with Jarmoan-type material.

At the base of the tell of Hassuna, on the Assyrian downlands, three aceramic occupation levels, apparently of a rather impermanent nature, were noted. It is possible that such encampments were used during the winter months by people from the foot-hills (Oates 1972). On the high piedmont, where the rainfall was somewhat greater than further south and more dependable, there are hints of more established communities at Tamerkhan and Choga Mami, both near Mandali. But the sites have not been excavated.[23] At both sites there is obsidian and they may mark the trade route between Anatolia and Khuzistan (Oates 1966).

22 There is polite disagreement on the precise technique used. Fragments of pins, a rounded-square section awl and beads were found.
23 On the surface of the mound of Tamerkhan there was pottery, chipped artefacts and stone bowls all similar to the upper levels at Jarmo, and these seem to represent the topmost occupation of a 6 m. tell. It would be very interesting to know what lies below. Not far away, at Choga Mami, some of the sherds are similar to those from Jarmo, others are similar to those from Ali Kosh.

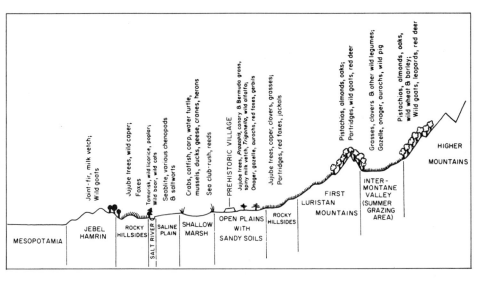

Labels in figure, left to right:

Joint-fir, milk vetch; Wild goats

Jujube trees, wild caper; Foxes

Tamarisk, wild licorice, poplar; Wild boar, wild cats

Seablite, various chenopods & saltworts

Crabs, catfish, carp, water turtle, mussels, ducks, geese, cranes, herons

Sea club-rush, reeds

PREHISTORIC VILLAGE

Jujube trees, *Prosopis*, canary & Bermuda grass, spiny milk vetch, *Trigonella*, wild alfalfa; Onager, gazelle, aurochs, red foxes, gerbils

Jujube trees, caper, clovers, grasses; Partridges, red foxes, jackals

Pistachios, almonds, oaks; Partridges, wild goats, red deer

Grasses, clovers & other wild legumes; Gazelle, onager, aurochs, wild pig

Pistachios, almonds, oaks, wild wheat & barley; Wild goats, leopards, red deer

HIGHER MOUNTAINS

Bottom labels:

MESOPOTAMIA | JEBEL HAMRIN | ROCKY HILLSIDES | SALT RIVER | SALINE PLAIN | SHALLOW MARSH | OPEN PLAINS WITH SANDY SOILS | ROCKY HILLSIDES | FIRST LURISTAN MOUNTAINS | INTER-MONTANE VALLEY (SUMMER GRAZING AREA)

24 Cross-section of northern Khuzistan between Jebel Hamrin and the first Luristan mountains, showing micro-environments and the site of Ali Kosh. (Hole, Flannery and Neely 1969)

Further west, still within the piedmont area, at Bouqras on the Euphrates in Syria the two lowest levels have rectangular houses of mud-brick with rammed earth floors similar to those at Jarmo, and the next four levels have still more solid rectangular mud-brick houses, some with plastered floors. The chipped-stone industry, the polished stone bowls and the figurine types are most closely paralleled at Jarmo. But the economy is totally different. Here once again a settled community was apparently completely dependent on wild resources, hunting wild aurochs, sheep and goat. Only in the seventh occupation level, associated with pottery, is there evidence of herding (Contenson 1966; Reed 1969).[24]

Finally, down in the south on the northern edge of the Khuzistan steppes which form the southern outlier of the piedmont zone, there is Ali Kosh – a small farming settlement established well beyond the natural habitat zone of both wild cereals and herd animals. The assemblage is similar though not identical to Jarmo. The carbon-14 dates for the first occupation phase, the Bus Mordeh, range between 7900 and 5400 b.c. (fig. 18). The excavators place it between 7500 and 6750 b.c., thus somewhat earlier than Jarmo (Hole and Flannery 1967). Their estimate seems a little high.

24 A site, tell Ghazal, with Jarmoan material has even been reported from the arid Jazirah region (Oates 1968).

The first phase could equally well run from 7000 to 6500 b.c. and the second phase, the Ali Kosh, from 6500 to 5800 b.c.

The North Khuzistan steppes are a marginal area with only 300 mm. of rain per year. Today crops fail regularly three years out of five. It would seem that conditions were not much better in the seventh millennium b.c. and to counteract this unpredictable regime the settlement was built right next to a swamp in the lower Deh Luran valley. Some of the crops were planted out on the mud flats and club rushes got entangled with the harvest. When the swamp silted up, some time in the sixth millennium, farming became impracticable.

There were many potential resources close at hand. The plain was rich in game – deer, gazelle, onager and cattle – there were fish and clams in the rivers, migratory birds and wild boar in the swamps, and in the hills to the north stands of wild cereals, acorns, pistachio and almond, as well as wild sheep and goat (figs. 24 and 25). Already in the first phase, the Bus Mordeh, the villagers utilised a large number of these resources and achieved a diet that was both more reliable and better balanced than that of their modern counterparts. They hunted, mainly gazelle,[25] less often onager, aurochs and boar. They caught carp and cat-fish, collected mussels and water-turtles and brought down wild fowl. Although they herded goats, domestication had not, apparently, been under way for any length of time. The age-structure (only one-third of the animals were over three years) and the sex structure (a disproportionate number of males were killed) certainly suggest control but there were no morphological changes. They may have kept a few sheep and Flannery interprets a hornless skull as evidence of morphological change following domestication (but see chapter 3, p. 44).

The villagers collected nuts and fruits and large quantities of tiny wild legumes – a lot of work but very nourishing. They grew small amounts of emmer (*Triticum dicoccum*), six-row barley (*Hordeum vulgare* var. *nudum*) and einkorn (*Triticum monococcum*).[26] They also collected crop-weeds such as goat-face and rye grasses. In terms of seed numbers the wild legumes made up 94% of the total, the cultivated grains only 3%. But in terms of weight the proportions were about equal, for the cereal grains were very much larger (Helbaek 1969a).

It is unlikely that the wild progenitors of the cereals and of the

25 Legge (1972b) suggests that bone experts did not pay sufficient heed to the possibility of gazelle manipulation.
26 Helbaek (1969a) includes einkorn among the domesticates; Hole, Flannery and Neely (1969, 343) place it among the wild resources.

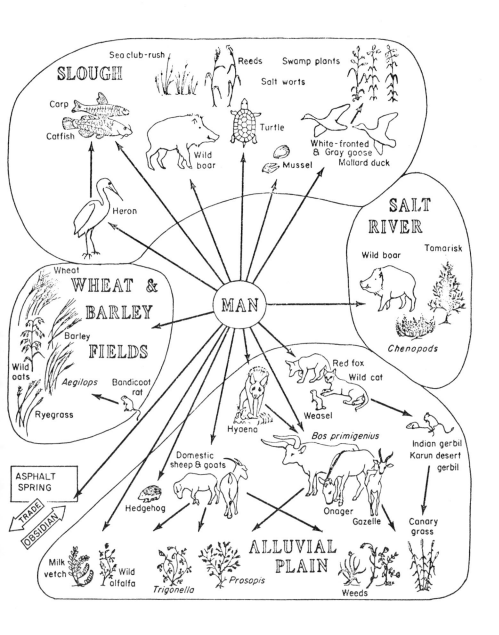

25 Simplified representation of man's exploitation of wild and domesticated resources in south-west Iran during the seventh and eighth millennia b.c. (Hole, Flannery and Neely 1969)

goat and sheep were indigenous to the plain; they must have been brought down from the hills. Hole (1971) found wild barley a few kilometres from the site.

The first settlement was very small, probably covering less than half a hectare and housing perhaps 50 to 100 inhabitants. The excavation uncovered some small rectangular rooms, one was 2 × 2.5 m., made of narrow clay slabs, with sunken, sometimes paved, floors and no evidence of hearths or ovens. It is not clear whether these were habitations; they may have been for storage or used as pens.

As at Jarmo, 'imports' show contact both with the north and south: tiny amounts of obsidian from the north, cowrie shells from the Persian gulf. Traces of flax apparently also indicate trade. Helbaek (1969a) does not believe that it could have been grown locally.

Given the well-balanced diet and the high risk involved in crop cultivation in this marginal area it is surprising that the villagers ever took to farming. The major advantages would seem to be in-creased productivity and probably less back-breaking labour (Flan-nery 1969). At any rate by the second phase, the Ali Kosh, 40% of the foodstuffs were being cultivated.[27] It was mainly emmer (*Triticum dicoccum*) and two-row barley (*Hordeum distichum*) plus minute amounts of six-row barley. As the area under cultivation increased, the wild legumes were gradually displaced and made up only 20% of the plant remains, while crop-weeds and pasture-plants like plantain and mallow increased in importance (18%). One lentil attests to contact with the hills. Querns, grinding stones, pestles and mortars begin to be manufactured. There are many stone bowls and good water-tight baskets lined with asphalt. The goats now show morphological evidence of domestication, sheep become slightly more important and herding methods seem to have improved for more animals survive to three years (40%). However, hunting actually increased in importance. There is a nice assort-ment of butchering tools, such as pebble choppers and 'slicing slabs'.

The houses are more solid than in the first phase, larger, and divi-ded into several rooms. The walls are made of larger clay slabs and plastered. The ovens are outside, and so is a brick-lined 'roasting pit'. There are tightly flexed intra-mural burials sometimes with fine offerings of turquoise, stone and shell ornaments. Though there

27 Dennell (1972) however, makes an interesting point: the samples from the Bus Mordeh phase were from midden deposits; from the Ali Kosh phase they were from inside hearth deposits. The latter are more likely to contain a higher proportion of cultivated plants.

is still only a small amount of imported obsidian there are now contacts with the high Iranian plateau: the turquoise probably comes from the Mashed region near Afghanistan and a piece of native copper, cold-hammered into a bead, must also have come from the highlands.

(9) ANATOLIA

Turning finally to Anatolia we find a similar economic diversity. Knowledge of early settled communities in this area is still very sketchy, offering tantalising glimpses but not much detail.

On the south coast there is still a gap in the cultural sequence: the Belbaşi culture was probably contemporary with the Late Aurignacian (Kebaran); the overlying Beldibi deposits were probably contemporary with the Natufian and then, after a lapse in time, there is pottery and obsidian dating to about 6000 b.c.

Nothing much is known about the interior basins prior to the seventh millennium b.c. It may be that the first occupation coincided with the recession of the inland lakes at the end of the Pleistocene and the exposure of fertile tracts of alluvium.

One of the early inland settlements was Hacilar, founded *c.* 6750 b.c., not far from the edge of the lake within the Burdar basin (figs. 18, 19). It was well placed. Not only was there the lake and the alluvium but it was sited on a dry gravel terrace close to a river. Rainfall was just adequate, between 300 and 500 mm. a year, or perhaps a little more in the seventh millennium, and the surrounding plain was probably covered with an open woodland that supported herds of wild aurochs and deer. Einkorn and barley grew wild in the surrounding hills but, so far at least, wild emmer has not been found in this region and the nearest stands are a long way off in the Anti-Tauros and Tauros mountains.

Only nineteen bones were retrieved from the aceramic levels of the site. Eleven were from sheep or goat and the rest were from cattle, dog, fallow deer and hare (Payne 1972b). With such a sample it is impossible to know which animals, if any, were domesticated.

There is more evidence on plant foods. Despite the probability that wild emmer was not indigenous to the region, it was grown at the site (fig. 20). There were larger quantities of hulled two-row barley (*Hordeum spontaneum*). It shows no morphological change but Helbaek believes that it was in process of being domesticated. There was a little domesticated naked barley, probably six-row *Hordeum vulgare* var. *nudum*. Einkorn was present and could be either wild or cultivated. There were a variety of field-weeds: white goosefoot (*Chenopodium album*), mallow (*Malva* cf. *nicaëensis*), heliotrope (*Heliotropium* cf. *suaveoleus*), field gromwell (*Lithospermum arvense*) and vervain (*Verbena officinalis*). Purple pea (*Pisum elatius*) and lentils (*Lens esculenta*) were also found. The latter are apparently not indigenous to the area but grow wild in the Zagros-Cacausian region to the east.

The range of crops found, including several that are well outside their present-day natural habitats, suggests either that present-day distributions are not trustworthy or that there was an infiltration by, or contact with, groups living to the south and east. The chipped-stone industry is insufficiently represented to allow comparison with contemporary cultures further afield.

Hacilar was a small village which, like many of the contemporary settlements already examined, consisted of small rectangular mud-brick houses, mud-plastered and grouped around courtyards. Some of the rooms had stone foundations, the more important ones had fine lime-plastered floors on a pebble base, red and burnished. Again as at other settlements there were internal hearths and others out in the courtyards along with ovens and storage bins. There was also a 'skull cult'. There were at least seven aceramic occupations and then the site was abandoned for nearly a thousand years (Mellaart 1970c).

Recently a rather similar settlement has been excavated in the plain of Konya at Can Hasan III. Again it is an aceramic community, with at least seven structural phases. And again the houses were small rectangular dwellings. The walls abutted on to each other and were mainly built of slab pisé, coated with mud plaster and sometimes painted red. Again floors were sometimes of compacted clay with an admixture of small pebbles.

In the lower levels of this site there is evidence that einkorn (*Triticum monococcum*), emmer (*Triticum dicoccum*) and lentils (*Lens culinaris*) were grown, and wild einkorn (*Triticum boeoticum* ssp. *aegilopoides* and *Triticum boeoticum* ssp. *thaoudar*), bitter vetch (*Vicia ervilia*), common vetch (*Vicia sativa*), legumes (*Medicago* and/or *Trifolium* spp.), small-seeded grasses (*Gramineae*), bullrush (*Scirpus lacustris*) and large amounts of hackberry (*Celtis tournefortii*) were collected.

There are bones of sheep or goat, cattle and pig, but it has not yet been determined whether they were domesticated. Cattle seem to have been the most important meat source.

In the upper levels einkorn drops out, emmer is less important and free-threshing wheat – club-wheat and bread-wheat – begins to be grown. Also two-row hulled barley *Hordeum distichum* and probably a little naked two-row *Hordeum distichum* var. *nudum*. A similar range of wild plants are found with, in addition, a little walnut (*Juglans regia*), wild grape (*Vitis sylvestris*), *Prunus* sp. and *Chenopodium* sp. Again the bone sample has not yet been analysed (French 1972).

Suberde, another small, contemporary site on the plain of Konya was relatively short-lived. There were only two occupation levels, with traces of hut floors in the lower level and mud-brick rooms with plastered floors in the upper level. There is some uncertainty about the economic base. There is no information on the plant remains. The excavators thought that all the bones, of which there were many, were from wild animals. The one exception was the dog (Perkins and Daly 1968). They further suggested that the wild sheep or goat,[28] which made up 70% of the meat supply in the lower level and 50% in the upper (fig. 1), were hunted by means of co-operative drives. However, Payne (1972b) has pointed out that nearly all the sheep / goat are less than three years old, which rather invalidates the idea of wholesale slaughter by co-operative drives and seems more indicative of early domestication, prior to morphological change.

There is no reason to doubt that the cattle bones were from wild animals. The lack of leg bones is consistent with a technique which involved the butchering of the animal at the kill-site and the 'schlepping' back to base of only the meatier parts of the carcase. Cattle provided 14% of the total meat supply in the lower level, then increased to 30% in the upper. Boar remained constant at 14% and obviously had some particular significance since clay models and boars' tusk ornaments were found. There were also red deer (7% in the upper level) and occasional jackal, fox, bear, wild cat, marten, badger, hedgehog, hare, roe and fallow-deer. Despite the proximity of water, fishing and fowling were unimportant.

Yet another small site, Erbaba, 50 km. from Suberde, has recently been discovered. It has a carbon-14 date of 6570 b.c. and domesticated animals have been reported. The excavation results have not yet been published (Drew, Perkins and Daly 1971).

At all these small sites obsidian is found, but of course the source is relatively close at hand. At Suberde a piece of worked copper was also found (Perkins and Daly 1968).

Not only were there small communities practising herding and cultivating crops, there were also far larger settlements. Just as the township of es-Sultan stands out among the galaxy of small communities in the Levant, so Çatal Hüyük east on the plain of Konya dominates in Anatolia.

28 Only 10% of the sheep/goat bones could be used to distinguish one from the other: of these 85% were sheep and 15% were goat.

It is not clear when the township began. Mellaart has excavated twelve occupation levels. The earliest of these, with evidence of priestly quarters, fine wall paintings, a great bull cult and pottery, dates to *c.* 6000 b.c. (fig. 18). A deep sounding touched another three levels, encountered pottery throughout, and did not reach the base. There are still many metres to be excavated and the settlement must go back well into the seventh millennium b.c. We know nothing about these earlier occupations and cannot even guess how large the settlement was. Did it start as a small village and expand slowly? Or was there a sudden upsurge at the end of the seventh millennium, similar to the sudden expansion at es-Sultan? Was the community originally dependent on hunting and gathering or were there herds and crops right from the start? Did it become a trading centre relatively late on? Or could the inhabitants have been traders before they became farmers and herders (chapter 2, p. 22)?

There can be no answers until further excavation takes place. Certainly Çatal Hüyük was well situated for trading. It occupied a dominant position in the Calycadnus valley, on a natural routeway between the high plateau and the Mediterranean. And certainly even in the earliest excavated levels, the community exploited this position. The trade network was impressive. Greenstones, lava, limestones, alabaster and obsidian were all obtained from relatively close by. White marble came from the west, flint from northern Syria, large cowries from the Red Sea and copper from the Tauros mountains (Mellaart 1967).

The evidence also indicates a flourishing food-producing economy. Although today much of the plain is arid and saline this is probably the result of over-grazing, erosion and irrigation. In the seventh millennium b.c. it was probably a great grassland region supporting vast herds of aurochs (Cohen 1969). Since the excavation concentrated on the priestly quarters the faunal remains are scarce, but it appears that already in level X the aurochs had been domesticated – the earliest known occurrence in South-west Asia. The large size of the domesticated beasts rather suggests that domestication was a local achievement. Later on, by level VI (5600 b.c.), the size decreases.

Dogs were also domesticated. There is less certainty about sheep and goat. Perkins (1969) considers they were wild; Mellaart (1967) believes them to be domesticated.

We do not know what, if anything, was grown during the early occupations – no plant remains were retrieved from levels X to VII. By level VI (5600 b.c.) there was a varied range of crops: einkorn (*Triticum monococcum*), emmer (*Triticum dicoccum*), bread-wheat (*Triticum aestivum*) and large amounts of six-row naked barley (*Hordeum vulgare* var. *nudum*). The two-row hulled barley (*Hordeum spontaneum*) may have been wild, or it may have been cultivated but not have had time to alter morphologically. There were peas (*Pisum elatius* and *Pisum sativum* var. *arvense*) and vetch (*Vicia noeana, Vicia ervilia*) (J. Renfrew 1969).

Çatal Hüyük was not the only township in Anatolia. There is another important settlement at Asilki Hüyük which may be even earlier than Çatal Hüyük for it is aceramic and has carbon-14 dates ranging between 6600 and 7000 b.c. (fig. 18). Unfortunately it has not yet been excavated.[29] But, like Çatal Hüyük, it seems to have been an important obsidian trading centre. Herein may lie the key to the precocious development of large settlements in Anatolia.

The chapter ends with a string of unanswered questions. The problem of the relationship between the large and small settlements and of the inter-connection between them and the beginning of food-production has hardly been touched upon. It is very difficult and costly to excavate the basal levels of the great tells because of the vast overlying accumulation of material. For this reason most of the detailed evidence on early farming comes from small unimportant settlements. But we urgently need evidence from some of the great tells. In northern Iraq, for example, sites like Nineveh, tell al Hawa, Erbil and Kirkuk are all situated at important crossing points and would have been ideally placed to handle the obsidian trade from Anatolia, shells from the Persian coast and semi-precious stones from the mountains to the east. The tells have obviously been occupied for millennia but we know virtually nothing about their initial development (Oates 1972). If it is found that alongside the small village settlements there were a series of large centres the whole question of how the transition to food-production in South-west Asia occurred would have to be re-examined. Nodal trading points, to which a great variety of wild produce, including plants and animals, was brought as barter, could have been innovating centres, not only in terms of technology but in methods of plant and animal manipulation. They could also have acted as important centres of diffusion.

Here we return to the realm of hypothesis and the attempt to fuse theory and fact must wait until the concluding chapter.

---

29 Bones taken from a section of the tell exposed by river cutting included cattle, dog, fallow-deer and hare (Payne 1972b).

7   Meso-America and Peru

The first evidence of plant domestication in Meso-America and Peru dates *c.* 7000 b.c. – only a couple of thousand years later than in South-west Asia. Nothing, however, suggests that there was contact between the two regions. Since they are separated by ten thousand miles this is not particularly surprising (Riley, Kelley, Pennington and Rands 1971, 448).

In the New World early food-production took the form of plant cultivation rather than animal rearing. The number and geographical range of potential animal domesticates were small. In the Andes there were such intractable beasts as the llama, alpaca and vicuña, as well as guinea pigs. Muscovy ducks, turkeys and stingless bees were wider-ranging but hardly a substantial food source. There was also the dog, again widely distributed. Given this limited choice, animal domestication remained unimportant and even the most advanced societies had to rely heavily on hunting.

On the other hand there was a great variety of potential root, fruit and seed crops (Appendix B, p. 233).

It is very probable that seed- and root-crop cultivation began independently in many different parts of the New World. But the search for evidence has been limited by the availability of plant remains. Attempts to establish the origins of root-crop cultivation in the tropical lowlands are hampered by the rapid and almost total decay of organic material (Appendix A, p. 228). Tropical seed-crop cultivation stands a better chance of being recorded because pollen preserved in peat or lake sediments may indicate vegetational changes concomitant with agriculture. Recent coring of lake Gatún in Panama has yielded interesting results (p. 191). But, in general, the main environments with reasonable plant preservation are arid regions such as the desert coast of Peru, or semi-arid regions wherever there is additional protection in caves and rock-shelters, for example the high Andean basin of Ayacucho in Peru, some of the caves and rock shelters at lower elevations on the western flanks of the Andes, the Meso-American highlands, and the plateaus of the American south-west. In all these arid and semi-arid areas food-production was based on seed crops. In the Meso-American highlands and the American south-west there were no indigenous root crops; in the Ayacucho basin root crops were available but, initially at least, were ignored.

Three of these arid and semi-arid areas seem to have been early, independent, centres of cultivation – the Meso-American highlands, the Ayacucho basin and the western slopes of the Andes. On the arid coast of Peru cultivation began quite early but was based on introduced cultigens. And again, in the American south-west, although attempts may have been made to cultivate the indigenous amaranth and chenopods, it was not until maize was introduced around 3000 b.c., probably from Mexico, that cultivation began to assume an economic importance (Haury 1962).

It is probable that there was contact in Peru between the highland basins, the western hillslopes and the coastal plain. Indeed there are similarities in the material equipment. There must also have been contact between different parts of the Mexican highlands. It is much less clear whether, during the time that early attempts at plant domestication occurred, there was any contact between the Mexican highlands and Peru. During the Late Pleistocene the Panamanian isthmus and Pacific coast were probably areas of savanna, and communication would not have been difficult, but by the early Post-Pleistocene and certainly by 8000 b.c., dense jungle and mangrove swamps had developed and created a considerable barrier. There could, of course, have been contact along the coast (Green and Lowe 1967, 60) but on the whole the early cultigens in the two regions are sufficiently different to suggest virtually independent development rather than diffusion from one area to another (Heiser 1965). It seems possible that somewhat later, *c.* 3000 b.c., there was contact – early maize from the Ayacucho basin in the Andes is very similar to the primitive Mexican Nal-Tel type (Flannery 1973). The distributions of the wild progenitors of the early cultigens is too poorly known to help clarify the matter (Appendix B, p. 233).

This chapter focuses on the beginning of seed-crop cultivation in the highlands of Meso-America and Peru. A short detour is made into the Meso-American lowlands where recent information indicates the possibility of early maize cultivation (Linares and Ranere 1971). A section on coastal Peru is also included although it was not an independent centre. It was an area where the indigenous hunter-gatherers gradually accepted the 'imported' domesticates and began to produce their own food. This is a very different pattern from that of south-east Europe and the Aegean where cultivation, herding and associated village communities made an abrupt appearance, probably as the result of colonisation from South-west Asia (p. 107).

Before considering the transition to food-production in these different regions, a résumé of the general background and earlier cultural developments in Meso-America and Peru must be attempted.

CULTURAL BACKGROUND

Man did not evolve in the Americas, he arrived, probably via the Bering Strait, some time during the Pleistocene. Whether it was a hundred thousand years ago or fifty thousand or closer to thirty thousand is not known. Indeed until *c.* 14,000 years ago the record is sparse, ill-dated and frequently disputed.

Recently a very crude assemblage was uncovered in the Pikimachay cave (Flea cave) in the Ayacucho basin in the Peruvian Andes. MacNeish was excavating the cave to find evidence of early cultivation. He found his evidence and below, in a basin in the cave floor, he found a series of levels (from the base, *k* to *i*) with coarse core tools, occasional worked flakes and such extinct fauna as the giant sloth (*Megatherium*) and horse. Not all authorities accept all of MacNeish's 'worked' pieces, but most accept some – especially since some are made of basalt which does not occur naturally in the cave (MacNeish, Nelken-Terner and Cook 1970, 31). This Paccaicasa complex has been carbon-14 dated to 20,000 years ago (MacNeish 1971b). Such an early date from Peru suggests that human infiltration across the Bering Strait into North America must have occurred many millennia earlier. So far there are no similar well-authenticated sites in North America, with the possible exception of the much disputed Calico site in the Mojave desert of California (MacNeish 1971b).

In the Pikimachay cave the Paccaicasa complex merges into the Ayacucho (zone *h*-1, *h*)[1] with better-made tools, a higher percentage of flake tools, rough, unifacial points and a considerable bone industry. This has a carbon-14 date of *c.* 13,000 b.c. There are still many extinct species (sloth, paleo-llama, horse, an extinct form of deer and perhaps sabre-toothed tiger and mastodon).

There are no exact parallels for this complex in either South or North America. Willey (1971, 70) mentions the Chivateros Red

---

1 It is not yet clear whether the Paccaicasa should really be considered as a separate complex or be included in the Ayacucho (MacNeish, Nelken-Terner and Cook 1970, 33).

Zone complex from the lower Chillón and Lurín valleys of coastal Peru, perhaps the Guitarrero I of northern Peru (although MacNeish, Nelken-Terner and Cook (1970) consider the parallels are with the later Puente complex of the Ayacucho basin), the Chuqui complex in northern Chile, the Catalanian in western Uruguay and wide-spread finds from eastern Brazil. Lynch and Kennedy (1971) add the Laguna de Tagua-Tagua of central Chile and MacNeish (1971b) notes parallels with the material from the Santa Elena peninsula of coastal Ecuador, the lower levels of Hueyatlaco in northern Mexico, the Friesenhahn cave and Lewisville site, both in Texas, and possibly (but the evidence is very slight) the Old Crow site in the Canadian Yukon. The latter is carbon-14 dated between 28,000 and 23,000 years ago. Many of these parallels seem to be very vague, often the main unifying factor is the crude workmanship.

MacNeish makes a distinction between the Ayacucho and related industries and a more skilful later tradition which includes many blades and burins and rather crude leaf-shaped points. Lanning (1965), however, lumps the earlier industries together with the blade/burin tradition. This blade/burin tradition, at most faintly represented in the Ayacucho basin, is more adequately documented in the Oquendo complex of coastal Peru, the El Jobo in Venezuela and at Tlapacoya and Hueyatlaco in Mexico. The two latter assemblages are carbon-14 dated to 23,000 and 22,000 years ago.

This unsatisfactory catalogue improves *c.* 14,000 years ago. At about the time that the climate ameliorates and the ice-sheets inch back, three major traditions begin to emerge in North America. They are not so clearly registered in either Meso-America or Peru. It is simplest to consider the North American manifestations first and then see if, and how, the southern evidence fits in.

The Desert tradition is found in the American south-west. In this arid basin-and-plateau country there were no herds of large game. Small game such as rabbits and rodents could be snared or shot down with bows and arrows or throwing sticks. But such game was not a very reliable food source and seed, berry and nut-collecting assumed great importance. A fairly specialised plant-collecting and processing equipment evolved, including baskets and net containers, querns and grinding stones.

The second tradition, Big Game Hunting, was orientated towards hunting the large herbivorous herd animals of the open plains of North America. Around 10,000 b.c. these plains supported a wide range of game, not just great herds of mammoth, bison, horse and llama but also antelope, deer and wolf, as well as many smaller animals. Most of the cultural evidence comes from kill-sites, for the ordinary camp-sites are less easy to find. While the Desert way of life was best undertaken by small groups, Big Game Hunting required a certain amount of co-operation, a banding together of groups, though perhaps only for short periods of time. The hunting also required good, stout, projectile points and the various phases of the Big Game Hunting tradition are recognised by changes in these points.

The third tradition in North America, the Old Cordilleran, is less easily defined and less widely accepted. The confusion seems to arise because of the rather different interpretations given to the term. Some authorities (Lynch 1967; MacNeish 1967d) define it very loosely and are able to include widely dispersed sites in a variety of environments. There seems to be greater validity in defining it more precisely and restricting it, in North America, to the early assemblages found in the Pacific north-west and other temperate mountain regions. These were areas with abundant forest game and river, lake and often coastal resources. There were large animals but not herd animals. There were fruits, berries, nuts and seeds. The utilisation of a wide variety of these resources is associated with a fairly unspecialised tool-kit. There were knives and scraping tools, hammerstones and burins, only occasional milling and grinding stones. The 'type-fossil' of this assemblage is a rather large bi-point (leaf-shaped), called the Cascade point.

Turning now to Meso-America, one finds bi-points, known as Lerma points, which are rather similar in shape to the Cascade point. But they are much heavier and are closer in size to the Big Game Hunting points. Apart from these points there is little evidence of the Old Cordilleran tradition. This is not unexpected since there are no comparable biomes.

There is plenty of evidence of the Desert tradition, both in northern and central Mexico. Indeed, the Mexican upland forms an extension of the basin-and-plateau country of the American southwest. A similar range of equipment reflects a similar life-style.

There is no environmental equivalent to the North American high plains in Meso-America. None the less, Big Game Hunting points are found. In northern Mexico there is a scatter of early types, such as the Clovis and Folsom points. In central Mexico later varieties are more common. They are found both at kill-sites in the central valley of Mexico and in caves in the semi-arid uplands. In the caves they are found in association with the Desert tradition tool-kit. MacNeish, who has excavated a number of Desert sites, has suggested that, rather than a real Big Game Hunting tradition, the kill-sites in the valley may be the result of occasional forays by

Desert groups: 'They probably only ever found one mammoth in their life-time and, like some archaeologists, never stopped talking about it' (MacNeish 1964b).

Information on the early cultural stages in the Peruvian Andes is so sparse that one cannot define distinct traditions. There are fluted points, somewhat similar to the Big Game Hunting points but with fish-tails. These are so widely scattered in South America that it is unlikely that they represent a specialised life-style. In the Jaywamachay cave in the Ayacucho basin they are found in the Huanta complex dating between 8800 and 7700 b.c. (fig. 32) (MacNeish 1971b).

There are also a great many bi-points. Some authorities interpret these as part of the Old Cordilleran tradition. But they are not found in the same sort of environmental setting as in North America and the points are generally smaller. They have been found in the desert and on the *lomas* (the fog-meadows) of the Peruvian coastal plain (the Chivateros II and Arenal complexes), on the western slopes of the Peruvian Andes (Lauricocha I/II and Guitarrero II), and way up in the Ayacucho basin (Puente complex) (Lanning 1967a, 49; MacNeish, Nelken-Terner and Cook 1970, 36; Lynch and Kennedy 1971). In all these different environments they seem to be roughly contemporary, dating around 7500 b.c.

Even the Desert tradition is not readily discernible. The Peruvian coast is a desert region; collecting activities were very important and from about 3500 b.c. a specialised equipment is found. But the availability of, and heavy reliance on, marine resources gave rise to a very different subsistence and settlement pattern to that of the American south-west.

It is too early to have any clear idea of the cultural background from which experimentation with plant and, to a lesser extent, animal domestication occurred in upland Peru. In the Meso-American uplands the slow transition from plant collecting to cultivation developed out of the Desert tradition; a tradition that was already geared to the intensive exploitation of local plant resources.

THE TRANSITION TO FOOD-PRODUCTION IN THE MESO-AMERICAN UPLANDS

The great highland plateau of Mexico, the Mesa, is flanked by two series of mountain ranges, the Sierra Madre Oriental to the east, the Sierra Madre Occidental to the west. These ranges form escarpments with small, steep-sided valleys and narrow ridges. One of the

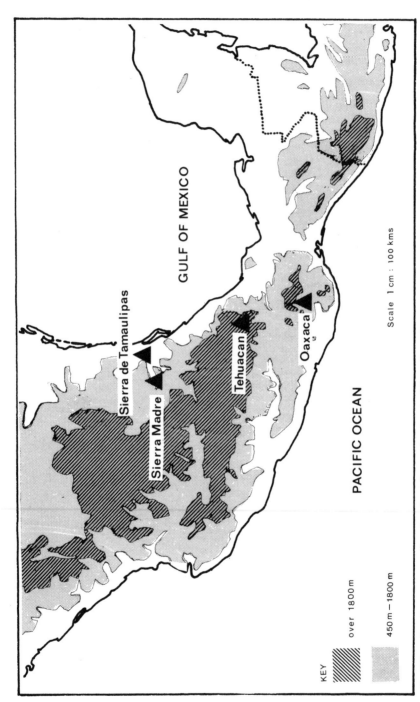

26 Map showing centres of early plant domestication in Meso-America.

early centres of plant cultivation is located in the northern part of the Sierra Madre Oriental, in the state of Tamaulipas (fig. 26).

The northern part of the highland plateau is the continuation of the basin-and-plateau country of the American south-west. There are great stretches of level land, so arid that nothing but short grass, mesquite (*Prosopis juliflora*) and cacti can grow. The rainfall is rarely more than 120 to 500 mm. a year. In the southern part of the plateau precipitation increases to between 500 and 1000 mm. and the terrain is more diversified, with a number of intermontane basins and valleys (Wellhausen *et al.* 1952). In two of these, the Oaxaca basin and the less extensive valley of Tehuacán, other early centres of plant domestication have been discovered (fig. 26).

The initial search for early centres was closely linked with the search for the beginning of maize domestication, for the Meso-American subsistence pattern is dominated by the maize-bean-squash triad and it was assumed that maize would be among the initial domesticates. One man in particular, Richard MacNeish, devoted himself to this search and much of what follows derives from the surveys and excavations that he has carried out since the late 1940s.

The primary difficulty in locating probable centres of early maize cultivation is the total absence of any wild prototype and therefore lack of information on the wild distribution pattern (Appendix B, p. 233). However, in 1948/50 remains of a primitive form of domesticated maize were found at Bat Cave, New Mexico, carbon-14 dated *c.* 3600 b.c., and in 1949 MacNeish, working in the arid Sierra Madre de Tamaulipas in north-east Mexico, found other primitive cobs, carbon-14 dated to 2500 b.c. More surveying between 1951 and 1955 suggested that the probable area of primary domestication lay somewhere south of the valley of Mexico and north of Chiapas. Since preservation was best in dry caves and since the best caves were in deeply dissected country, a process of elimination pinpointed three possible regions: Tehuacán in southern Puebla/northern Oaxaca, the Oaxaca valley in the southern part of that state, and Rio Balsas in Guerrero. MacNeish decided to concentrate on Tehuacán and after a preliminary survey in 1960 a major project got under way. It lasted three years, from 1961 to 1963, and, to give some idea of its magnitude, 454 sites were surveyed, 5 caves were excavated, 156 occupation levels were recorded and 50 specialists were brought in, including one who examined 2 cotton bolls, one who dissected 237 coprolites (faeces), another who handled 11,000 pieces of bone and a fourth who was faced with 100,000 plant fragments (MacNeish 1967b). The final publication

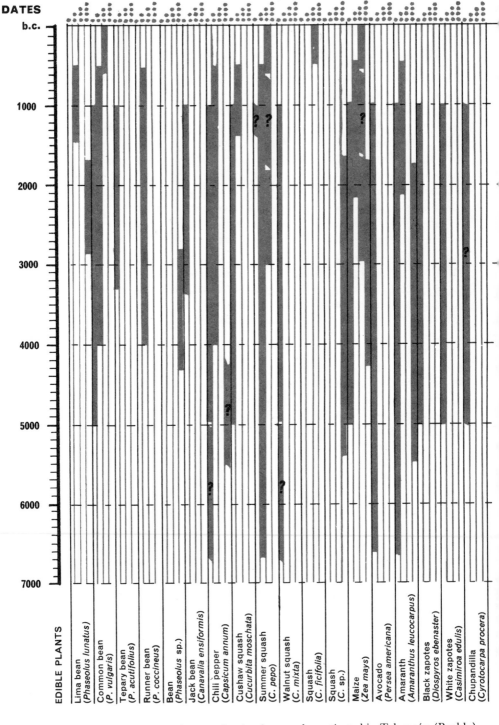

1000

2000

3000

4000

5000

6000

7000

EDIBLE PLANTS

Lima bean (*Phaseolus lunatus*)
Common bean (*P. vulgaris*)
Tepary bean (*P. acutifolius*)
Runner bean (*P. coccineus*)
Bean (*Phaseolus* sp.)
Jack bean (*Canavalia ensiformis*)
Chili pepper (*Capsicum annum*)
Cushaw squash (*Cucurbita moschata*)
Summer squash (*C. pepo*)
Walnut squash (*C. mixta*)
Squash (*C. ficifolia*)
Squash (*C.* sp.)
Maize (*Zea mays*)
Avocado (*Persea americana*)
Amaranth (*Amaranthus leucocarpus*)
Black zapotes (*Diospyros ebenaster*)
White zapotes (*Casimiroa edulis*)
Chupandilla (*Cyrotocarpa procera*)

27 Sequence in which plants and animals were domesticated in Tehuacán (Puebla), Tamaulipas and Ayacucho, Peru.

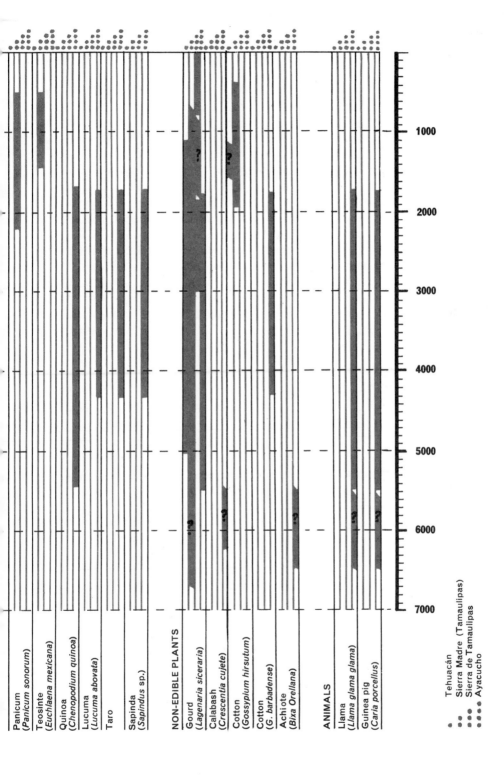

Panicum
(*Panicum sonorum*)

Teosinte
(*Euchlaena mexicana*)

Quinoa
(*Chenopodium quinoa*)

Lucuma
(*Lucuma abovata*)

Taro

Sapinda
(*Sapindus* sp.)

NON-EDIBLE PLANTS

Gourd
(*Lagenaria siceraria*)

Calabash
(*Crescentia cujete*)

Cotton
(*Gossypium hirsutum*)

Cotton
(*G. barbadense*)

Achiote
(*Bixa Orellana*)

ANIMALS

Llama
(*Llama glama glama*)

Guinea pig
(*Caria porcellus*)

1000

2000

3000

4000

5000

6000

7000

• Tehuacán
•• Sierra Madre (Tamaulipas)
••• Sierra de Tamaulipas
•••• Ayacucho

will run to six volumes of which three have been published (Byers 1967a, b; 1970).

Kent Flannery, who analysed the bones from Tehuacán, then undertook another very large project in 1966, this time in the second potentially favourable area, the valley of Oaxaca. The final report on this project has not yet been published (Flannery unpub.).

By the end of the 1960s, with MacNeish's early work in Tamaulipas plus the two big projects in Tehuacán and Oaxaca, the patterns of development in highland Mexico were fairly clear and rather similar. However, in each area plants were domesticated in a different order (fig. 27). This suggests that there was no one centre but rather several in which experimentation began at about the same time. One cannot, of course, rule out the possibility of some contact and diffusion of ideas.

At present there is much more information from Tehuacán than from the other two regions, so this area will be used to illustrate how the transition from hunting and gathering to food-production occurred. The variations found in Oaxaca and Tamaulipas can then be examined in less detail.

(1) Tehuacán valley (Puebla)

The valley of Tehuacán, drained by the river Salado, straddles the border between the states of Puebla and Oaxaca (fig. 26). The floor of the valley is about 1500 m. above sea level. To the north-west rise the peaks of the Sierra Madre de Oaxaca, often shrouded in cloud, while the south and west are enclosed by the Mixteca Alta ranges. The mountains effectively stop the rain-bearing winds from the Gulf of Mexico so that the valley is a rain-shadow area with only 400 to 500 mm. of rain a year. The rain falls between mid-May and mid-July and then again between late August and late September (Byers 1967d, e).

The area with prehistoric occupation is about 130 km. long. Evidence is derived partly from surveys, partly from excavations. The cave of Coxcotlan had 28 occupation levels, the cave of Purron had 25, and these long sequences plus information from shallower deposits in other caves and open-air sites make it possible to follow developments through from *c*. 10,000 b.c. to the fifteenth century A.D.

The early occupation, probably *c*. 10,000 b.c., is contemporary with the retreat of the ice-sheets over North America. Evidence of how far the valley was affected by the more northerly climatic fluctuations is conflicting. The analysis of plant remains

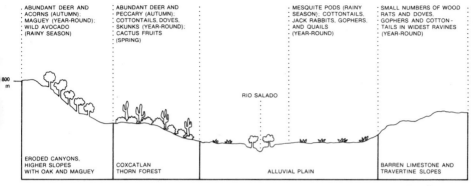

| ABUNDANT DEER AND
ACORNS (AUTUMN);
MAGUEY (YEAR-ROUND);
WILD AVOCADO
(RAINY SEASON) | ABUNDANT DEER AND
PECCARY (AUTUMN);
COTTONTAILS, DOVES.
SKUNKS (YEAR-ROUND);
CACTUS FRUITS
(SPRING) | MESQUITE PODS (RAINY
SEASON); COTTONTAILS.
JACK RABBITS, GOPHERS,
AND QUAILS
(YEAR-ROUND) | SMALL NUMBERS OF WOOD
RATS AND DOVES.
GOPHERS AND COTTON-
TAILS IN WIDEST RAVINES
(YEAR-ROUND) |

RIO SALADO

| ERODED CANYONS.
HIGHER SLOPES
WITH OAK AND MAGUEY | COXCATLAN
THORN FOREST | ALLUVIAL PLAIN | BARREN LIMESTONE AND
TRAVERTINE SLOPES |

1km

28 East/West cross-section of the central part of the Tehuacán valley showing major ecological zones.
(Reproduced from *America's First Civilization* by Michael D. Coe, 1968, by courtesy of American Heritage Publishing Co. Inc.)

showed no obvious changes in vegetation from 10,000 b.c. onwards – other than that brought about by over-grazing in Post-Conquest times. But the faunal evidence shows a quite sharp break around 7000 b.c. Before this time there were animals such as the horse (*Equus* sp.), antelope (*Antilocápra americana*), large jack rabbit (*Lepus* sp.), large fox, gopher (*Gopherus* cf. *berlandieri*), quail and small ground squirrel or prairie dog. After 7000 b.c. these disappeared, either becoming extinct or moving northwards to cooler latitudes. They were replaced by present-day fauna. The rodent population – always a sensitive indicator of environmental change – was also modified. Before 7000 b.c. there were many deer mice (*Peromyscus melanophrys*); afterwards these were replaced by cotton rats (*Sigmodon hispidus*) and kangaroo rats (*Dipodomys phillipsii*). All these changes suggest that conditions prior to 7000 b.c. were cooler and wetter. As a result grassland and mesquite covering were probably more extensive (Flannery 1967a). Even so, the valley was probably never a very hospitable place and early hunters and gatherers had to wander over a large territory utilising plant and game resources from many ecological niches.

In order to understand more clearly the relationship between potential food resources, site locations and patterns of exploitation, MacNeish and his team sub-divided the valley into micro-environments, and indeed micro-micro-environments (MacNeish 1972). Fig. 28 shows the four main sub-divisions. The first, the alluvial plain or western valley floor, is covered with short grass with gallery forests stretching along the waterways and terraces. The second, the western limestone and travertine slopes, is particularly

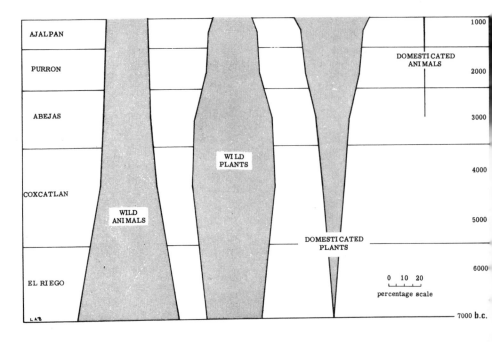

AJALPAN				1000
PURRON			DOMESTICATED ANIMALS	2000
ABEJAS				3000
		WILD PLANTS		4000
COXCATLAN				5000
	WILD ANIMALS		DOMESTICATED PLANTS	
				6000
EL RIEGO			0 10 20	
			percentage scale	
LAB				7000 b.c.

29 Tehuacán: changing patterns of subsistence 7000–1000 b.c.
(Reproduced from 'A Summary of the Subsistence' by Richard S. MacNeish in *The Prehistory of the Tehuacán Valley*, Vol. I, ed. Douglas S. Byers, University of Texas Press, 1967.)

inhospitable with hardly any rain even in the rainy season, thin soils and meagre plant and animal resources. The third, the eastern alluvial slopes, has slightly more moisture since some of the rain falling higher up the mountains flows down the gullies. The soils are more fertile and there are thorn forests, with trees like the maguey (*Agave* ssp.) and prickly pear (*Opuntia* ssp.) and stands of giant cacti, sometimes over 10 m. tall. The fourth sub-division, the higher alluvial slopes, is broken by canyons and has a covering of oak and maguey.

The first phase of human occupation, lasting from *c.* 10,000 b.c. to *c.* 6700 b.c. is called the Ajuereado phase. The thinly distributed population lived by hunting and gathering. The proportion of plant to bone remains from this phase suggests that hunting was of prime importance for meat made up two-thirds of the diet (fig. 29). The orientation towards hunting is reflected in the stone industry which includes projectile points (Lerma and Abasolo types), flake and slab choppers, crude blades, well made end-scrapers, side-scrapers, gravers and some 'spoke-shaves' – notched tools possibly used for straightening lance shafts (MacNeish 1967d).[2] Despite the previously mentioned changes in the faunal composition pre- and post-7000 b.c. this assemblage does not seem to change (fig. 30). But probably hunting techniques, and perhaps social organisation, were modified. The early groups hunted the jack rabbit and occasional antelope, both of which could most easily be killed by communal hunts, for the antelope is a herd animal and the jack rabbit nests on the ground and cannot escape down burrows. Since the vegetation was more open than today both could have been driven towards canyons or enclosures. Thus it is probable that in the early Ajuereado phase small bands sometimes amalgamated for hunting trips. After 7000 b.c., in the late Ajuereado phase, hunters would have concentrated on the cotton-tail rabbit (*Sylvilagus audubonii* and *Sylvilagus cunicularius*) and white-tailed deer (*Odocoileus virginianus*). Communal hunting would not have been practicable for the cotton-tail disappears rapidly down burrows, and the deer move swiftly in small herds. Both are more easily killed by individual hunters (Flannery 1966; 1967a). It must be admitted that such nuances are not clearly visible in the archaeological record, although the communal hunting of the jack rabbit may be reflected in the find of 400 bones, representing no less than 40 rabbits, neatly concentrated in one square metre within an early Ajuereado occupation level.

The meat supply was supplemented by plant foods such as setaria grass seeds *Setaria* cf. *macrostachya* HBK. (particularly important in the late Ajuereado), prickly pears *Opuntia* ssp. (important in the dry season), mesquite *Prosopis juliflora* and wild avocado *Persea americana* Mill. (C. E. Smith 1967).

Ajuereado sites, both cave and open-air, were small and temporary, usually less than 100 m. square with only one or two hearths. They were probably used by small nomadic groups, perhaps a couple of families. The sites were scattered throughout the different micro-environments and the plant analysis from eight sites where preservation was reasonably good seems to indicate that all were 'of a single brief season and that little correlation exists between any particular season and any particular micro-environment' (Mac-Neish 1972).

Changes in the pattern begin to be noticeable in the El Riego phase, 6700 to 5000 b.c. (fig. 32). MacNeish (1971a) suggests that

2 Similar artefacts, associated with mastodon, mammoth, horse, antelope, dire wolf and smaller animals and birds, have been found in the same state at Baltasar Tetela on the north side of the Valsequillo reservoir (MacNeish 1967d).

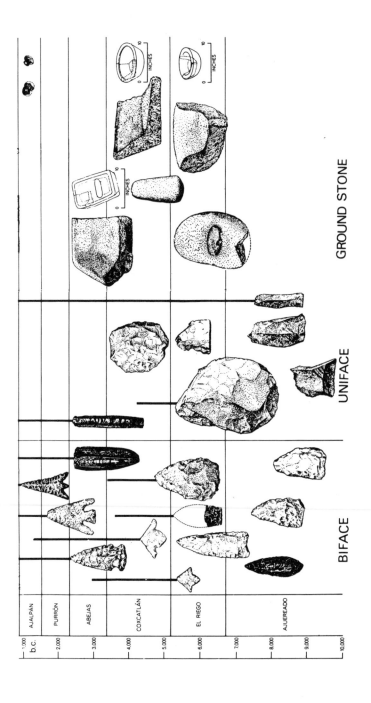

30 Tehuacán: changes in the flaked and ground stone industry, 10,000–1000 b.c. (from 'The Origins of New World Civilization' by Richard S. MacNeish. Copyright © 1964 by Scientific American Inc. All rights reserved.)

the changes in technology, settlement patterns and social structure represent a belated response to earlier (late Ajuereado) adaptations, and ultimately reflect Post-Pleistocene environmental changes. The disappearance of herd animals and other fauna meant that hunting was no longer so dependable or remunerative. As a result, plant gathering began to assume greater importance. In the El Riego phase plant foodstuffs increase from about 30% to 46% of the total food supply (fig. 29). The stone industries show corresponding adaptations. Stones were ground and pecked to make mortars and pestles, querns and grinding stones (fig. 30). There were many multifaceted scraper-planes which could have been used for pulping food and there were baskets and nets, suitable for plant collecting.

Not only was plant gathering increasingly important, but there were attempts at plant cultivation. It is hard to know how important they were, or precisely what was being grown, for morphological changes were slight or non-existent. C. E. Smith (1967) and Mac-Neish (1967a) offer conflicting lists of cultigens in the same volume of the Tehuacán report. Both suggest that avocados were cultivated – some of the stones were small and definitely wild, others were larger and could be the result of domestication.[3] They also add chili peppers (*Capsicum annum* L.), amaranth (*Amaranthus* spp.) and walnut squash (*Cucurbita mixta* Pang.) (fig. 27).[4] It is not clear whether avocados and chili peppers were indigenous to the valley. If they were 'imported' the valley people must have been in contact with neighbouring groups and perhaps gained their knowledge of cultivation from them.

These few cultigens are the only ones on MacNeish's list. He postulates 'the most incipient kind of incipient horticulture', involving the planting out of a few cultigens on the alluvial slopes of the *barrancas* or on the banks of the river Salado, or near springs. Such activities provided no more than 5% of the plant foodstuffs and did not conflict with the needs of a mobile society.

C. E. Smith, however, greatly extends the list and maintains that many of the important 'wild' plants were, in fact, cultivated. He includes, by the end of the El Riego phase, maguey, prickly pear, setaria and hog-plum (*Spondius mombin*). If he is correct, not only

3 Definite evidence of domestication is not available until 1500 b.c.
4 However, there are only 8 fragments of *Capsicum* and no way of really knowing whether they were domesticated. There are only 3 fragments of walnut squash, of which 2 are dubious and amaranth does not alter with domestication. There is a fragment of pumpkin (*Cucurbita pepo* L.) but it is thought to be wild (Cutler and Whitaker 1967). Two large cotton bolls (*Gossypium hirsutum* L.) found in the El Riego deposits are considered to be out of position and to have derived from a higher level (Stephens 1967).

horticulture (the planting out of individual cultigens like the avocado and chili) but also agriculture (the sowing of small fields with grain) had begun. The percentage of cultivated foodstuffs would be quite considerable and activity patterns must have been affected. None of these plants show evidence of morphological change so the question cannot be resolved. The chart (fig. 29) follows MacNeish's reconstruction.

Analysis of the food remains from individual sites suggests a more careful scheduling of seasonal activities than in the earlier phase. Hunting and trapping were important during the winter dry season and animals and humans probably concentrated in the valley bottoms and on the alluvial slopes. The meat diet was supplemented with opuntia and agave leaves. In spring the groups scattered more widely and seed collecting and pod-picking were major activities. Seed collecting continued into the summer, supplemented – if we follow MacNeish – by a few cultigens grown on the *barrancas*. Then in the autumn fruit collecting on the alluvial slopes became important, supplemented by hunting, cutting opuntia and agave leaves and perhaps cultivating avocados (Flannery and Coe 1968; MacNeish 1971a).

The social organisation becomes a little more complex. There are eleven larger sites, from 50 to 500 m. square with three or more hearths, and forty-eight small sites. In no case do the associated assemblages suggest that the sites served particular functions such as base-camps, hunters' camps or butchering sites. They represent a range of activities and include both men and women's gear. They must have been occupied by a number of families. In this they differ from many of the early sites in South-west Asia (p. 115) (Flannery 1972).

The larger sites represent the temporary coalescing of a couple of micro-bands into a bigger macro-band. These sites are situated in the better-watered areas – the humid valley bottoms and eastern alluvial slopes – and, of the nine sites that have sufficient plant evidence to indicate the season of occupation, seven were settled in the wet summer months when wild plant supplies were most abundant. In autumn, as food supplies dwindled, the macro-bands split up into micro-bands. Of the forty-eight small sites representing micro-bands, only three were summer encampments and they were in less well-favoured areas. Most of the rest were either spring sites (twenty-nine) or winter sites (nine). There was one autumn site. Even in this early phase six micro-bands were apparently able to stay put for two seasons, four during the spring–summer and two during the summer–autumn. One unexplained feature in this careful analysis by MacNeish is the relative dearth of autumn sites.

MacNeish (1964b) considers that a certain amount of territoriality is indicated by a series of clusters of large and small sites within the optimal areas. These clusters are, however, very irregular: one consists of six large sites and nineteen small, another has three of each, another two large and four small.

The El Riego emphasis on plant collecting and the associated equipment (including mortars and pestles, querns and grinding stones, baskets and nets) is typical of the Desert tradition (fig. 30). The El Riego is a regional variant which is also found in other parts of Puebla, for example in the Oaxaca valley and at Texcal near Valsequillo, and also further to the south, in the Santa Marta cave in Chiapas (fig. 32) and in the Tecolote cave near Huapalcalco in Hidalgo. With the exception of the Oaxaca valley, there is no further evidence of incipient agriculture (MacNeish 1967d).

In the next phase, the Coxcotlan, 5000 to 3400 b.c. (fig. 27) the evidence for plant cultivation is less ambiguous. But cultigens still represent only a very small percentage of the total food supply, no more than 14% (fig. 29). Wild plants are still far more important. Cultivated species are thought to include chili peppers, avocados, amaranth, bottle gourds *Lagenaria siceraria* (represented by a few rinds) and, by the end of the phase, black and white zapote (*Diospyrus digyna* and *Casimiroa edulis*). Chupandilla (*Cyrtocarpa procera*) was probably grown for its fruit. C. E. Smith (1967) adds the palm tree, Coyol (*Acrocomia mexicana*). MacNeish (1967a) does not.

There is also the token appearance of the three cultigens that later came to dominate the economy: 93 fragments of maize,[5] 3 fragments of squash and a solitary bean pod.

The maize cobs (*Zea mays* L.) are tiny, no more than 19 to 25 mm. long, usually with only eight rows of kernels. The glumes are long and soft, and as with most wild grasses the rachis is brittle. Since the ancestry of cultivated maize is still disputed (p. 235) and no definite examples of wild maize are known, it is impossible to make a firm distinction between wild and early cultivated forms. The Tehuacán report (Mangelsdorf, MacNeish and Galinat 1967) suggested that both wild and cultivated examples were present in the Coxcotlan phase. But recently a strong case has been made that they were all early cultigens (Flannery 1973).

The squash remains included 2 seeds of cushaw squash (*Cucurbita moschata* Duch.) and a seed of walnut squash (*Cucurbita mixta* Pang.)

5 Maize may already have been present in the El Riego phase – embedded in a coprolite (Callen 1967b).

(Cutler and Whitaker 1967). The bean pod was from a common bean (*Phaseolus vulgaris* L.) (Kaplan 1967).

From the total list of cultigens it is thought that only maize (or teosinte), amaranth, chupandilla and probably walnut squash were native to the valley. All the rest must therefore have been introduced. Presumably group movements up and down the valley system increased the potential for contact with neighbouring areas.

It is likely that some planting activities now began in the spring and then went on into the summer, and cultivation included both horticulture and agriculture. It is a little difficult to assess the effect of changes in the subsistence base on the size and location of sites but it would seem that a more efficient exploitation affected both group size and length of stay. There are fewer sites (twenty in all) but the macro-band camps are often two or three times larger than in the earlier phase. Moreover, all nine macro-band sites and seven of the eleven micro-band sites were occupied for two or even three seasons. The macro-band sites were all in favourable locations, either on the alluvial slopes or in the humid river bottoms or in the dissected canyons. Half (eight out of sixteen) of the two-season macro- and micro-band sites were spring–summer occupations. Another two were summer–autumn (one even went on into winter). Thus just over 60 % of the two- or three-season sites made use of the more bountiful wet summer season resources – including the fairly small amount produced by cultivation. More surprisingly, four of the nine macro-bands were able to stay put through autumn and winter or winter and spring, utilising the wild resources of the humid valley floors supplemented perhaps with cultivated amaranth and avocados (MacNeish 1972). The chart opposite sets out the relationship between site location and season(s) of occupation.

The Coxcotlan assemblage is still within the Desert tradition and forms part of the central Mexican variant. Similar assemblages occur in the upper levels of the Texcal cave in Puebla and the upper levels of the Tecolote cave in Hidalgo and in the Oaxaca basin (MacNeish 1967d).

It takes three thousand years for plant cultivation to become really important in the valley. By the Abejas phase, between 3400 and 2300 b.c., a quarter of the food supply is cultivated (figs. 29 and 32). The range of cultigens is much as before (fig. 27). Maize begins to bear larger cobs and a race can be distinguished which is ancestral to the present-day primitive Chapalote and Nal Tel races. There are a few hybrid maize cobs, evidence of the beginning of an important genetic break-through (chapter 3, p. 61).

	Humid river bottom (within western valley floor)	Alluvial slopes	Higher alluvial slopes	Oasis (transition western valley floor/western travertine slopes)	Dissected canyons (higher alluvial slopes)	Travertine slopes	Canyons (travertine slopes)
Winter–spring–summer	—	I M	—	—	—	—	Im
Spring–summer	I M/2m	—	Im	—	2 M	—	—
Summer–autumn	—	Im	—	—	—	—	—
Summer–autumn–winter	—	I M	—	—	—	—	—
Autumn–winter	2 M	—	—	—	—	—	—
Winter–spring	2 M	—	—	Im	Im	—	—
Winter	Im	Im	—	—	—	Im	—
Summer	—	—	—	—	—	—	Im

Coxcotlan site location and season(s) of occupation. M = Macro-band, m = Micro-band.

New cultigens appear towards the end of the phase. There are a great many tepary beans (*Phaseolus acutifolius* Gray var. *latifolius* Freeman), probably native to the valley, and jack beans (*Canavalia ensiformis* (L.) DC.), probably imported (Kaplan 1967).[6] Contacts beyond the valley are also demonstrated by the first 'imports' of obsidian.

The increased emphasis on food-production allowed a curtailment of the seasonal round and permitted longer-term residence. MacNeish considers three of the twenty-two Abejas sites to be semi-permanent or permanent 'hamlet'-type settlements. They are situated in optimal areas along the *barrancas*. Unfortunately none have been fully excavated. Part of one house was excavated and the contents suggested year-round occupation but this may not be truly representative (Flannery 1972). The other Abejas sites were, as before, seasonally occupied by macro- and micro-bands (chart overleaf). The two- or three-season sites were apparently all occupied during the spring and summer and sometimes longer. This may link up with the increasing importance of maize cultivation. But in order to understand the pattern one would need to know at which time of year the 'hamlets' were occupied and what the

6 The common bean, as in the Coxcotlan phase, remains documented by a solitary pod (Kaplan 1967).

inter-connection was between 'hamlet', macro-band and micro-band. In terms of total population, the valley probably still did not support more than 120 to 240 people (Flannery 1968).

	Humid river bottom (within western valley floor)	Alluvial slopes	Dissected canyons (higher alluvial slopes)	Canyons (travertine slopes)
Winter–spring–summer	I M	—	—	—
Spring–summer	2 M	I m	I M	I M
Spring–summer–autumn	I M	—	—	—
Winter	3 M	I m	6 m	—
Spring	—	—	I m	—

Abejas site location and season(s) of occupation. M = Macro-band, m = Micro-band.

Just at the point where a more sedentary pattern is emerging and it would be reasonable to talk of 'farming' rather than 'incipient agriculture', information almost dries up. For reasons unknown, only two thin occupation levels have been found to cover almost a thousand years. The only notable feature of this Purron phase, 2300 to 1500 b.c., is the appearance of some of the earliest pottery found in America.[7] It is simple and fairly crude and imitates the shapes of stone bowls found in the preceding phase.

When the story resumes, in the Ajalpan phase, beginning *c.* 1500 b.c., a simple, more or less sedentary society is established (fig. 32). Most of the population spends most of the year in small hamlets of wattle-and-daub huts, each hamlet with a population of perhaps 100 to 300 people. There were probably three or four such hamlets in the valley (MacNeish 1972).

The Ajalpan plant remains were poorly preserved but by extrapolation from the earlier Abejas and the later Santa Maria it is probable that about 40% of the food was grown (fig. 29). This means that nearly two-thirds of the food supply still came from wild resources (31% from wild plants and 29% from game). Occasional seasonal camps were found. They may have been used by people from the hamlets while out hunting or collecting. The heavy reliance

7 Pottery dating to about this time was also found in the Cotorra complex in the Santa Marta caves, Chiapas.

on wild resources suggests that food supplies were still fairly tight and this must have placed a limit on settlement size.

During this phase, pumpkin (*Cucurbita pepo* L.) may have been grown and perhaps also cotton (*Gossypium hirsutum* L.). There is more hybrid maize, which seems to have been back-crossed with both wild and early domesticated maize.

Pottery has now developed into a major craft, weaving has become more refined, a wider range of ground stone equipment is produced, and burials are more complex and are associated with figurines. We have reached a time when much of the economic effort is geared to cultivation and where many of the attributes of a sedentary life have been established. The sequence goes on in the valley, but the next phases, with the introduction of irrigation between 900 and 200 b.c., are primarily important in documenting the development of a more complex, more highly stratified, society.

(2) OAXACA VALLEY (PUEBLA)

Only 100 km. south of Tehuacán another early sequence has been established in the valley of Oaxaca. The environment is very similar: a highland valley 1550 m. above sea level, screened by mountains and with a summer rainfall of 500 to 700 mm. The valley is about 85 km. long and, like the Tehuacán valley, has been sub-divided into ecological zones (fig. 31). There is a much greater expanse of river alluvium, divided into a narrow strip of 'low alluvium' which is the present flood plain of the river Atoyac and the much wider strip, sometimes up to 15 km., of 'high alluvium', which is mainly the abandoned Pleistocene flood plain. As in the Tehuacán valley the alluviums are covered with grasses and mesquite with gallery forests of alders, fig-trees, bald cyprus and willows along the watercourses. The piedmont slopes are the equivalent of the alluvial slopes of Tehuacán, much dissected by tributary streams and covered with thorn forest, with a scattering of oaks above 1800 m. Above this are the mountain slopes with oak and pine and manzanita (*Arctostaphylos*). At the eastern end of the valley there are tuff outcrops riddled with small caves and rock-shelters (Flannery, Kirkby *et al.* 1967).

The earliest occupation dates to the ninth millennium b.c.[8] Hunter-gatherers concentrated on plant gathering, like the El

8 The carbon-14 dates from the lowest level (E) of the cave of Guilá Naquitz are too recent; the overlying level D has two ninth millennium dates as well as an aberrant third millennium date. The lowest level of Cueva Blanca has ninth millennium dates (fig. 32).

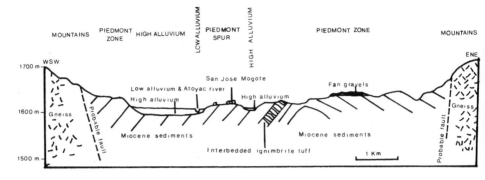

31 Cross-section of the north-western valley of Oaxaca near Etla showing major ecological zones.
(after Flannery, Kirkby, Kirkby and Williams 1967)

Riego people of Tehuacán, but seem to have been much less wide-ranging. Sites are located in the tuff outcrop zone close to the transition with the piedmont. This is the zone with the maximum variety of edible wild plants. Much information comes from the Guilá Naquitz cave, 300 m. above the valley floor. This cave was re-occupied several times (zone D), each time for a couple of months in late autumn. The cave inhabitants gathered an extra-ordinary variety of wild fruits and nuts – acorns, pinyon nuts, mesquite beans, prickly pears, organ cactus fruits, onion bulbs, hackberry, maguey, nanche (*Malpighia* sp.), susí (*Jatropha* sp.), small wild black runner beans (*Phaseolus* sp.) and pumpkins (*Cucurbita* sp.). They also hunted deer and caught turtles (Flannery, Kirkby *et al.* 1967; Flannery unpubl., 12).

The associated equipment was similar to the El Riego assemblage in the Tehuacán valley and was typical of the Desert tradition. There were knotted nets, basketry, cordage and grinding stones.

The first cultivated plants may appear at the beginning of the seventh millennium. The cave of Guilá Naquitz was still being occupied for single seasons by small groups but now, among the plant remains of zone C one finds some pumpkin seeds and peduncles (*Cucurbita pepo* L.) which may be wild or cultivated. These become more common in zone B, *c.* 5000 b.c. (Flannery unpubl., 13, 14). Thus the sequence in which plants were brought into cultivation differs from the Tehuacán valley.

As time goes on the variety of plants increases and maize begins to be grown. The Oaxacan equipment is very similar to the Coxcotlan. It belongs to the same Tehuacán variant of the Desert tradition. One novel feature in the Oaxaca valley is a 'ceremonial area', probably dating before 4000 b.c. At Gheo-Shih, which seems to be a summer-season macro-band encampment, there is a carefully cleared area, 7 m. wide, delimited by boulders. According to Flannery (unpubl., 23) 'what they most resemble are the borders of a cleared "dance ground" '. At the same site different areas of activity can be distinguished, one where animals were butchered, another where pendants were made.

Just as at Tehuacán, and perhaps for a similar, as yet unknown, reason, information peters out between 3500 and 1400 b.c. It picks up again in the Tierras Largas phase (1400–1150 b.c.) (fig. 32) and the assemblage, including the pottery, is very similar to the Tehuacán Ajalpan material. However, the settlements are more complex (Flannery unpubl., 48). The site of San José Magote, on a piedmont spur just above the valley, covers at least 100 m. square, and more probably 150 m. square. There are three varieties of house construction. All are rectangular wattle-and-daub structures, but some have small, evenly spaced post-holes, others have large post-holes and still others have staggered post-holes. There are also platforms – large, rectangular structures made of stout posts filled with a mixture of crushed tuff, lime and sand and then coated, several times over, with white lime plaster.

One of the differences between the Tehuacán and Oaxaca valleys is that the water-table along the band of high alluvium is 20 m. below the surface in the former, and often no more than 3 m. in the latter. This means that simple pot irrigation, involving the sinking of shallow wells, is practicable in Oaxaca. Although there is no evidence that such irrigation was practised until the next phase, the three Tierras Largas villages are all suitably located on or near the high alluvium. If the Oaxacans had begun to use this very simple technique they could have taken two or even three crops a year. In which case they could have grown a considerable proportion of the total food supply and this could explain why the settlements are both larger and apparently more permanent than in the Tehuacán valley (Flannery, Kirkby *et al.* 1967). When the Oaxaca report is published a more detailed assessment will be possible.

(3) TAMAULIPAS

The third area of early plant cultivation is in Tamaulipas, north-east Mexico. This was one of the first regions explored by MacNeish, between 1946 and 1955. He began in the Sierra de Tamaulipas which is an eastern spur of the Sierra Madre Oriental.

TEHUACÁN	OAXACA	TAMAULIPAS	GUATEMALA

4000 b.c.
San Marcos:
Coxcotlan ph:
  4150 ± 200 (I 573)
Coxcotlan:
Coxcotlan ph:
  3525 ± 230 (I 664)
,, (Zne. XI)
  4375 ± 200 (I 459)
,, (Zne. I)
  4975 ± 200 (I 567)			

5000 b.c.
 	
,, (Zne. K)
  5050 ± 220 (I 457)
,, (Zne. XVI)
  5750 ± 250 (I 458)
Coxcotlan:
El Riego ph:
  4550 ± 200 (I 661)
,, 4750 ± 180 (I 651)
,, 4825 ± 200 (I 668)
,, 5400 ± 300 (I 675)
,, 5570 ± 250 (I 660)
,, (Zne. Q)
  5850 ± 250 (I 574)			

6000 b.c.
 	
,, 6425 ± 275 (I 769)
,, 6475 ± 250 (I 764)
,, (Zne. Q)
  6600 ± 250 (I 460)
Abejas:
El Riego ph:
  5725 ± 250 (I 765)
,, 5975 ± 250 (I 658)
,, 6040 ± 225 (I 759)
,, 6040 ± 300 (I 758)
	Guilá Naquitz:
	  (Zne. C)
	,, 6670 ± 160 (SI 515)
	,, 6910 ± 180 (GX 0785)
		Sierra Madre:
		Infiernillo ph:
		  6244 ± 450 (M 498)
		,, 6544 ± 450 (M 500)	

7000 b.c.	,, 7280 ± 120 (GX 0873)
	,, 7450 ± 300 (M 2097)
	,, (Zne. D)
	  7840 ± 240 (GX 0783)
		Sierra de Tamaulipas:
		Lerma ph:
		  7320 ± 500 (M 499)	

8000 b.c.	,, 8750 ± 350 (M 2099)
	Cueva Blanca:
	  (Zne. E)
	  8100 ± 350 (M 2093)
	,, 8780 ± 220 (SI 511R)
	,, 8960 ± 80 (SI 511)
	,, 9050 ± 400 (M 2094)		

32   Carbon-14 dates for Meso-America and Peru.

		Puente:
		Chihua ph:
		  (Zne. Ih1)
		    4086 ± 120 (I 5273)
		  '' (Zne. IIA)
		    4520 ± 125 (I 5274)
		Piki ph:
		  (Zne. IIA)
		    4680 ± 120 (I 5131)
		  '' (Zne. IIB)
		    4665 ± 120 (I 5129)
		  '' (Zne. IV)
		    4610 ± 120 (i 5128)
		  '' (Zne. VI)
		    4720 ± 120 (I 5132)
			Cerro Pucusana:
			  4315 ± 55 (GrN 5545)
			Ancón:
			Canario complex:
			  4750 ± 100 (UCLA 203)
			Ancón:
			Luz complex:
			  4570 ± 120 (Y 1304)
				4000 b.c.

				5000 b.c.

	Guitarrero II, Ancash:
	(Upper section):
	  5625 ± 220 (GX 1860)
	'' 5730 ± 250 (GX 1861)
		'' (Zne. VIII)
		  5210 ± 125 (I 5024)
		Jaywa/Piki ph:
		  (Zne. IX)
		    5470 ± 125 (I 5056)
			'' 5190 ± 100 (UCLA 202)
			'' 5350 ± 100 (UCLA 201)
			'' 5430 ± 120 (Y 1303)	

				6000 b.c.

		Jaywamachay:
		Jaywa ph:
		  (Zne. C)
		    6300 ± 135 (I 4503)
		  '' (Zne. D)
		    6410 ± 125 (I)
		Puente:
		Jaywa/Puente ph:
		  (Zne. XIIA)
		    6910 ± 125 (I 5057)		

				7000 b.c.

		Jaywamachay:
		Puente ph:
		  (Zne. H)
		    7030 ± 140 (I 5277)
		Huanta ph:
		  (Zne. J1)
		    7510 ± 145 (I 5275)		

				8000 b.c.
	Guitarrero II: (Lower section): 8625 ± 300 (GX 1780) '' 8585 ± 290 (GX 1778)			

Chart continued overleaf

TEHUACÁN	OAXACA	TAMAULIPAS	GUATEMALA

Coatepec:
Ajalpan ph:
   690 ± 130 (I 908)
   '' 745 ± 120 (I 914)
   '' 745 ± 120 (I 915)
   '' 860 ± 130 (I 931)
   '' 890 ± 120 (I 916)
Ajalpan:
Ajalpan ph:
   860 ± 120 (I 901)
   '' 900 ± 190 (I 767)
   '' 915 ± 130 (I 923)
			Salinas la Blanca:
			   765 ± 105 (Y 1151)
			  '' 814 ± 90 (Y 1166)
			  '' 928 ± 105 (Y 1154)
			  '' 978 ± 105 (Y 1150)

1000 b.c.

TEHUACÁN	OAXACA	TAMAULIPAS	GUATEMALA

'' 1030 ± 130 (I 935)
  '' 1050 ± 350 (I 752)
  '' 1090 ± 300 (I 927)
  '' 1150 ± 140 (I 934)
  '' 1270 ± 130 (I 929)
  '' 1575 ± 180 (I 895)
San Marcos:
Ajalpan ph:
   1025 ± 200 (I 566)
Purron:
Purron ph:
   1425 ± 170 (I 670)
  '' 1425 ± 200 (I 666)
  '' 1500 ± 175 (I 570)
  '' 1775 ± 180 (I 753)
  '' 1900 ± 190 (I 757)
  '' 1950 ± 180 (I 762)
	Tierras Largas:
	Tierras Largas ph:
	   1010 ± 150 (M 2351)
	  '' 1070 ± 150 (M 2352)
	  '' 1080 ± 150 (M 2353)
	San José Mogote:
	Tierras Largas ph:
	   1170 ± 150 (M 2351)
	  '' 1320 ± 160 (M 2372)
	  '' 1330 ± 180 (M 2330)
		Sierra Madre:
		Mesa de Guaje ph:
		   1490 ± 250 (M 505)
		  '' 1700 ± 250
		Sierra Madre:
		Flacco ph:
		   1995 ± 334 (C)	

2000 b.c.

TEHUACÁN	OAXACA	TAMAULIPAS	GUATEMALA

Purron:
Abejas ph:
  '' 2725 ± 200 (I 755)
  '' 2775 ± 190 (I 572)
	Cueva Blanca:
	Coxcotlan ph:
	   2800 ± 190 (M 2092)
		Sierra Madre:
		Guerra ph:
		   2780 ± 300 (M 504)
		Sierra de Tamaulipas:
		Late La Perra ph:
		   2500 ± 280 (C 687)
		Sierra Madre:
		Late Ocampo ph:
		   2624 ± 350 (M 503)
		Early Ocampo ph:
		   3280 ± 350 (M 502)	

3000 b.c.

TEHUACÁN	OAXACA	TAMAULIPAS	GUATEMALA

Coxcotlan:
Abejas ph:
   2820 ± 175 (I 653)
  '' (Zne. IX)
   3000 ± 200 (I 594)
  '' 3075 ± 180 (I 654)
  '' (Zne. VIII)
   3200 ± 220 (I 593)
  '' 3250 ± 180 (I 652)
  '' 3300 ± 200 (I 766)
Purron:
Coxcotlan ph:
   3850 ± 220 (I 754)
  '' 3945 ± 200 (I 768)
	'' 3295 ± 105 (GX 0782)		

4000 b.c.

PANAMA	WESTERN ANDES	AYACUCHO	COASTAL PERU
			_____ 1000 b.c.

		Kotosh, Huánuco:*
		    1670 ± 100 (Gak 766a)
		  ,, 1950 ± 900 (Tk 42)
		  ,, 1950 ± 100 (Gak 776 b)
		Pikimachay:
		Cachi ph:
		    (Zne. F)
		    1900 ± 120 (I 4154)
		
		* Not in Ayacucho
			Ancón:
			El Paraiso complex:
			    1545 ± 40 (GrN 5544)
			Chuquitanta:
			    1494 ± 59 (P 1214)
			  ,, 1620 ± 150 (I 1676)
			Gaviota ph:
			    1505 ± 105 (GX 1231)
			  ,, 1670 ± 100 (GX 1232)
			  ,, 1830 ± 100 (GX 1230)
			  ,, 1860 ± 150 (N 86)
			Conchas ph:
			    1810 ± 95 (GX 1130)

			_____ 2000 b.c.

Chiriqui:
grillo ph:
2125 ± 105
		Puente:
		Cachi ph:
		    (Zne. Ic)
		    2045 ± 105 (I 5131)
		  ,, 2090 ± 105 (I 5055)
			Ancón Tank site:
			Conchas ph:
			    2250 ± 80 (UCLA 968)
			Playa Hermosa ph:
			    1935 ± 95 (GX 1132b)
			  ,, 2175 ± 105 (GX 1132a)
			  ,, 2490 ± 110 (GX 1141)
			Pampa:
			Pampa ph:
			    2500 ± 110 (GX 1134)
			Encanto:
			Encanto ph:
			    2770 ± 80 (UCLA 967)

			_____ 3000 b.c.

Chiriqui:
gote ph:
3900 ± 110
			Chilca Quebrada:
			Encanto ph:
			    2270 ± 65 (GrN 5520)
			  ,, 3180 ± 110 (GrN 5547)
			  ,, 3420 ± 120 (UCLA 664)

			_____ 4000 b.c.

The cultural sequence was incomplete and had to be supplemented by excavations in the Sierra Madre, a little further to the south-west (MacNeish 1958, 152). The excavations were on a much smaller scale than those in Tehuacán and Oaxaca and the results can be dealt with fairly summarily.

The sequence begins with the Diablo phase, probably dating *c.* 10,000 b.c. Somewhat shadowy hunters, known only from finds of crude chopping and scraping tools inhabited the Sierra de Tamaulipas.[9] It is not until 8000 b.c., in the Lerma phase, that information increases. There are small micro-band sites and evidence that hunting provided much of the total food supply.

The record then fades out between 7000 and 5500 b.c. in the Sierra de Tamaulipas but can be picked up in the Sierra Madre where, in the Infiernillo phase, plant gathering begins to assume more importance. In this region cultivation probably begins *c.* 5500 b.c. and, just as in Tehuacán and Oaxaca, it is on a tiny scale. Pumpkins (*Cucurbita pepo* L.), which grew wild in the valley, probably begin to be grown (fig. 27). Perhaps, too, bottle gourd (*Lagenaria siceraria*) and chili peppers (*Capsicum annum* L. or *Capsicum frutescens* L.) (Mangelsdorf, MacNeish and Willey 1964).

The Infiernillo assemblage is another variant of the Desert tradition. The netting and basketry are different from the Tehuacán and Oaxacan types and there is no evidence of weaving or of mortars and pestles (MacNeish 1967d).

For the next part of the sequence we return to the Sierra de Tamaulipas, with the Nogales phase from 5500 to 3000 b.c. and the La Perra from 3000 to 2200 b.c. (fig. 32). These cultures, like the contemporary ones in Tehuacán and Oaxaca, are still part of the Desert tradition, but belong to the more northerly Abasola variant. There is evidence of macro-bands congregating in the wet season and dispersing in the dry.

MacNeish believes that cultivated foodstuffs were still a very minor part of the total subsistence. Even by 3000 b.c. they accounted for only 9% of the total diet. This percentage is based on the assumption that the foxtail millet (*Setaria geniculata Beauvais*) which forms a major constituent of the coprolites was harvested wild. However, the grains in the coprolites tend to be larger than in a random wild sample (Callen 1967a, b). This could simply be due to selectivity in collecting or it could be the result of cultivation. If cultivated, then the importance of food-production would be radi-

9 There are no carbon-14 dates for the Diablo phase.

cally increased. If collected, then gathering remains the most important activity, while the meat supply is eked out with such occasional delicacies as snails roasted and eaten in the shell or raw grasshoppers.

A wider variety of cultigens begins to be grown. There is a small amount of cultivated maize. It is a primitive race, Nal Tel A and B and the cobs are already somewhat larger than the early Tehuacán examples.

Between 4000 and 2200 b.c. contemporary groups in the Sierra Madre (Ocampo phase) were experimenting with slightly different crops: no maize, but a larger-seeded variety of pumpkin, common beans (*Phaseolus vulgaris*), runner beans (*Phaseolus coccineus*) and chili peppers (fig. 27). However, the Sierra Madre is handicapped by a very low rainfall, often less than 400 mm. per year, and the percentage of cultivated plants creeps up even more slowly than in the Sierra de Tamaulipas. At 2200 b.c. it is still less than 9% of the total (unless one includes the foxtail millet, again abundantly present in the coprolites) and by 1800 b.c. it is no more than 20%. In the Flacco phase, between 2200 and 1800 b.c., maize (Chapalote type) and amaranth (*Amaranthus* ssp.) were grown and foxtail millet becomes less important. By 1800 b.c., the Guerra phase, there is cotton (*Gossypium hirsutum* L.) and perhaps cushaw squash (*Cucurbita moschata* Duch.). By 1400 b.c., the Mesa de Guaje phase, there is hybrid maize (Breve de Padilla), teosinte (*Zea mexicana*), pumpkin (*Cucurbita pepo* L.) and small lima bean (*Phaseolus lunatus* L.) (fig. 27).

Even *c.* 500 b.c. the population remains nomadic. Groups coalesce in the wet season and hive-off in the dry. There is only one rather dubious village before 500 b.c.

By comparison, in the Sierra de Tamaulipas, where the rainfall is a little higher (600 to 800 mm.), cultivated plant foods increase in importance more rapidly and already in the Almagre phase between 2200 and 1800 b.c., there are fairly large seasonal camps with, in one case, wattle-and-daub houses.

There is an unfortunate gap in the Sierra de Tamaulipas sequence between 1800 and 600 b.c. When information picks up again, in the Laguna phase, *c.* 600 b.c., there is a fully sedentary society with villages ranging from 2 or 3 houses to 300 or 400, some in the valleys, some in defensive positions, some with plazas and temple mounds. Nearly half the food supply is cultivated and there are five different hybrid races of maize. There must have been a relatively structured society including a priesthood. There was probably some sort of irrigation. There was fine pottery and a complex weaving industry;

also many figurines. Until we know what happened in the valley between 1800 and 600 b.c. it is impossible to judge whether this is an indigenous development, or, as seems more likely, the result of colonisation, or at least very considerable outside influence.

The most obvious feature of all three areas of Meso-America examined here is the length of time it took for food-production to be sufficiently stable and productive to support sedentary communities. If amaranth and foxtail millet are excluded from the list of cultigens then the percentage of food produced creeps up inordinately slowly. If they are included (the evidence being inconclusive) cultivation makes a more rapid impact on the total economy but seemingly does not affect the need for seasonal mobility. Over a span of 5000 years the variety of cultigens gradually increases, often as the result of contact between different regions. And through selectivity and, particularly in the case of maize, cross-breeding, yields increase. But in these arid marginal areas primitive techniques could only produce one crop per year and wild plant gathering supplemented by hunting remained a vital part of the economy. Because the wild resources were scattered through the different micro-environments a pattern of scheduled seasonal movement continued to operate. Only when irrigation began to be practised, and it became possible to take more than one crop each year, could sedentary societies really become established.

THE MESO-AMERICAN LOWLANDS

Evidence of the transition to food-production in the lowlands is sparse and the degree to which it is an indigenous development remains unclear.

Until very recently nearly all the evidence of pre-ceramic and early ceramic settlements came from coastal shell-middens. Coe and Flannery (1964a) postulated that indigenous lowland hunter-gatherer communities gained their knowledge of plant cultivation and of pottery-making from the highlands shortly after 1600 b.c. Ocós pottery from coastal Chiapas and Guatemala, dated c. 1300 b.c., has strong affinities with the contemporary highland Ajalpan. Unfortunately no plant remains are preserved at the Ocós sites (Altamira and Colonia Aquiles Serdan in coastal Chiapas and La Victoria in Guatemala) or at the roughly contemporary Chiapa I site of Grijalva further inland in Chiapas (Coe 1961a; Green and Lowe 1967).

Definite evidence of cultivation comes from the following Cuadros phase, *c.* 1100 b.c. By a fortunate freak, the high calcium content of the clay floors at Salinas la Blanca in coastal Guatemala preserved both plant impressions and fossilised plants and these included both maize and avocados. The maize was of the Chapalote, or perhaps Nal Tel, type, similar to that found in the upland Ajalpan.

Coe and Flannery (1964a) went on to suggest that the introduced maize quickly became a staple and in conjunction with the estuarine-riverine resources provided a well-balanced diet. The maize could be grown on the well-drained fertile soil along the edge of the tropical forest and two, or even three, crops could be taken each year. The lagoon-estuaries provided fish, the mud banks molluscs and the mangrove swamps crabs. A wide variety of resources were thus locally available and this made it easier for the lowland communities to become sedentary.

Green and Lowe (1967, 61) query this interpretation. They suggest that maize was not introduced until the Cuadros phase and point out that grinding equipment appears only at about this time. They believe that the preceding Ocós culture, and the still earlier Barra culture (stratified below the Ocós at Altimira) were based on root-crop cultivation. Although there are no plant remains, they emphasise the lack of grinding equipment and note that some of the pottery can be matched with the Chorrera ware of coastal Ecuador. They suggest that root-crop cultivation derived from northern South America and diffused northwards along the coast. The only problem is that there is no evidence that the Chorrera people grew root-crops and indeed the direction of diffusion may easily be reversed. Estrada and Evans (1963) consider that the Chorerra pottery probably derives from coastal Guatemala and that its advent heralds the introduction of maize!

Another alternative is that the Meso-American coastal areas were not in the forefront of economic developments and that lowland cultivation began further inland and diffused to the coast. This hypothesis has been stimulated by recent work in the drier tropical inland lowlands of the Gatún lake area and Azuero peninsula of Panama. Hunter-gatherers inhabited this area at an early date and may have begun to cultivate maize independently (Linares and Ranere 1971). The evidence is rather tentative. Four maize grains were found in a core from Gatún lake at a level dating between 5300 and 4300 b.c. They are thought to be wild and could therefore indicate that maize was indigenous to the area. Four, however, is a very small sample and might be intrusive in the core. Higher up the core more maize pollen appears in conjunction with much grass pollen (*Gramineae*) and Ambrosia-type pollen (*Compositae*). The association is thought to imply that agriculture has begun. Unfortunately, this section of the core dates anywhere between 3100 b.c. and 200 a.d. and is therefore of little help in assessing how and when cultivation began in this region. The only other evidence is the early appearance of grinding equipment. Already in the Panamanian Cerro Mangote (3900 b.c.) and Monagrillo (2125 b.c.) cultures there is a predominance of pebble grinders and basin querns. However, this only shows that plant processing was important, it does not necessarily imply agriculture.

Though not conclusive this recent work indicates the importance of broadening the inquiry on the origins of cultivation to include the tropical lowlands. The picture of how and where cultivation began may yet be radically altered.

THE TRANSITION TO FOOD-PRODUCTION IN PERU

Peru is a country of enormous geographical and climatic diversity (fig. 33). Four major topographical units can be defined.

Starting from the west there is the coastal plain: a narrow, low-lying strip of cool desert. It is rainless because the cold Humboldt current sweeps along the coast and the rain-bearing winds from the west deposit their moisture long before reaching land. The current, however, nurtures a vast plankton colony which in turn supports a quite extraordinary abundance of marine life. Some 225 species of fish are found as well as shellfish, sea-mammals and shore birds (Lanning 1967a, 7; Parsons 1970). But these resources could not be exploited if the coastal desert were without fresh water. Fortunately there are numerous small rivers, some permanent, others intermittent. These provide fresh water, plant and game resources and, particularly along the lower reaches, fertile alluvial soil for farming. Such valleys were once extensively wooded with algarroba and similar trees. Virtually all the rivers rise on the western slopes of the Andes, so they run high during the highland wet season from January to April.

The desert is also broken by patches of fog-meadow, called *lomas*. This is a scrub vegetation that forms under the banks of fog that accumulate as the winds are forced to rise over the foothills of the Andes at elevations between 250 and 800 m. These *lomas* could be used for hunting and grazing during the winter months (June to September). In summer both fog-bank and *lomas* disappear (Lanning 1967a, 10; Patterson 1971b).

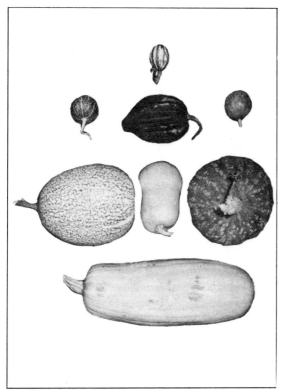

III Wild and cultivated species of squash and gourds. *Top: Cucurbita sororia. First row, left to right: C. cylindrata, C. pepo, C. okeechobeensis. Second row, left to right: C. ficifolia, C. moschata, C. maxima. Bottom: C. mixta. (reproduced by courtesy of T. W. Whitaker)*

The second topographical zone is the western slopes of the Andes. These slopes are heavily dissected and, lacking rain, are generally covered with a sparse xerophytic vegetation (Kaplan, Lynch and Smith 1973). The grazing is suitable for camelids – wild or domesticated llamas, alpacas and guanaco. From early times there may have been seasonal movement up and down the hillslopes, utilising the high *puna* during the wet months and the lower highland valleys in winter (Lanning 1967a, 47).

The third of the four zones is the high Andes. In northern Peru there are three principal ranges: the Cordilleras Occidental, Central and Oriental. Further south the Central range fades out. The peaks rise to 5000 and in places nearly 7000 m. and even the upland basins and plains are sometimes over 3300 m. above sea level. Although Peru lies within tropical latitudes (4 to 18°S) the high altitudes of the intermontane basins and ranges produce a

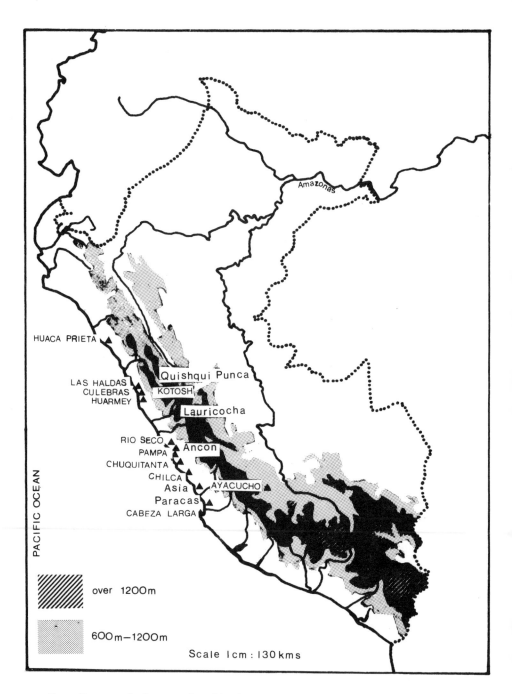

HUACA PRIETA

Quishqui Punca

LAS HALDAS
CULEBRAS   KOTOSH
HUARMEY

Lauricocha

RIO SECO
PAMPA   Ancon
CHUQUITANTA
CHILCA   AYACUCHO
Asia
Paracas
CABEZA LARGA

Amazonas

PACIFIC OCEAN

over 1200m

600m–1200m

Scale 1cm : 130kms

33   Peru. Pre-ceramic sites mentioned in the text.

temperate to cool climatic regime and nightly frosts are not un-
common in the southern basins and high plains (Willey 1971, 5).

These high basins, such as Titicaca, Cuzco and Ayacucho, are
in many ways similar to the Mexican basins. They have stretches
of fairly fertile soil; they tend to be rain-shadow areas and to have a
semi-arid vegetation covering. There are potential cultigens, both
root- and seed-crops (Appendix B, p. 233), and potential animal
domesticates such as the vicuña, guanaco and guinea pig.

Finally, to the east the Andes slope down to the great Amazonian
plain. The high eastern slopes are covered with montane forest
giving way lower down to montane rain forest and eventually to
Amazonian rain forest. It is quite probable that root-crop cultivation began early in the Amazonian lowlands but because of the
lack of preserved plants the beginnings remain completely speculative
(Appendix A, p. 228).

Until quite recently archaeologists excavating early farming
settlements tended to concentrate on the coastal sites. Preservation
is excellent – it is often hard to believe that some of the organic
remains are thousands of years old (photograph V). But, in fact,
cultivation was not initiated in this area. Hunter-gatherers were
present from *c.* 10,000 b.c., but plant cultivation, based on imported
cultigens, did not begin much before 4000 b.c.

Excavations have now begun on sites on the western hillslopes
and high intermontane basins of the Andes. Preservation is good on
the semi-arid hillslopes and reasonable in some of the intermontane
basins, particularly where there are rock-shelters or caves.

In both areas evidence of early domestication is being uncovered.

(1) THE AYACUCHO INTERMONTANE BASIN

The Ayacucho basin is one of the high intermontane basins (fig. 33).
It is a huge, roughly triangular, depression, each side about 112 km.
long. It lies nearly 2000 m. above sea level and is ringed on three
sides by mountains rising over 4200 m.

It is here that MacNeish, turning his attention from Meso-America
to points further south, discovered another early centre of
food-production. Initial attempts to produce food probably began
c. 6000 b.c., and are thus roughly contemporary with developments
in Meso-America. But unlike Meso-America, food-production was
not limited to plant cultivation. Animals – the llama and the guinea
pig – were also utilised.

The surveys and excavations in the Ayacucho basin are not yet
complete and only preliminary reports have been published.

Eventually it should be possible to reconstruct the transition from hunting and gathering to food-production in some detail.

The basin has been sub-divided into 5 micro-environments. The semi-desert basin floor lies below 2100 m. Grassland and open thorn forest extend to 2520 m., to be replaced by predominantly dry thorn forest up to 2700 m. Between 2700 m. and 3900 m. precipitation increases and there is a covering of thorn scrub (humid scrub forest) and finally above 3900 m. there is tundra-alpine vegetation.

Five hundred occupation levels have already been found. Several caves have long stratigraphic sequences. In particular the Pikimachay cave was occupied more or less continuously from nearly 20,000 years ago, and the Jaywamachay cave from 10,000 years ago.

The earlier parts of cultural sequences from these two caves have already been discussed (p. 162). In the Jaywamachay cave the Huanta complex (fish-tail points, burins and blades) gave way to the Puente complex *c.* 7700 b.c. (fig. 32). By this time the local Andean glaciers had receded and the fauna and vegetation had become similar to that of the present day.

The Puente complex continued through to *c.* 6500 b.c. Plant remains are unfortunately lacking but the heavy concentrations of animal bones and the very wide variety of rather small projectile points may indicate that hunting was the dominant activity. Bones of deer, horse, llama, and perhaps paleo-llama, are present, and towards the end of the phase llama bones outnumber deer.

Small Puente sites, probably micro-band encampments, are found in at least three micro-environments: the humid scrub forest, the dry thorn forest and the desert-like part of the grassland. There is little evidence of seasonal scheduling; both wet and dry season sites are found in the dry grassland zone.

A more organised pattern seems to appear after 6500 b.c., associated with the Jaywa complex (6500–5500 b.c., fig. 32). All the micro-environments are utilised and a superficial examination of sites in different zones seems to indicate that activities were being scheduled. Unlike the contemporary Meso-American upland sites, there is no evidence of a shift from hunting to plant gathering. Large mammal hunting, of llama and deer, seems to be important and there is an even greater variety of projectile points, as well as knife-like tools and end-scrapers which may have been used for butchering and skin preparation (MacNeish, Nelken-Terner and Cook 1970, 36).

It is possible that the first attempts at herding and cultivation began during this phase. A great quantity of llama dung was found in the Jaywamachay cave (altitude 3300 m. in the humid scrub zone) in association with Puente artefacts. The dung could simply be that of wild llama, collected and brought into the cave as an excellent source of fuel. Or it may have been dropped by animals herded into the cave and living alongside the human occupants. Small bones found in the same level may be guinea-pig bones, possibly of animals kept in captivity. Other small bones, again possibly from guinea-pigs, were found in the Jaywa levels of the Puente site. These 'domesticates' still need more rigorous identification.

Again in the Jaywamachay cave there were a couple of achiote seeds (*Bixa orellana* L.) while in the Pikimachay cave there were odd fragments of bottle gourd rind (*Lagenaria* sp.). There is no way of knowing whether either species was cultivated but achiote, at least, is not native to the basin. It probably comes from the eastern slopes of the Andes.

Domestication is not firmly attested in this phase and if there was food-production it was a very minor activity. Evidence picks up a little in the following Piki phase, 5500 to 4300 b.c. (fig. 32). Large numbers of small bones, probably of guinea pigs, were found. In the Pikimachay cave, in a level which is apparently Piki, there were remains of squash, amaranth, quinoa (*Chenopodium quinoa*), gourd and perhaps chili peppers, all of which MacNeish (personal comm. 1972) thinks were cultivated.[10]

It is noticeable that the early cultigens were primarily seed-crops even though many varieties of roots and tubers were locally available. It may partly be a question of preservation – the fleshy roots preserve less well than hard grains. But so far at any rate, Sauer's dictum that root-crop cultivation antedates seed-crop remains unproven (chapter 2, p. 20).

Gradually plant foods, whether wild or cultivated, become more important. In the next phase, the Chihua (4300–2800 b.c.), there is cultivated maize, cotton, lucuma, sapindas fruits, tara and possibly bean (*Phaseolus vulgaris*) (MacNeish, Nelken-Terner and Cook 1970, 38).[11] The maize is interesting because it seems to belong to the primitive Nal Tel-like race, similar to that found in Meso-America (Flannery 1973). Perhaps there was some contact between the two areas.

There are milling stones, pestles, mortars and perforated stones

10 This list is rather longer than Flannery's (1973). He only mentions bottle gourd and quinoa, and expresses caution about the latter.
11 Again Flannery (1973) only includes maize, lucuma and beans.

which may be digging stick weights.

Domesticated llama are definitely attested (MacNeish personal comm. 1972). Groups begin to live out in the open as well as in caves and rock-shelters. The population seems to increase and at least one open-air site is large enough to suggest occupation by a macro-band which perhaps remained together for a couple of seasons. Seasonal movement is well documented: one cave site in the valley bottom has 34 occupation levels – all, with one exception, wet season occupations.

Between 2800 and 1700 b.c., in the Cachi phase, cultivation and herding become well established, the population continues to increase and there seem to be villages. Hoes have been found which may indicate root-crop cultivation. Squash (*Cucurbita moschata* Duch.) and lima beans (*Phaseolus lunatus* L.) are grown and possibly coca. The squash might indicate contact with Meso-America, the lima beans certainly indicate contact with the eastern slopes. Terraces, perhaps part of a water control system, may date to this phase.

Although there is no evidence of ceremonial centres in the Ayacucho basin before 1700 b.c., there is, just over the crest of the Andes, on the eastern flanks at an elevation of 1950 m., a ceremonial centre at Kotosh (fig. 33). This has a carbon-14 date of *c.* 2000 b.c. (fig. 32) (Izumi and Sono 1963). There appears to be no pottery in the early levels at this site but unfired clay figurines and other unbaked objects were found in a wall niche of a structure known as the 'white temple'. The most interesting building is the 'temple of the crossed hands'. Two walls remain, 9.4 and 9.2 m. long, built of stones and plastered (fig. 34). A pair of crossed hands were sculpted in plaster below an internal niche (fig. 35). This construction was filled in and another complex of rooms, the 'temple of the little niches' was built on top. This complex had stone staircases.

Little has been published on the economic base of this ceremonial centre. Many charred seeds were found and there were llama bones in one of the temple niches. It seems probable that some of the food was being produced. Indirect evidence of cultivation on the eastern slopes is provided by the presence of species native to these slopes as 'imports' in the intermontane basins, the western hillslopes and the coastal plain. These species include lima beans (*Phaseolus lunatus*), guavas (*Psidium guajava*), manioc (*Manihot esculenta*) and peanuts (*Arachis hypogaea*).

With the emergence of villages and even ceremonial centres we can leave the uplands and move down to the western hillslopes.

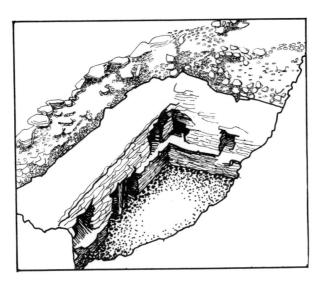

34   'Temple of the Crossed Hands', Kotosh, Peru.
(after Izumi and Sono 1963)

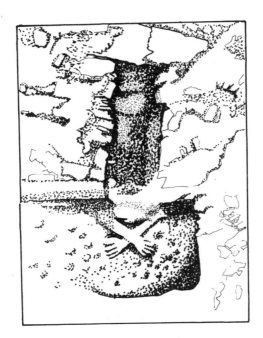

35   'Temple of the Crossed Hands' (close-up)
Kotosh, Peru.
(after Izumi and Sono 1963)

(2) The western Andean slopes

Several rock-shelters and open-air sites with pre-ceramic occupation levels have been excavated on the western slopes of the Andes. Until very recently there was no associated evidence of domestication. It was assumed that a hunter-gatherer subsistence continued long after food-production had begun in the intermontane basins and on the coast. Assemblages found in the Lauricocha caves (Lauricocha I to III) in the central section, at an altitude of 3000 m. were similar to those in the lower highland valleys at Quishqui Punca (Lauricocha I to III) in the Calléjon de Huaylas, at Ambo (Lauricocha II) in the Upper Huallaga and at Viscachani (complex related to Lauricocha III) in western Bolivia. Lanning (1967a, 47) suggested that the high caves were abandoned in winter and the hunter-gatherers followed the wild herds of guanaco and deer to less inhospitable lower elevations.

There may also have been movements between the coastal plain and the hillslopes. Groups may have occupied the coastal *lomas* from June to September and then during the dry season, when both fog and meadow disappeared, moved up into the hills. The *lomas* Arenal and Luz complexes are fairly similar to the Lauricocha I and II and the later coastal Canario and Encanto complexes have parallels with Lauricocha III (Patterson 1971b).

But this mobile hunter-gatherer economy was only one of the subsistence patterns. A very interesting discovery, so far only briefly published, has been made in the cave of Guitarrero in the Calléjon de Huaylas, Ancash department (Kaplan, Lynch and Smith 1973).

The area around the cave has a covering of thorn scrub with a scattering of such xerophytic cacti species as *Trichocereus peruvianus* and *Opuntia maxima*. Although no longer present, wild beans (*Phaseolus vulgaris*) could have flourished in such a setting. In stratum II of the cave, associated with equipment that has affinities with the *lomas* Arenal, the Lauricocha II and the Ayacucho Puente, cultivated common beans (*Phaseolus vulgaris*) were found. They differ from the wild forms in colouring, size, thinness of coat and lack of dehiscent characteristics (chapter 3, p. 63). A fairly high level of this stratum was carbon-14 dated to 5700 b.c. (fig. 32) (Lynch and Kennedy 1971). The cultivated beans were found at this level and also lower down although none came from the lowest part which had a carbon-14 date of 8000 b.c. (fig. 32). Cultivated Lima beans (*Phaseolus lunatus*) were also found but the context was less secure. Lima beans are not native to the region and must have derived from the eastern slopes.

It would seem therefore that *c.* 6000 b.c., at a time when the first evidence of domestication is found in the Ayacucho Puente complex, comparable developments were taking place on the lower slopes.

(3) THE COASTAL PLAIN

Scattered hunter-gatherer groups occupied the coastal plain *c.* 10,000 b.c. Various early complexes – the Red Zone, Oquendo, Chivaterros I and II – are known primarily from lithic workshops in the lower Chillón valley of the central coast (Lanning 1965; 1967a, 41).

Early sites found on the inland *lomas* date some time before 8000 b.c. The earliest *lomas* complex is the Arenal and it includes projectile points and a few milling stones. The *lomas* groups may have led a fairly marginal existence collecting wild potatoes and catching a motley assortment of snails, lizards, burrowing owls and occasional deer and guanaco. Bottle gourds (*Lagenaria siceraria*) were probably gathered locally and used as containers. It has already been mentioned that during the dry season Arenal groups may have moved up into the hills. The Arenal complex is similar to the Guiterrero II of the hillslopes and the Puente/Jawya of the Ayacucho basin.

The subsistence and settlement patterns begin to change *c.* 5200 b.c. Patterson (1971a; 1971b), somewhat emending Lanning's earlier scheme (1967a, 41), defines three cultures between *c.* 5200 and 2500 b.c.: the Canario (5200–4200 b.c.), the Corbina (4200–3750 b.c.) and the Encanto (3750–2500 b.c.). The dates are fairly arbitrary for there are many odd discrepancies in the Peruvian carbon-14 sequence (fig. 32).[12]

The change that emerges is that, particularly during the dry season, some *lomas* groups moved down to the coast and to the mouths of the small river valleys and began to exploit marine and littoral resources. Other *lomas* groups probably still moved up into the hills.

Fourteen seasonal camps have been found on the *lomas* north of Ancón. They were probably occupied from July to October and the economy was still geared to local hunting and collecting although occasionally marine resources were brought in from the coast, a distance of 3 to 5 km. (Patterson and Moseley 1969; Patterson 1971b). There is far more plant processing equipment: numerous querns, shaped and unshaped grinding stones and mortars.

12 Rowe (1965) has noted that the two main processing laboratories come up fairly consistently with an 'earlier' and 'later' set of dates.

Contact between the *lomas* and the hills, and even the intermontane basins, is indicated by the similarity of the Canario, the Lauricocha II and III, the Guiterrero IV and the Piki complexes (MacNeish, Nelken-Terner and Cook 1970; Patterson 1971b).

The Canario settlements down on the coast and near the mouths of the river valleys are thinly dispersed. They seem, with one exception, to be dry season encampments. For example, one site on the south bank of the Chilca, only a few kilometres away from an extensive *lomas*, had no *lomas* resources – probably because the *lomas* had temporarily dried up. This community seems mainly to have utilised the valley resources and to have gathered shellfish from the beach 6 kilometres away as a secondary resource (Patterson 1971b). The exceptional permanent site is on a hill above the Lurín valley in a position to exploit marine, beach, valley, desert and *lomas* resources. Fish and shellfish seem to be the dietary staples but wild plants were also gathered from the valley and *lomas*. It is possible that cultivation had just begun. Patterson (1971b) mentions that domesticated bottle gourds and an unidentified squash (*Cucurbita* sp.) were found.

In the following Corbina and Encanto phases the seasonal pattern, between *lomas* and upland and *lomas* and coast, seems to continue. But on the *lomas*, although plant gathering remains important, there is a shift of emphasis from hunting local game to obtaining (by expedition or barter) marine and littoral resources. This shift may simply be part of a widespread trend towards more intensive exploitation of the marine and littoral environments, or it may reflect a diminution in *lomas* resources. Lanning (1965) postulates a general reduction of the *lomas* due to increasing desiccation and points out that the relic *lomas*, marked by an abundance of snail-shells, are more extensive than today. Parsons (1970) disagrees with the idea of increased desiccation and suggests that the more extensive relic *lomas* mark the rare occasions, about every 25 to 40 years, when the warm El Niño sea current pushes further south and results in a sudden increase in rainfall. It is also possible that the *lomas* game was depleted by over-exploitation as the population increased. Patterson (1971a, b) suggests that there may have been a six-fold population increase, at least on the central coastal plain, between 3000 and 2300 b.c.

An increased utilisation of marine resources is also recorded from the coastal settlements. Chilca I on the bank of the Chilca river, 4 kilometres from the sea, seems to have been seasonally occupied by a group that primarily exploited shellfish (*Mesoderma donacium*, *Mytilis chorus*, *Mytilis magellanicus* and *Pecten purpuratus*)

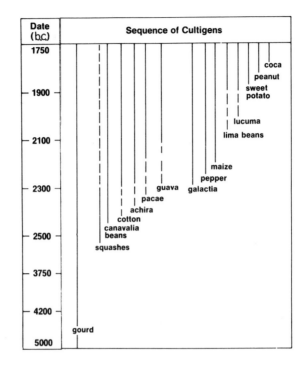

36 Sequence in which plants were brought into cultivation on the central coast of Peru. (after Patterson 1971a)

as well as sea fish, sea mammals and off-shore birds. The equipment includes a fish-hook made from a cactus spine and others made from stone and bone (Engel 1966b).

It is difficult to ascertain how important cultivation was, or even what was being cultivated. Patterson (1971b) mentions no more than bottle-gourds and perhaps squash (fig. 36). Engel (1972, 102) confidently maintains that at Chilca I gourds, lima beans (*Phaseolus lunatus*) and cotton were being grown before 3500 b.c.[13] There is a possibility, however, that these cultigens do not belong in the early midden horizon but are intrusive from a higher level (Patterson and Moseley 1968). The same authors also suggest that the domesticated common beans (*Phaseolus vulgaris*) reported from Cabeza Larga on the Paracas peninsula in the south are intrusive. Of all these possible or probable cultigens only the bottle-gourd is likely to have been indigenous, the rest would have been obtained by contact, presumably with groups on the Andean hillslopes or high basins.

13 Engel (1972, 103) also mentions Asia, Rio Grande de Nazca and Paracas 514, all on the south coast, as sites where cotton and beans were domesticated prior to 3500 b.c. But these are generally thought to be later.

Generally speaking the Encanto coastal sites are small, probably inhabited by no more than 50 people. Chilca I may be an exception. Although considerably eroded, Engel (1966b; 1972, 106) estimated that there may have been as many as 100 to 150 huts and a population of 250 to 350 people. One very well-preserved round hut was reconstructed (Donnan 1964). The floor was slightly sunk into the sand, the walls and roof were made of bundles of canes (*Gynerium sagittatum*) bent inwards and secured at the centre. They were tied with ropes of junco (*Cyperus* sp.) and the frame was strengthened by lashing on cane bundles and bracing the interior with whale ribs. The whole thing was then covered with bundles of junco grass.[14] There seems also to have been a large ovoid house at this site, 11 m. in diameter with 150 post-holes (Engel 1972, 106).

Relatively few sites are known for the period between 2500 and 1900 b.c. which includes the Pampa, Playa Hermosa and Conchas phases (fig. 32). Coastal settlements seem to show an increasingly intensive orientation towards marine and littoral resources. At the Ancón Yacht site and at Pampa, Ventanilla, fishing seems to be the most important activity, followed by shell-fishing and the hunting of marine mammals and shore-birds. The location of these settlements appears to be orientated towards the exploitation of only one micro-environment rather than, as earlier, a wide variety (Patterson 1971b). A few crops may have been grown at Pampa. There were remains of *Cucurbita moschata* and possibly *Cucurbita ficifolia*. At the Ancón Yacht site maize pollen was found in coprolites in the Playa Hermosa level. This site is far from any suitable farm land and presumably cultivated plants were obtained by barter. Maize was probably being grown in neighbouring valleys (Patterson personal comm. 1972).

Information on food-production and settlement patterns increases in the Gaviota phase (1900–1750 b.c. fig. 32).

Maize is recorded primarily from north and north central coast sites (fig. 36). Some was found at the large site of Playa Culebras on the north central coast. Some was found in the pre-ceramic shell midden of Huarmey. Kelley and Bonavia (1963) report two types, both apparently domesticated, from a low level in this midden, and more devolved forms plus a solitary peanut (*Arachis hypogaea* L.) from higher up. There may have been maize at Las Haldas and at the Aspero site at Puerto de Supe on the northernmost edge of the central coast (Patterson personal comm. 1972). Squash, guavas, chili peppers, avocados, beans and cotton (*Gossy-*

14 The hut was used as a communal grave for seven burials, each mat-wrapped and extended.

pium barbadense) were also being cultivated by 1750 b.c. The cotton is a different species from the Mexican *Gossypium hirsutum* L.

The importance of food-production in the Gaviota phase varied greatly from community to community. There were at least three main subsistence patterns: coastal communities still largely dependent on marine resources, communities in the lower river valleys cultivating the flood-plains and exploiting marine and littoral resources, and communities higher up the valleys, where there is little or no flood-plain, apparently cultivating with the aid of very primitive water management, probably involving short irrigation canals. Only a small amount of marine foodstuffs filtered through to these upper valley settlements (Patterson 1971b).

Not only did the subsistence pattern vary but also settlement size and form. By now the inland *lomas* sites had been abandoned. Coastal and valley sites were permanently occupied. Rather than seasonal movement there seems to have been a system of barter between coastal, flood-plain and upper valley sites. There are more sites. There are hamlets (50 to 100 inhabitants), villages (200 to 500) and a few much larger settlements (up to 1000 or even 1500). The latter are located mainly on the north and central coastal plain at, for example, Culebras I, Río Seco and Chuquitanta (El Paraíso) (fig. 33).

A description of a few sites will give some idea of the variety. Huaca Prieta on the north coast was partially excavated by Junius Bird in the 1940s (Bird 1948). It is a huge midden site, 125 m. long and 12 m. high. It represents the accumulation of all the domestic debris thrown out over centuries by a fairly small community. It is close to the sea and to the flood-plain of the Chicama river.

The inhabitants lived in small, roughly square houses built into the midden. Each comprised one or two rooms and were made of beach cobbles set in a mortar of midden dirt and water, roofed over with wood and whale bones weighed down with rubble.

The midden debris contained a fine cross-section of equipment and foodstuffs. There were matting and baskets, fragments of bark cloth, some finely decorated textile fragments, and gourd containers – very occasionally decorated with incised patterns (Bird 1963). There were crude pebble tools and fire-crackled stones probably used for heating water.

Cultivated plant remains included two types of squash (*Cucurbita moschata* and *Cucurbita ficifolia*), lima beans (*Phaseolus lunatus*) and jack beans (*Canavalia ensiformis*). There were plants that occur wild in the area and may either have been cultivated or gathered: chili peppers (*Capsicum baccatum*), cotton (found both as yarn and as textile fragments), achira (*Canna edulis* or *Canna indica*) and canavalia (*Canavalia plagiosperma*). There were starchy rootstocks and tubers of cattail, junco (*Cyperus*) and sedges (*Scirpus*), and edible fruits such as circuelade fraile (*Bunchosia armaniaca*), guayaba (*Psidium guajava*) and lucuma (*Lucuma splendens*), all of which were available from the neighbouring Chicama valley (Parsons 1970).

A second village site is Asia I (Omas) on the south-central coast. Here one of a series of small, refuse-covered mounds was excavated by Engel (1963). He uncovered a multi-roomed complex built of stone and adobe. Unfortunately, little has been published on the economy other than that beans and cotton were grown. Not only cotton textiles but spindles and spindle-whorls were present.[15]

The economic viability of the large site of Río Seco (90 km. to the north of Lima) is hard to understand. Settlement debris covered 10 hectares and there was a large number of rather flimsy houses as well as at least two artificial platforms built up by the super-imposition of well-constructed stone-and-adobe room complexes, each back-filled with boulders and lumps of adobe. Several stone columns or blocks were set on top of the platform. The curious feature is that the settlement is located on a terrace above the sea with no visible source of water and no land suitable for farming. Apparently marine resources still provided the bulk of the diet although some cultivated foodstuffs may have been brought in from neighbouring valleys.

At Culebras I on the north-central coast, on the south side of the Culebras delta and 100 m. from the sea, there were no platforms but an impressive amount of labour had gone into terracing the hillside and facing the terraces with basalt blocks. Several semi-subterranean, square or rectangular houses, between 1.5 and 3 m. a side were built on each of the terraces. The houses were divided into two or three rooms. The subterranean portions were lined with basalt blocks and mortar, while the upper parts were probably of adobe or wattle-and-daub. There was a large cemetery on the top of the hill as well as many intra-mural burials. The dead were wrapped in layers of cloth and mats and were accompanied by fairly lavish grave-goods – necklaces, pendants and other ornaments of shell, stone and bone, as well as gourd containers and food-offerings (Lanning 1967a, 68). At this site the inhabitants could and

---

15 Asia I has a carbon-14 date of 1314 ±100 b.c. This may be aberrant. Or this may be a late site (perhaps even contemporary with neighbouring ceramic-using settlements), or it may have been occupied for a long time. Elaborate grave-goods include jet mirrors set in baked clay holders, snuff trays and tubes, lime bottles of gourd or wood, and lime and coca leaves (Lanning 1967a, 72).

IV   Chuquitanta (El Paraiso), Peru.
(*reproduced by courtesy of W. Bray*)

V   Remains of basket from Pre-ceramic Chuquitanta, Peru.
(*reproduced by courtesy of W. Bray*)

did exploit both marine resources and flood-plain agriculture. Maize was among the crops grown (Lanning 1967a, 67; Willey 1971, 96). Lanning (1967a, 63) mentions that small guinea-pig runs (stone-lined tunnels) were constructed between rooms and guinea-pig bones were found inside them. This is the earliest evidence for the introduction of these small animals from the highlands.

We can end with Chuquitanta (El Paraiso), 5 km. from the sea, close to a permanent spring and to a valley flood-plain. Marine resources were exploited. Lima beans, cotton, perhaps squash (*Cucurbita moschata*) and various fruits such as pacae and lucuma were grown. The economy was sufficient to underwrite the construction of seven large, more or less contemporary, platform mounds, the largest 300 m. long, as well as a series of ancillary units, all within an area 900 × 700 m. (photograph IV). As at Río Seco, the mounds were made up of super-imposed, back-filled room complexes. These complexes were well planned with joining passages, staircases and courtyards. The lower courses were of stone and mud mortar and were surmounted by mud-brick walls, polished and painted – black, red, ochre and white. Complex I, which was restored, had a patio surrounded by platforms on three sides, each with an access stairway. The structure had been enlarged at least five times. Only the upper level was excavated and included a 'ceremonial' chamber with a large hollow in the floor with two small cavities at each of the four corners (Engel 1966b; 1972, 110).

There is not enough evidence on the connection between the establishment of these large settlements, with or without ceremonial complexes, and changes in the subsistence base. Was increased food-production an important factor? Was the increased stability dependent upon a broad-based economy involving the exploitation of marine resources and plant cultivation? Or was there an important barter system between communities with rather specialised economies? Alternatively, was food-production of little importance in the development of these large centres? At a number of the sites where there is evidence of cultivation many of the cultigens were non-foodstuffs such as cotton or bottle-gourds, or were condiments such as chili pepper. It may be that the Peruvian coastal plain affords an example not only of a sedentary way of life based primarily on wild resources but also of large settlements and ceremonial complexes whose economic viability had little to do with the transition to food-production.

To answer these questions and to clarify the importance of contact and exchange between fishing villages on the coast and flood-plain and upper valley farming settlements requires much more detailed information on the subsistence base of the individual sites. Such information might also further an understanding of the relationship between the coastal plain and the highlands. It is surely not fortuitous that the Pampa – Playa Hermosa – Conchas and Gaviota material shows links with the Cachi complex of the Ayacucho basin (MacNeish, Nelken-Terner and Cook 1970), or that the Kotosh ceremonial centre on the eastern high flanks of the Andes is contemporary with Chuquitanta and Río Seco on the coastal plain. The cultigens grown on the coastal plain are not indigenous, and they therefore indicate contact with other regions. They could have arrived by sea trade,[16] but the evidence – slight as it is – suggests that seed-crops, including maize, were not grown on the coastal lowland to the north until quite late, perhaps 1500 b.c. (Appendix A, p. 228). The much earlier dates for cultivated beans on the west Andean hillslopes (6000 b.c.) and for squash, beans and maize in the Ayacucho intermontane basin (all by 3000 b.c.) indicate that the highlands were probably a far more important source of cultigens than the neighbouring coastal regions.

16 The designs on gourd vessels from Huaca Prieta are very similar to those on the earlier (*c.* 2300 b.c.) South Valdivian III pottery from Ecuador (Lanning 1967a, 76).

Conclusions

The evidence has been sorted, analysed and criticised. But few definitive statements emerge. Despite substantial research, particularly in the last decade, the material is still too meagre, both in quantity and quality.

Let us consider some of the imponderables. First, the coverage on the transition to food-production is limited to a few geographic areas. These areas tend to have features in common – conditions are usually arid or semi-arid (so organic preservation is reasonably good) and most of the plant staples are seed-crops. This concentration on limited and relatively similar environments means that attempts to elevate cross-cultural regularities into generalisations on how food-production began throughout the world must be suspect.

Secondly, even in the areas which have been studied, the coverage is frequently piecemeal. In South-west Asia excavators have concentrated on small tell sites and, as a direct result, early farming is usually seen in terms of the development of small peasant communities living in scattered villages. The two large tells that have been excavated, revealing the townships of Çatal Hüyük and Jericho, fit very awkwardly into this picture. But who knows what lies below Nineveh, Kirkuk and other great piedmont tells? There may have been many townships (p. 23). Perhaps, as Jane Jacobs suggests (p. 22), such towns were early trade centres and played a vital part in the transition to food-production.

To take another example, much recent theorising has emphasised population pressure as a major factor behind the shift to food-production. Yet, at least in South-west Asia, few regional surveys have been attempted and there is no detailed information on the increase in number or size of sites through time (compare G. Wright's [1971] vague estimates for South-west Asia (p. 122) with MacNeish's [1972] detailed analysis for the Tehuacán valley (p. 178) or Patterson's work [1971b] in central coastal Peru). There is therefore no way of assessing the validity of Binford's demographic model or the different versions suggested by Meyers or Smith and Young (pp. 32–36).

There is also frequent reference in the literature to the significance of human movements up and down the valleys as a means of promoting the exchange of information and domesticates. But in South-west Asia there is not one detailed coverage of a valley system to illustrate the connection between sites occupied at different times of the year or with different subsistence orientations. For example, what, if any, is the relationship between a 'herding' camp such as Tepe Sarab and mixed-farming villages such as Jarmo (p. 148)? Detailed surveys and excavations along the lines of the work in the Tehuacán, Oaxaca and Ayacucho valleys are needed.

But even in the latter areas the coverage is not complete. In the Tehuacán valley in Mexico small 'hamlets' appear *c.* 3400 b.c. But not one has been extensively excavated. We cannot tell whether they were permanent or semi-permanent or how large they were. We cannot therefore assess the variety of settlement patterns, the subsistence scheduling or the inter-connection between these 'hamlets' and the macro- and micro-band camps (p. 179).

Thirdly, the quality of the excavations varies considerably. This may be a reflection of when the excavation took place and what techniques were available at the time (Hole 1971: 'Flannery and I once wrote that seeds were rare at Ali Kosh, when in fact it was our technique for recovering them that was at fault'). It may partly be a matter of cost (in time, equipment and the need for specialists). Or perhaps a failure to recognise the importance of retrieving as much data on the subsistence base as possible (Reed 1960: 'Too often the animal bones have been shovelled upon the refuse heap').

Fourthly, if the archaeological coverage is inadequate – in both quality and quantity – coverage by other disciplines is still more haphazard. We do not know a fraction of the wild distributions of potential domesticates (and have an overly narrow view of what constitute 'potential domesticates'). In some cases we do not even know which the wild progenitors were (chapter 5). Discussion on how to recognise that domestication has occurred is still fierce and unresolved (chapter 3). We have only a hazy idea of the effect of widespread climatic development on the areas under review, and an impossibly foggy knowledge of local past environments (chapter 4). How then can we talk of sites being just beyond the wild distribution zones, or be sure that present-day 'optimal resource areas' were optimal 12,000 years ago, or that present-day 'marginal' sites really were marginal? Much more pollen and soil sampling is needed.

In sum there is not only a need for work in a variety of environments but for more detailed work in the areas covered in this book. There is a need for local environmental studies and for more problem-orientated research. If, for example, population pressure is hypothesised as important, then detailed surveying (without necessarily undertaking costly excavations) should be attempted and ways must be found to quantify 'density' and 'pressure'.

These criticisms are not meant to imply a state of unalleviated chaos and confusion. The increasing attention paid to the problem of the beginning of food-production has not only resulted in many more excavations in the last ten years but has also effected a sharpening of the analytical tools. There are new and better ways of retrieving evidence (p. 50), of sampling (and of correcting for bias) and of analysing (p. 47). Specialists are not only being employed, but their work is being promoted from learned (and often unread) appendices to an integral part of the project. Instead of waiting at home for samples to arrive, many specialists now go out in the field, collect precisely what they require, gain a better general understanding, and are able to feed their specialist knowledge into the work in progress.

On the theoretical side an important development is the use of a systemic approach. The ability to view culture as an adaptive system comprising a series of articulated parts – environment, technology, subsistence activities, social structure and beliefs – makes it easier to visualise the inter-action between these parts and the way change in one causes adjustments in the others (p. 26). The use of the cybernetic principles to explain the mechanism by which change occurs within the system again provides a more incisive method for tackling the question of how specific hunting-gathering economies evolved towards food-production (p. 27).

Bearing in mind the inadequacies of the available evidence, are any patterns beginning to emerge? If we restrict the field to Meso-America and South-west Asia (information from upland Peru still being limited) are there significant cross-cultural regularities? Some perhaps, but not many. In both cases domestication occurs in areas where there are many micro-environments and a correspondingly wide range of food resources. In both areas, some time prior to early attempts at domestication, human groups began to utilise many of these resources and to practise a broad-spectrum economy. Such an economy presupposes not only a detailed knowledge of the micro-environments but the ability to procure and process different types of plants and animals (p. 29). In both areas considerable technological competence is shown. A variety of projectile points for hunting was found there, together with grinding stones and querns for processing seeds and nuts.

We may suspect that the variety of terrain might encourage attempts to manipulate plants, for seasonal scheduling would be eased by transplanting to accessible locations, for example from hillslopes to valley-floors. The diversity of food resources would also give considerable scope for experimentation and would provide a hedge against failure – if one resource failed there were others to fall back on. The utilisation of several micro-environments engendered a mobility which would promote contact. Neighbouring valleys would have somewhat different resources which could usefully be exchanged. Diffusion of information, domesticates, etc., might therefore be quite rapid.

It is unlikely that even these limited cross-cultural regularities will hold good in other environments. It seems probable that tropical lowland root-crop cultivation began on the river banks and while these provide a wide range of resources and the possibility of a broad spectrum economy, there need not have been much mobility, for the micro-environments are crammed close together (river/mud-flat/bank/forest edge) and the lack of diversity in the lowland terrain would not promote resource exchanges. Nor is much technological ability required in the procuring and processing of root-crops.

Changes in the environment may have affected subsistence patterns in both Meso-America and South-west Asia. But this hardly constitutes a significant 'regularity'. It is likely that many shifts in subsistence (both hunting-gathering and food-producing) are partly a reflection of environmental change – which may be long-term, short-term, widespread or local. It is possible that in both regions environmental changes are to some degree associated with the recession of the Pleistocene ice-sheets but this has not yet been adequately demonstrated. At any rate, the effect of environmental change is markedly different in the two regions. In Meso-America MacNeish (1971a) suggests that drier conditions *c.* 7000 b.c. led to a decrease in available herd animals and this resulted in an increased focus on plant resources. Food procurement became more, rather than less, difficult. In South-west Asia a rise in temperatures and rainfall around 9000 b.c. led to an extension of the oak–pistachio zones. Since wild cereals are associated with this zone they probably became more widespread. Seed collecting may have become more important but it does not seem to have been at the expense of hunting. Nor do any game species disappear. At about this time, or a little later, tracts of fertile alluvium were exposed by the recession of the inland lakes. Such tracts were ideal for early dry farming. It would seem that in parts of South-west Asia ameliorating conditions made the food quest less arduous.

So if environmental change was a factor it operated in different ways in the two regions, and we find very different resulting economies and developments.

In Meso-America there is a concentration on plant resources. These are widely scattered within the valley systems and necessitated a scheduled seasonal round of activity. Although some micro-environments are sufficiently rich to allow groups to stay put for a couple of seasons they do not have adequate wild food resources for year-round occupancy. No food plants grew in extensive stands – wild maize (or teosinte) was a low-yielding plant and was certainly not a staple. There was no question of pre-agricultural sedentism. Early cultivation appears to have involved non-staple and frequently non-edible plants, such as bottle-gourds (containers) and chili peppers (condiment). For over 3000 years cultivated plants played only a minor part in the economy and *barranca* cultivation was incorporated into the seasonal round. It took several millennia for cultivated maize to become an important crop – partly because the favourable genetic changes were polygenetic and involved considerable crossing and back-crossing, partly because maize is wind-pollinated so that favourable mutations were constantly being bombarded by wild pollen. Maize is deficient in protein, there were no herd animals to make up this lack and the only protein cultigens were beans and peanuts. Until the bean–maize combination developed, hunting or legume or nut gathering continued to be essential and so promoted the continuance of a mobile, low density population. Thus, although plant domestication began *c.* 5000 b.c., it was not until 1500 b.c. that a viable food-producing economy sufficient to support sedentary groups emerged.

In South-west Asia the picture is quite different. Herd animals – sheep, goat, cattle and pig – were available. In favoured locations great stands of wild cereals flourished. In optimal areas where wild cereals and lake or river resources were at hand pre-agricultural sedentism was possible. It seems probable that in some parts of South-west Asia herding of sheep or goat began very early – not necessarily in conjunction with cereal cultivation. In other parts (or perhaps just other communities) there was experimentation with various cereals and legumes. Where wild barley and wheat were available they were probably grown together; where there was only one or other wild cereal it alone was cultivated. Both wild and early domesticated cereals and herd animals gave good returns (in contrast to maize) and the domesticates could quickly become an important part of the economy. Through contact and exchange mixed farming rapidly became the predominant economic strategy and with the transfer of domesticates beyond their natural habitat sedentary communities became far more widespread.

Some authorities have suggested that pre-agricultural sedentism in optimal areas led to increased population within these areas (p. 33). Population pressure could have led to an exodus into more marginal lands and an attempt to simulate the conditions of the optimal areas by transferring and cultivating cereal crops. Alternatively, cultivation may have occurred in the optimal areas in an attempt to maintain food supplies despite increased population (p. 35). Neither theory explains the beginning of herding. Nor has the role of the townships been elucidated. The importance of the obsidian trade as a means of diffusing knowledge and commodities has been recognised by many archaeologists but the possibility that strategically placed trade centres may have played some important innovating role in the shift to food-production has not yet been investigated.

This brief résumé of developments in Meso-America and Southwest Asia surely underlines the fact that food-production must not be viewed as a unilinear development. There is a wide gamut of possible plant/animal manipulations; there are many forms practised by hunter-gatherers and many forms practised by food-producers. There is no single hypothesis that will explain the shift to food-production in different parts of the world. For the foreseeable future we would do better to leave to one side the vague similarities and concentrate instead on the particular processes that operated in particular areas.

Appendix A

AFRICA, INDIA, CHINA, SOUTH-EAST ASIA, TROPICAL
SOUTH AND CENTRAL AMERICAN LOWLANDS

It is often very difficult to distinguish between primary centres
where the transition to farming was an entirely indigenous
development, and secondary centres where the knowledge and often
the actual plants or animals were externally derived by colonisation
and/or diffusion. It is often also an academic distinction, for within
the secondary areas locally available plants and animals were added
to the repertoire and new techniques and farming systems evolved.
It is also quite possible that some communities in 'recipient' areas
had, independently, experimented with local plant or animal
domestication but because this was relatively unsuccessful it has not
been recognised (chapter 5, p. 89).

Another book could be written on why and how local groups
came to accept and modify a food-producing economy, for certainly
they never acted as passive recipients. There have been very interesting studies on the introduction and impact of pig-breeding and horticulture in New Guinea (Brookfield and White 1968; Allen 1972;
Golson 1972), and there have been studies from many parts of Europe
on how farming was introduced, adopted, and adapted (among
recent contributions: Bökönyi 1971a; Tringham 1971; Whitehouse
1968, 1971; Jarman 1972b).

But in this Appendix the emphasis is on areas where the process
may have been indigenous.

AFRICA

'Any consideration of the beginnings and development of agriculture in Africa in the present state of our knowledge must be a survey
of our ignorance and a reasoned essay in speculation' (Shaw
in press).

(1) THE NILE VALLEY

On present evidence the Nile valley is a recipient area.

Domesticated wheat and barley, sheep and goat appear *c.* 4000 b.c. in Upper and Lower Egypt and are associated with large sites and well-made pottery. The importance of innovations in the lithic industry is disputed. Clark (1971) considers that the lithic assemblages were still predominantly in the indigenous tradition. Another opposing view is that they are distinctive and have little affinity with local assemblages.

The Nile valley is, however, of interest in that there is good evidence that grain collecting assumed a considerable importance in the economy as early as 12,000 b.c. – without apparently leading to cultivation. At Tushkla near Abu Simbel (with a possible carbon-14 date of 12,550 ± 490 b.c., WSU-315) there were many grinding stones and microliths with silica gloss. At Kom Ombo below Aswan, there were many grinding stones and carbon-14 dates of 11,610 ± 120 b.c. (Y-1447) and 11,120 ± 120 b.c. (Y-1375), and at Isna near Luxor there were again both grinding stones and blades with silica gloss, associated with very large sites. It is suggested that between 12,000 and 10,000 b.c. conditions along the Nile ameliorated and grains were more plentiful than previously. Long-grained grasses such as *Echinochloa, Aristida, Eragrostis, Cenchrus* ssp., *Panicum, Setaria* and *Digitaria* may have been utilised. At Isna *c.* 10,500 b.c. a sudden increase in a large-grained cereal, tentatively identified as barley, has been recorded. If correct this indicates that wild barley extended well beyond its present-day habitat.

After 10,000 b.c., perhaps as a response to slight climatic changes, grain assumes less importance in the economy and the grinding equipment and lustrous blades decline in number. Renewed emphasis on grain is then associated with the sudden influx of cultigens *c.* 4000 b.c., probably from South-west Asia.

It is also possible that prior to the advent of domesticated sheep and goat attempts were made to domesticate local animals such as cattle (*Bos primigenius* and *B. ibericus*), gazelle and oryx (Clark 1971).

(2) The Sahara and the North African coast

There is good evidence of Post-Pleistocene moist interludes in the highlands and along the major wadi systems and depressions that drained the higher country. Favourable open grassland habitats were created. Moisture peaks are recorded at 8250 (or ?9700) to 6400 b.c., 5100 to 2200 b.c. and 1600 to 500 b.c. (Butzer 1971, 582).

Evidence of early animal herding in North Africa may go back as early as the sixth millennium b.c. At Uan Muhaggiag, south-west Libya, sheep and cattle bones are carbon-14 dated to 5590 ± 220 b.c., but it is not entirely clear whether they were domesticated. At Haua Fteah, Cyrenaica, *c.* 4800 b.c., there is evidence of domesticated sheep and goat and perhaps domesticated cattle. Rock art depicting cattle, probably domesticated, mostly dates to the fifth and fourth millennia b.c. It is not clear how far these were independent developments, or how far they were influenced by developments further east.

Nor is it clear whether plant cultivation occurred equally early, and, if it did, whether it was an independent development or due to contact. Present-day distributions of sorghum and pearl millet extend no further than the south Sahara, but originally they may have extended further north (Butzer 1971, 591). Several northern sites, including Haua Fteah, have lithic elements which could have been used for processing either wild or cultivated plants. These include stone 'hoes', mortars, pestles and digging-stick weights (Hugot 1968).

In the central Sahara at Amekni in the Hoggar, 2 pollen grains are thought to be cultivated pearl or bullrush millet (*Pennisetum*) and other grains may be wheat. The site is carbon-14 dated between 6100 and 4850 b.c.

Nearby at Meniét, carbon-14 dated to 3450 ± 150 b.c., there are mortars, pestles and pollen which may be of cultivated grass, but this is dubious (Hugot 1968; Shaw in press).

Further south at Adrar Bous in the Aïr region, a pottery impression of 1 grain of *Brachiaria* is dated *c.* 4000 b.c., and another grain, of *Sorghum*, is dated *c.* 2000 b.c.

To the south-west, in the Dhar Tichitt region of Mauretania there are settlements dating between the mid-second millennium and the mid-first millennium b.c. Seven phases have been recognised. In the first three phases there are many pottery impressions of bur-grass seeds (*Cenchrus bifloris*) and 1 grain of *Pennisetum* sp. In the fourth phase there are impressions of fonio (*Brachiara deflexa*) and *Panicum laetum*, and *Pennisetum* rises to 3%. In the fifth phase, *c.* 1100 b.c., *Pennisetum* is up to 60%, and in the sixth and seventh up to 80%. By the fifth phase it is definitely cultivated. *Pennisetum* is indigenous to Senegal and southern Mauritania and this region, including the Tichitt sites, may well have been an early centre for the domestication of the crop. *Panicum turgidum* appears in the seventh phase. The slow augmentation in the importance of seed-crops suggests local domestication but does not rule out contact (Shaw in press). Domesticated cattle are recorded at Dhar Tichitt *c.* 1500 b.c.

(3) WEST AFRICA

The origin of agriculture in this region remains completely speculative: 'The archeobotanical evidence is essentially nil at the present time' (Harlan 1972).

There is fairly good agreement on the indigenous cultigens but it is not possible to establish when or in what order they were brought into cultivation. Nor is it known how far the process was indigenous. There are three possibilities. Either the process was entirely indigenous. Or cultivation began through stimulus from Saharan agriculturists. Or indigenous proto-cultivation occurred, involving, for example, the collecting and tending of tubers, and then, later, as the result of contact with the northern agriculturalists, plants were introduced and vegeculture was practised. (D. Harris in press). As proof of some form of contact, there are savanna-type artefacts on the tropical forest margins by the third millennium b.c. In Ghana and Nigeria ground-stone tools and pottery related to Saharan types are found in the second and first millennia b.c. (Alexander and Coursey 1969).

Murdock's hypothesis that there was a major centre of indigenous domestication in the region of the Niger headwaters and that *c.* 30 species were brought into cultivation in this area, is no longer acceptable (Shaw in press). Harlan (1972) proposes almost the opposite case – that there was no real centre of domestication since different crops were brought into cultivation in different areas in a broad belt south of the Sahara and north of the Equator: 'There is no center, unless you wish to refer to something 7000 kilometres across as a center.'

D. Harris (in press) recognises three West African zones in which different indigenous species were brought into cultivation.

(1) The vegeculture zone where cultigens include yams (*Dioscorea cayenensis, D. rotunda*) and other minor root-crops such as Hausa or Kaffir potato (*Plectranthus esculentis*), and perhaps piasa (*Solenostemon rotundifolius*) and yam pea or bean (*Sphenostylis stenocarpa*). The oil palm (*Elaeis guineensis*) – often protected rather than cultivated – provided edible oils and vitamin A and complemented the carbohydrate-rich root-crops. Kola trees (*Cola acuminata, C. nitida*), akee (*Blighia sapida*) and Liberica coffee (*Coffea liberica*) were also cultivated.

Vegeculture may first have developed on the edge of the forest zone. Shaw (in press) suggests that the Sangoan pick (43,000 to 13,000 b.c.) may have been used to grub up wild species. Since yams regenerate even after the tubers have been removed – as long as the vines and roots are reasonably undamaged – this practice may have resulted in natural vegetative reproduction, localised around living places.

(2) Rice zone. African rice (*Oryza glaberrima*) domestication may have begun as simple hydraulic cultivation on the inland delta of the Niger and perhaps in the Senegambian area of the Upper Gambia and Casamance rivers. Later, with dry rice cultivation, the area of cultivation extended throughout the savanna region, from Cape Verde to Lake Chad.

(3) Millet zone. Fonio millet (*Digitaria exilis*) cultivation extends throughout the savanna belt from Cape Verde to Lake Chad, but the greatest variety is found on the Fouta Djallon plateau and in the valleys of upper Senegal and Niger. Like rice it may originally have begun as hydraulic cultivation on the inland delta of the Niger. Later, with swidden cultivation, and in conjunction with pearl millet (from north tropical Africa) and sorghum (from the central Sudan) it spread widely – probably at the expense of vegeculture. Black fonio (*D. iburua*) has a more limited distribution, concentrated in the Atacora mountains of Dahomey and on the Jos plateau. It may have originated in the Aïr region of the southern Sahara. Another millet (*Brachiaria deflexa*) is limited to Guinea.

Other less important cultigens in this zone are bambara groundnut (*Voandzeia subterranea*), Kersting's groundnut (*Kerstingiella geocarpa*) and black beniseed (*Polygala butyracea*). The shea butter tree (*Butyrospermum paradoxum*) is quite important.

(4) ETHIOPIA/EAST AFRICA

Vavilov postulated an independent centre of domestication in Ethiopia based on the variability of the winter cereals. His views have been disputed (chapter 5, p. 92) and it now appears that these cereals, plus sheep and cattle, were introduced from the north, from the Nile valley.

Local plants were brought into cultivation, but it is not known whether this process began before Nilotic influences were felt, or only afterwards. Polished stone 'hoes', grinding stones and bowls are found in Ethiopia, Kenya and northern Tanzania. It is not certain that they denote plant cultivation, and, anyway, the associated cultures have not been dated.

Local plants brought into cultivation in Ethiopia are: finger millet (*Eleusine coracana*), teff (*Eragrostis abyssinica*) ensente – known as African banana – (*Musa ensente*), chat (*Catha edulis*), arabica coffee

(*Coffea arabica*) and noag (*Guizotia abyssinica*) (Harlan 1972; Shaw in press).

Wild races of sorghum (*Sorghum bicolor*) are abundant and wide-spread. Domestication may have occurred in a wide zone in the broad-leaved savanna belt from lake Chad to east-central Sudan.

Pearl millet (*Pennisetum americanum*) may have been domesticated throughout an even more extensive zone, from the Nile to Senegal and Mauritania (Harlan 1972).

INDIA

Evidence from India has not been included in this Appendix. It is too sparse and uneven in quality. Hutchinson (1972) sums up one theory on the origin of food-production on the sub-continent: 'A natural and convenient frame of reference is provided by the hypothesis that agriculture was introduced into India from the centre of origin of temperate agriculture in the Middle East. The crop plants of the Middle East – in particular wheat, barley, peas and lentils – were brought in by the first farmer invaders. Then . . . as the farmers approached the climatic limits of their crops they domesticated local plants to replace them and to provide the means of spread into further regions. Thus rice, the *Brassica* oilseeds, and the *Phaseolus*, *Cajanus* and *Dolichos* pulses were added to the list of crops.' He adds that African cereals such as sorghum, bulrush millet (*Pennisetum*) and finger millet (*Eleusine coracana*) and South-east Asian crops such as sugar cane and bananas were also introduced at an early date.

Hutchinson then casts doubts upon this interpretation: the earliest evidence of agriculture on the sub-continent comes from the Harappan culture. But this culture, c. 2000 b.c., already had Middle Eastern crops, African crops and indigenous crops, including cotton. 'It seems unlikely that Harappan agriculture could have arisen . . . without a long antecedent gestation period. And for this, Neolithic farming in the Baluchistan valleys seems inadequate. Until we know more of the human cultures that preceded the Harappan, we cannot assess the importance of culture spread and indigenous innovation, in the establishment of agriculture in India' (Hutchinson 1972).

CHINA

The dating of the early Chinese cultures is very arbitrary for there are no carbon-14 dates from the mainland. The estimated dates mentioned below should be treated with great caution.

Pleistocene glaciation extended over the Tibetan plateau and over scattered highlands in the rest of the Far East. The glacial retreat began between 14,000 and 12,000 years ago (Smalley 1968; Chang 1970b).

Pollen from a core taken from lake Jih-yüeh-T'an (Sun-Moon lake) in central Taiwan, showed changes in vegetation suggestive of climatic amelioration between 14,000 and 12,000 years ago. Between 8000 and 4000 years ago, temperatures were probably 2° to 3°C higher (Chang 1970a).

(1) NORTHERN CHINA

(a) Cord-marked pottery is found on the Lower Weishu river and Huang-Ho in western Honan. An arbitrary pre-sixth millennium b.c. date has been suggested by Chang (1970b). The pottery is apparently 'akin' to the Late Hoabinhian ware of southern China and South-east Asia but is associated with a distinctive lithic assemblage. There is no evidence of domestication (Chang 1970b).

(b) The Yang-shao culture is found mainly on the loess of northern China, on the confluence of the three great rivers – the Huang-Ho, the Fenho and the Weishu. This is a transitional environment between the wooded western highlands and the swampy eastern lowlands. The Yang-shao culture is later than the cord-marked.

Nucleated Yang-shao settlements are found on the lower terraces of the main rivers and on low hills near small rivers. Evidence of forest clearance/regeneration from Pan-p'o-ts'un, Sian, is thought to indicate shifting cultivation.

Remains of foxtail millet (*Setaria italica*) and Chinese cabbage (*Brassica* spp.) have been found in association with this culture. There are also rather dubious reports of broomcorn millet (*Panicum miliaceum* L.) and kaoliang (*Andropogon sorghum* Brot.). Mulberry trees were utilised for silk-worms. There were domesticated dogs and pigs and, less frequently, cattle, sheep and/or goat.

Is the domestication an indigenous process? Was there stimulus diffusion from South-west Asia? Where did the cattle, sheep and/or goat come from? Were they among the earliest domesticates? 'The assumption (of contact with South-west Asia) is as difficult to prove as to disprove when substantial evidence is totally lacking' (Chang 1968, 84).

Was there contact with India? Foxtail millet is found in India but is thought, on linguistic grounds, to derive from China, rather than vice versa.

Was there contact with South-east Asian cultivators? There is no evidence.

(c) The Lungshanoid cultures succeed the Yang-shao on the loess of northern China. Chang (1970b) suggests that they developed out of the Yang-Shao and then expanded eastwards and southwards to Honan, Shantung, Hupei, Kiangsu, Chekiang and Taiwan. This sequence is hypothetical. The northern Lungshanoid group may have emerged in the late fourth millennium b.c.

There is little direct evidence of cultigens from the northern Lungshanoid groups. Plant assemblages known from historical sources cannot be pushed back earlier than the second millennium b.c., at which time millets (foxtail millet, *Setaria italica* and broomcorn millet, *Panicum miliaceum* L.) predominate. Kaoliang (*Andropogon sorghum* Brot.), wheat (*Triticum aestivum*), rice (*Oryza sativa*), soybean (*Glycine* max.) and hemp (*Cannabis sativa*) are reported from late prehistoric and early historic sites. Hemp is apparently not indigenous. Rice is thought to be intrusive from the south (Chang 1970b).

Cereal crops, particularly millets, head Li's list (1970) of plants first cultivated, or with a long history of cultivation, in the north. He also considers that soybeans, a fairly large number of vegetables, some temperate fruit-trees and some industrially used trees are of northern origin. The list is mainly theoretical and is based on Vavilovian principles. Since, in more intensively studied areas, Vavilov's work has often had to be greatly modified and/or rejected, Li's list should also be treated with caution (see chapter 5, p. 92, for comments on Vavilov's work).

There is evidence of domesticated chicken as well as dog and pig (Chang 1968, 134).

(2) Southern China

(a) Late Hoabinhian groups are found mainly in south-western and southern coastal China. The assemblages contain both ground and edge-ground tools and cord-marked pottery. Some may date to the tenth millennium b.c.

In Taiwan the cord-marked pottery is localised on the lower coastal terraces near river estuaries. There is a lack of shellfish or animal bones but evidence of fishing. There is no direct evidence of cultivation but pollen from a section of the core from lake Jih-yüeh-T'an, central Taiwan, dated to 10,000 b.c., shows evidence of secondary forest growth and charred wood. It has been suggested that this could indicate cultivation – probably root and fruit (Chang 1970a). If correct this would suggest an early indigenous development, but the evidence is hardly conclusive.

(b) Lungshanoid influence from the north reaches the south-east coast, Taiwan and the Upper Yangtse perhaps during the third millennium b.c. There is a carbon-14 date from Teng-pi-t'ou, Taiwan, of *c.* 2500 b.c. The Lungshanoid affected, in varying degrees, the local Late Hoabinhian cultures.

Another section of the core from lake Jih-yüeh-T'an, dated 2250 $\pm$ 60 b.c., shows a sharp increase in grass pollen, of which one third was thought to be cereal pollen, and an increase in liquidambar and Chenopodiaceae. These changes are thought to correlate with the arrival of the Lungshanoid cereal cultivators (Chang 1970a).

Several southern Lungshanoid sites, Ch'ü-chia-ling (Hupei), Hu-shu (lower Yangtse), Ying-p'u (central coast Taiwan), have remains of both millet and rice. Associated rectangular and semi-lunate knives are thought to have been used in rice-harvesting.

Rice was clearly far more important in the southern Lungshanoid groups than in the northern. It may originally have been cultivated within the root-crop system of South-east Asia. Chang (1970b), however, points out that dry rice cultivation would be much lower yielding than either taro or yam. He therefore suggests that it could have developed in South-east Asia or southern China under the influence of the northern Lungshanoid cereal farmers. This idea does not seem to tally with the rather early dates for possible rice cultivation recently obtained in Thailand (see below).

At the Lungshanoid site of Ch'ien-shan-yang (Hangchow basin) there is evidence of rice (both *Ting* and *Keng*), peach (*Prunus persica*), melon (*Cucumis melo*), Chinese water chestnut (*Trapa natans* or *T. bispinosa*), broad bean (*Vicia faba*), sesame (*Sesamum indicum* or *S. orientate*) and ground-nuts (*Arachis hypogaea*) (Chang 1968, 146). Many of these are presumed to be local cultigens.

Li (1970) stresses that a great many cultivated vegetables, including aquatic vegetables, many fruit-trees and also fibre crops probably originated in southern China.

Domesticated dog, pig, cattle, water buffalo and sheep are found at southern Lungshanoid sites (Chang 1968, 146).

SOUTH-EAST ASIA

At the time of the maximum extent of the last glaciation (Würm II, *c.* 18,000 b.c.) there was a eustatic drop in sea-level of 120–140m.[1]

---

1 These estimates are based on work in the Timor Sea off the north-east coast of Australia.

(below present) (Andel and Veevers 1967, 100). This resulted in an expansion of the continental land mass to almost twice its present size (de Terra cited by Gorman 1971). After 16,000 b.c. sea-levels rose rapidly. By 9000 b.c. they were −60 m., by 7000 b.c. −30 m. Around 11,000 b.c. the Timor Sea cores show a change from colder- to warmer-water fauna (Andel and Veevers 1967, 100). The climate ameliorated, temperatures were 2 to 3°C above present levels (Hay cited by Gorman 1971).

Faunal remains from deposits in the Niah cave in Borneo dating to 30,000 b.c. are primarily modern extant species. Botanical evidence from Spirit cave, north-west Thailand, indicates no change in environment between *c.* 10,000 and 7600 b.c. and is little different from today (Gorman 1971).

'An impressive number of tropical crops, particularly vegetatively reproduced roots and fruits, derive from the region, but there is virtually no archaeological evidence by which to measure the antiquity of their domestication' (Harris 1967). The situation is, however, slowly changing.

There is a widespread belief that root and fruit cultivation preceded cereals in South-east Asia and that of the cereals, millets and sorghum preceded rice (*Oryza sativa*) (Chang 1970b). Suitable conditions under which root-crop cultivation could have emerged in South-east Asia were postulated by Sauer in 1952 (chapter 2, p. 19).

Li's list (1970) of primary domesticates or cultigens with a long history of cultivation again emphasises the importance of roots and tubers. It includes taro (*Colocasia antiquorum*), ape (*Alocasia macrorrhiza*), yam (*Dioscorea esculenta*), greater yam (*D. alata*), water chestnut (*Eleocharis tuberosa*), only a limited number of vegetables, and some tropical fruit-trees.

Harlan (1972) considers that South-east Asia and the South Pacific constitute a 'non-centre' where 'different crops were introduced into cultivation in different areas at different times' (chapter 1, p. 16). So, for example, the first step in the cultivation of the banana, which involves the establishment of the parthenocarpic, seedless, diploid *Musa acuminata*, seems to occur primarily in Indochina, Thailand and Malaya. The second step, producing triploids and tetraploids, either from *Musa acuminata* alone or in combination with *Musa balbisiana*, is found either side of the zone in which the diploids grow, from eastern India and Burma in the west and from the Philippines and Borneo in the east. Taro was perhaps domesticated in Burma, sugar-cane in New Guinea, tung and many citrus fruits in southern China and Indochina and the coconut 'anywhere, perhaps everywhere along the shores of this vast region'.

EVIDENCE

'Hard' evidence on early food-production in South-east Asia is fairly limited.

(i) Early plant cultiva'ion?

The Late Hoabinhian complex found in parts of Malaysia, Thailand, Vietnam and western Indonesia (and also southern China) is probably Post-Pleistocene in date. At Spirit cave, north-west Thailand, several Late Hoabinhian levels have been carbon-14 dated: layer 4 9400 ± 280 b.c., FSU 315 and 8950 ± 550 b.c., FSU 316; interface 3/4 8440 ± 310 b.c., TF 803[2] and 7230 ± 360 b.c., Gak 1845 (Gorman 1970; Radiocarbon 1971 [11]). Ongbah cave, west-central Thailand, is dated *c.* 9000 b.c. (Gorman 1971), Laang Spean, Cambodia, is dated 4290 ± 70 b.c., MC-273, and Gua Kechil, Malaya, is dated 2850 ± 800 b.c., Gak 0418 (Gorman 1970).

The Late Hoabinhian is associated with a wide-spectrum economy: shellfish, fish, game – pig, deer, bovids, goat/antelopes and primates – and with wild plants (Chang 1970b; Gorman 1971; Higham 1972). Groups on the coast and in upland karst/riverine areas utilised a wide range of intermontane or submontane resources and either coastal or riverine resources. There is a singular lack of specialised hunting equipment, perhaps because it was made from wood (Gorman 1971).

A wide range of plant remains were found in the Late Hoabinhian levels (4, 3, 2) at Spirit cave on the bank of the river Salween, north-west Thailand. In level 4 there were remains of almond (*Prunus*), kotamba (*Terminalia*), betel (*Areca*), bean (*Vicia* or *Phaseolus*), pea (*Pisum* or *Raphia*),[3] bottle-gourd (*Lagenaria*) and Chinese water chestnut (*Trapa*). Interface 4/3 contained pepper plant (*Piper*), butternut (*Madhuca*), edible oil nut (*Canarium*), candlenut (*Aleurites*) and *Areca*. Layer 3 contained *Canarium*, *Lagenaria* and cucumber (*Cucumis*). Layer 2 contained *Piper*, *Areca*, and *Canarium* (Gorman 1969).

2 Only given as a corrected date, with a half-life of 5730 years rather than the Libby half-life of 5570 years.
3 Harlan and de Wet (1972) point out that the presence of *Pisum* and *Vicia* which are cool-season genera associated with a Mediterranean climate in combination with South-east Asian tropical plants is very unlikely. They also add, scathingly, 'If the archaeobotanist cannot tell a pea from a palm the authenticity of the evidence is in serious doubt.'

Such a range may have served a wide variety of purposes. *Madhuca*, *Canarium* and *Terminalia* are foodstuffs, *Aleurites* was probably used for lighting or heating. *Piper* and *Areca* are stimulants. The presence of bottle-gourd, cucumber, Chinese water chestnut, leguminous beans and possibly peas suggests 'a development beyond simple food gathering. The beans in particular point to a very early use of domesticated plants' (Gorman 1969). However, in a later publication, Gorman (1971) is more cautious: 'whether they are definitely early cultigens remains to be established', while Higham (1972) says that Spirit cave is 'an unlikely site for farming'.

(ii) The beginning of rice cultivation

This may be an indigenous development (Li 1970). Chang (1970b), however, postulates that it represents northern Lungshanoid influences on the indigenous Hoabinhian sub-stratum. Such influences are supposedly recognisable in the Sa-Huỳnh assemblages in South Vietnam and Laos, the Ban-kao and Gua Cha assemblages in central Thailand and northern Malaya and in the Kalanay of Borneo and the Philippines. Sørensen (1972) supports this idea of Lungshanoid influences in the Ban-kao, comparing it with the Lungshanoid Ch'u-chia-ling culture of Hupei province. This interpretation is not widely accepted. Bayard considers that the Ban-kao pottery has, in fact, closer parallels with the indigenous Non Nok Tha, etc., than with the Lungshanoid.

At Spirit cave, north-west Thailand, interface 2/1 is carbon-14 dated 6600 ± 200 b.c., Gak 1846 and 5955 ± 195 b.c., FSU 314, and layer I is dated 5450 ± 150 b.c., FSU 317 (Gorman 1970; Radiocarbon 1971 [1]). Both interface and layer I have Late Hoabinhian artefacts associated with non-Hoabinhian artefacts – cordmarked and smooth-burnished pottery, simple, polished quadrangular adzes and bifacially ground knives. The knives have no known lowland parallels (though they are common in China and Kashmir), but the pottery and the adzes are found in early agricultural contexts on the lowland plain and their presence at Spirit cave may indicate that rice cultivation had been introduced to the highlands (Gorman 1971; Higham 1972).

Non Nok Tha in north-east Thailand is a lowland, open-air site. The lowest levels, I and II (1968 excavation) are pre-metal. There is a wide range of carbon-14 dates: 3420 ± 320 b.c., Gak 1034; 2485 ± 65 b.c., FSU 340; 1610 ± 130 b.c., FSU 348; 800 ± 130 b.c., GX 1612 and a thermo-luminescence date of 2995 ± 320 b.c., PT-277. Bayard considers that level I may have begun 4500/

4000 b.c. and level II may have terminated *c.* 3000 b.c. In the earliest level, sand-tempered, cord-marked pottery contained imprints and carbonised fragments of rice chaff (Bayard) – but does this necessarily indicate that the rice was cultivated? From the earliest levels onwards there are bones of bovines, osteologically identical to the modern Thai breed of zebu, *Bos indicus.* The overwhelming number of juvenile female animals would seem to suggest domestication but since they are found as grave offerings there may be a cultural/functional bias (Higham 1972). Pig bones are also found and may be from domesticated animals.

TROPICAL SOUTH AND CENTRAL AMERICAN LOWLANDS

There is no direct evidence from plant remains. 'Hard' evidence is therefore limited to associated equipment and in particular to the pottery griddles used for baking bitter manioc (*Manihot esculenta*). Less certainly, heavy querns and grinding stones may indicate maize cultivation. The evidence, and then the interpretations are summarised below.

(1) EVIDENCE (of varying exactitude)

Venezuela

(i) Rancho Peludo, extreme north-west Venezuela, has carbon-14 dates which range from 2820 to 1860 b.c. and later. There is a crude ceramic complex including two griddle fragments – indicating bitter manioc cultivation.
(ii) The Saladero culture along the Orinoco river has carbon-14 dates of 910 ± 130 b.c., 740 ± 130 b.c. and 610 ± 130 b.c. (Rowse 1962). This culture seems to have spread via lake Valencia to the north coast, Trinidad, the Lesser Antilles and Puerto Rico (Bennett and Bird 1960). Or was lake Valencia an early centre? (Lathrap 1970, 67, 112). There are a few griddle sherds – again indicating bitter manioc cultivation (Sanoja 1963).
(iii) The Barrancoid complex is found on the middle and lower Orinoco and has carbon-14 dates of 890 ± 120 b.c., 860 ± 80 b.c. and 840 ± 140 b.c. (Rowse 1962). The pottery shows connections with the Colombian Malambo. Sanoja (1963) mentions the presence of both griddles (= bitter manioc) and querns and grinding

stones (=? maize) but Lathrap (1970, 113) does not mention the grinding complex. He considers that the large urns with constricted necks may have held beer made from bitter manioc.

Colombia

(i) Puerto Hormigo shell-middens may date to about 3000 b.c. There is well-made pottery but no evidence of agriculture (Reichel-Dolmatoff 1965, 53).
(ii) The Barlovento complex has carbon-14 dates of 1510 ± 70 b.c., 1180 ± 120 b.c. and 1020 ± 120 b.c. (Rouse 1962). There are both coastal middens and inland settlements – for example, Bucarelia near Zambrana, 150 kilometres up the Magdalena river. The inland sites have pottery similar to that of the coast but the economy is no longer based on marine shellfish. Was there root-crop cultivation at the inland sites? Both bitter and sweet manioc are locally available. There are no griddles (Reichel-Dolmatoff 1965, 58; Lathrap 1970, 65).
(iii) The Malambo complex on the lower Magdalena river may date between 1120 b.c. and a.d. 70. There are large open-air sites. The pottery is not related to that of (i) or (ii) and there are abundant griddle sherds (= bitter manioc).
(iv) Momíl I on the lower Magdalena river may date to the first half of the second millennium b.c. (Reichel-Dolmatoff 1965, 78). Lathrap (1970, 56) considers that the presence of four horizons and the depth of the deposit means that Momíl I should go back well into the second millennium b.c. There are associated griddle sherds with sharply raised rims (= bitter manioc).

Momíl II may have started around 700 b.c. There is a sudden appearance of heavy querns and grinding-stones, small griddles and large storage vessels. All these are thought to indicate maize cultivation. Certain pottery traits suggest Meso-American influence – bowls with flanged bases, tall tripod vessels, bulbous mammiform supports and bird-shaped whistles. They are not unlike ware from Tlatilco in Mexico or Playa de Los Muertos and Yarumela in Honduras (Reichel-Dolmatoff 1965, 78).

Ecuador

(i) The Valdivia complex on the coast may date to 3000 b.c. There is evidence of a hunting-fishing-gathering economy and of fine pottery. There is no evidence of agriculture (Estrada and Evans 1963). Lathrap (1970, 67) notes, however, that the evidence of a marine-based economy is slight and believes that root-crop cultivation may have extended to the coast at this time.

(ii) The Machalilla complex, 2000–1500 b.c., is similar to (i).

(iii) The Chorrero complex is found in the Guayas basin, on the coast and in the southern highlands. It may date to 1500 b.c. The pottery is fairly similar to the Ocós pottery from coastal Guatemala. Was maize introduced at this time? (Estrada and Evans 1963; Meggers 1966, 61).

Peru

(i) The Tutishcayno complex found in the Ucayali river basin in eastern, tropical Peru, may date between 1800 and 1500 b.c. There are fairly large permanent settlements in situations suitable for both riverine and agricultural pursuits. There is pottery but no griddles.

(ii) Root-crops, *achira* and sweet potato (*Ipomoea batatas*), found at sites on the desert coast *c.* 2000 b.c., must derive from tropical environments.

Guatemala (*Central America*) (see chapter 7, p. 190)

(i) The Barra and Ocós phases date before 1100 b.c. The lack of fish-bones and shellfish, despite reasonably good preservation, suggests that the economy was not based on marine resources. There are no grinding equipment or griddles but there are numerous obsidian flakes. Green and Lowe (1967, 58) have suggested that there may have been root-crop cultivation, without bitter manioc. Today one of the main crops is sweet manioc. The pottery is 'orientated' towards South America (note that archaeologists in Ecuador reverse the position!).

At the sites of Altimira, Salinas and Colonia Aquiles Serdan there is apparently a hiatus after the Ocós phase. This could be a real time-lapse or might be due to a slight shift to locales more suitable for maize cultivation.

(ii) The Cuadros phase is carbon-14 dated to 1100 b.c. There are grinding equipment and preserved maize cobs. There is a drop in the number of obsidian flakes. Green and Lowe suggest that the pottery is now orientated towards the north – to the central Chiapas, Veracruz and Puebla. This interpretation of the Barra-Ocós-Cuadros material by Green and Lowe is not accepted by Coe (1961a) or Coe and Flannery (1967) who find no evidence to suggest root-crop cultivation.

(2) INTERPRETATIONS/THEORETICAL DEDUCTIONS

The evidence from Venezuela suggests that in this region root-crops, specifically bitter manioc, have priority over seed-crop culti-vation. Bitter manioc cultivation goes back to the second, and quite probably the third, millennium b.c. (Rancho Peludo and Saladero cultures). The later Barrancoid groups may have continued to culti-vate root-crops. However, the presence of querns and grinding-stones may indicate that they were beginning to grow maize.

Again in Colombia root-crop cultivation would seem to have priority. It is unproven for the Barlovento complex but certainly seems to be associated with both the Malembo and Momíl I. The distributions suggest that it is an inland rather than a coastal develop-ment. With Momíl II there is evidence of intrusive maize cultivation.

The neatness of the sequence is somewhat disturbed if the grinding equipment (suggesting maize cultivation) reported alongside griddles (indicating manioc cultivation) in the Venezuelan Barran-coid is correct, for the Barrancoid is supposed to be related to the Malambo.

Lathrap (1970, 47) suggests that bitter manioc, which is relatively difficult to process, would not be among the first root-crops brought into cultivation. If bitter manioc cultivation goes back to the second and third millennia b.c., then pre-bitter manioc root-crop cultiva-tion might begin as early as 7000 to 5000 b.c. Perhaps such crops as sweet potato (*Ipomoea batatas*), arrow-root (*Maranta arundinacea*), Ileren (*Calathea allonia*), Yautia, also known as ocuma or tania (*Xanthosoma sagittifolium*), arracacacha (*Arracacia xanthorrhiza*), kaffir potato (*Colens* spp.), taro (*Colocasia esculenta*) and Fiji arrow-root (*Tacca pinnatifida*) were grown (Lathrap 1970, 47; Hawkes 1969).

Rowse (1972) proposes two possible initiating centres for root-crop cultivation. The first is inland Venezuela, on the borders between the forests and the llanos, especially along the gallery forests fringing the banks of the Orinoco. The second is northern Amazonia, or the area between northern Amazonia and the Venezuelan llanos. Lathrap (1970, 67) also opts for an inland region. He believes that the initial development took place in the humid lowlands to the east of the Andes, in Amazonia and northern South America. Perhaps cultivation began early on the alluvial deposits around lake basins, for example, lakes Valencia and Maracaibo in Venezuela. Harris (1969), like Rouse, stresses the importance of the junctions between eco-systems (chapter 2, p. 31), for example between forest and river or lagoon. He notes that both the Orinoco basin and the Caribbean lowlands fit this pattern. He considers that vegeculture spread later to the Amazonian lowlands.

Why was root-crop cultivation supplanted in several areas by maize cultivation? Harris (1973) suggests that it is because maize cultivation is inherently less stable and is therefore likely to expand at the expense of root-crop cultivation (chapter 2, p. 16). On the other hand, maize rarely became the predominant crop in tropical forest areas, and Harris (1971) suggests that this is because, in such areas, maize suffers two disadvantages. Greater care is needed in burning down the vegetation in order to produce ash for maize cultivation, and maize depletes the soil faster than root-crops, for the latter 'mulch' the soil and give added fertility.

Appendix B

THE DISTRIBUTION OF POTENTIAL DOMESTICATES
IN MIDDLE AND SOUTH AMERICA

'The taxonomic studies of these . . . plants are still of such a preliminary nature that the all-important sub-species of races which
genetically may be of great importance, are still not recognised
nor described' (MacNeish 1965).

BEANS

1. *Canavalia* (domesticated: *C. ensiformis* (L.) DC. – jack bean).
   Wild *Canavalia* have a pan-tropical distribution:
   (i)   *C. brasiliensis*: moist tropical lowlands, as far south as Ecuador.
   (ii) *C. maritima*: ranges down to Ecuador and extreme north of
         Peru.
   (iii) *C. piperi* and *C. dictyota*: south Peru, Bolivia, adjoining Brazil
         and Argentina.
   (Sauer and Kaplan 1969; Pickersgill 1969b.)
2. *Phaseolus* (domesticated: *Ph. coccineus* L. – runner bean; *Ph.
   acutifolius* Gray, var. *latifolius* Freeman – tepary bean; *Ph.
   vulgaris* L. – common bean; *Ph. lunatus* – small lima bean,
   sieva bean; *Ph. lunatus* var. *macrocarpus* Bentham – big lima
   bean).
   It is frequently difficult to distinguish between wild and domesticated forms. Tentative distributions:
   (i)   *Ph. coccineus*. Found wild in cool humid uplands of Chiapas,
         Guatemala, Puebla, Zacatecas, Crahuila, Mexico and
         Jalisco. Within pine/oak forests over 1800 m.
   (ii) *Ph. acutifolius*: arid and semi-arid regions. Now has disjunct
         distribution: (*a*) from Sonoran desert, south through Jalisco,
         (*b*) Tapachula/Guatemala border region. These are prob-
         ably relics of a more extensive region.
   (iii) *Ph. vulgaris*. Wild form is found widely in Mexico, in sub-
         tropical areas, at 850 to 2000 m. A sub-species, *Ph.*

vulgaris spp. *aborigineus* is found in Argentina and Venezuela. Not entirely clear whether these are 'pre-human wildlings' or 'escapees' (Gentry 1969).

(iv) *Ph. lunatus*: tropical and sub-tropical regions, rarely over 1200 m. Wild form found in Chiapas and Guatemala.

(v) *Ph. lunatus* var. *macrocarpus*: tropical and sub-tropical regions. Probably true wild forms found in north-west Argentina, the Urabamba valley and Ancash region of Peru.

(Mangelsdorf, MacNeish and Willey 1964; Kaplan 1965, 1967; Heiser 1965; Smartt 1969; Pickersgill 1969b; Lathrap 1970, 58; Willey 1971, 106.)

CHILI PEPPERS

(Domesticated: *Capsicum baccatum* var. *pendulum*; *C. annum* – bell pepper, paprika, cayenne, Mexican chilis; *C. chinense*; *C. pubescens*; *C. frutescens* – tabasco pepper)

Wild distributions:

(i) *C. baccatum* var. *baccatum*: now has very restricted distribution, almost entirely confined to south Peru and Bolivia.

(ii) *C. annuum* var. *minimum*: southern United States, West Indies, Central America and Colombia.

(iii) *C. frutescens*: Mexico, Central America, lowland South America south to Bolivia and Brazil.

No wild form of *C. chinense* is known but it is closely related to, and may derive from, *C. frutescens*. It is found in the West Indies and lowland South America south to Bolivia and southern Brazil.

No wild form of *C. pubescens* is known. It is found in highland South America.

(Heiser 1965; Pickersgill 1969a, b.)

In contrast to this interpretation of a multiple wild distribution, Davenport (1970) suggests that *C. frutescens*, or a related wild form, is the likely ancestor of the other domesticated species: *C. baccatum* var. *pendulum*, *C. chinense* and *C. annum*.

COTTON

(Domesticated: *Gossypium hirsutum* L.; *G. barbadense* L.)

Both are probably hybrids of *G. raimondii*, or related ancestral form, found in Peru, and *G. arboreum* or *G. herbaceum*, thought to have floated across the Atlantic from the Old World. The ancestral forms both have thirteen chromosomes. Hybridisation, possibly in

eastern South America, doubled the chromosome number.
(Mangelsdorf, MacNeish and Willey 1964; Pickersgill 1969b.)

GOURD

(Domesticated: *Lagenaria siceraria*)
No wild form of *Lagenaria siceraria* known in the New World. Possibly
floated by sea from Africa to South America.
(Mangelsdorf, NacNeish and Willey 1964; Whitaker, Cutler and
MacNeish 1968.)

MAIZE

(Domesticated: *Zea mays*)
No wild form of *Zea mays* known. Fossil pollen of 'wild' maize was
supposedly found in a section of a core dating to 80,000 years ago,
from Bellas, Mexico City. However only 8 grains were found at a
depth of 69.30 m. to 74.20 m., then none until 2 more at 45.12 to
45.31 m., and then in quantities in late deposits above 9.80 m., by
which time it was from domesticated maize. None was found in the
lower levels of the nearby Madero core (Clisby and Sears 1955a, b;
Lorenzo 1967). There is always the possibility that the drill was
contaminated by wind-blown maize pollen.
4 grains of fossil maize pollen were found in a core from the Gatún
Lake area, Canal zone, Panama. Dates between 5300 and 4300 b.c.
and is considered to be wild (Linares de Sapir and Ranere 1971).
There are two contenders for the wild form:
(*a*) An ancestral pod-corn, thought to have been widely distributed
in various habitats in the temperate highland regions of South
America and Middle America (Mangelsdorf 1950; Mangelsdorf
and Reeves 1959; Towle 1961; Coe 1963; Brandolini 1970). It has
recently been stated that such a form could not have survived in the
wild since it would have had no mechanism for seed dispersal
(Flannery 1973).
(*b*) Teosinte (*Zea mexicana*). This grass has the same chromosome
number as domesticated maize and has 7–12 seeds in hard husks
set on a brittle rachis. The main difference between teosinte and
domesticated maize is that teosinte has a distichous spike (2 rows of
kernels), maize has a polystichous spike (several rows of kernels).
However some of the early maize from Tehuacán is distichous.
This early maize is fragile which could be due to the persistence of a
brittle rachis, has long soft glumes, and has cupoles that could have

evolved from the fruit case of teosinte.

Teosinte is native to the semi-arid, sub-tropical zones of Mexico and Guatemala, from southern Chihuahua to the Guatemalan–Honduran border. It has not been found in the Tehuacán valley, but has been recorded north of its modern day distribution in the Guilá Naquitz cave in Oaxaca, *c.* 7400–6700 b.c. and at Tlapacoya, valley of Mexico, *c.* 5000 b.c. Modern teosinte may be a 'weed' race; prehistoric teosinte may have been somewhat different and had a different distribution (Flannery 1973).

SQUASH

(Domesticated: *Cucurbita ficifolia* Bouché – squash; *C. moschata* Duch. – cushaw squash; *C. pepo* L. – pumpkin, summer squash; *C. mixta* Pang. – walnut squash; *C. maxima* Duch.) (See photograph III)

C. ficifolia is evolutionarily isolated from the other squashes and no closely related wild species are known.

C. moschata is thought to be the 'indispensable cog through which the species of *Cucurbita* are related'. *C. maxima* and the related wild *C. andreana* Naud. could either have evolved from *C. moschata* in Mexico and then migrated south, leaving no trace north of the Equator, or *C. moschata* may originally have been more widespread, giving rise to *C. maxima* and *C. andreana* Naud. in South America and other species in Middle America, and then may, later, have become extinct in South America (Pickersgill 1969b).

Wild distributions:

(i) Several wild species, including *C. lundelliana* Bailey, *C. martinezi*, *C. texana* Gray and *C. foetidissima* HBK. are indigenous to south-western North America, and Middle America. (Darlington 1963, 142; Whitaker and Cutler 1965; MacNeish 1965; Whitaker, Cutler and MacNeish 1968.)

(ii) *C. andreana* Naud., adapted to dry conditions, is found in Uruguay, Argentina and Bolivia (Cutler and Whitaker 1961).

Other assessments of origins are based on centres of diversity of domesticated squashes. But the diversity centres may be the result of convergence rather than an indication of origin. The diversity centres for the domesticated squashes are:

(i) *C. ficifolia*: highlands of Mexico and Central America.

(ii) *C. moschata*: the brown-seeded variety is found in the lowlands of northern South America; the white-seeded variety is found in the lowlands of Mexico.

(iii) *C. pepo*: lowlands of North America and north Mexico.
(iv) *C. mixta*: south Mexico.
(Cutler and Whitaker 1961, 1967; Mangelsdorf, MacNeish and Willey 1964; MacNeish 1967a; Whitaker and Bird 1949.)

LLAMA

Probably the wild ancestor is *Llama glama* guanicoe (or *L. guanicoe*), found in dry open country from sea level to 5600 m., from the southern tip of the Andes to central Peru (Lynch 1967).

GUINEA PIG

Wild *Cavia porcellus* is found in grassland or bush highland country throughout South America (Lynch 1967).

Bibliography

ADAMS, R.M. (1960) Early civilisation, subsistence and environment, in KRAELING, C.H. and ADAMS, R.M. (eds.), *City Invincible*, 269.
(1965) The origins of agriculture, in TAX, S. (ed.), *Horizons of Anthropology*, 120.
(1966) *The Evolution of Urban Society. Early Mesopotamia and Prehispanic Mexico.*
ALEXANDER, J. (1969) The indirect evidence for domestication, in UCKO, P.J. and DIMBLEBY, G.W. (eds.), *The Domestication and Exploitation of Plants and Animals*, 123.
and COURSEY, D.G. (1969) The origins of yam cultivation, in UCKO, P.J. and DIMBLEBY, G.W. (eds.), *The Domestication and Exploitation of Plants and Animals*, 405.
ALLAN, W. (1965) *The African Husbandman.*
ALLCHIN, F.R. (1969a) Early domestic animals in India and Pakistan, in UCKO, P.J. and DIMBLEBY, G.W. (eds.), *The Domestication and Exploitation of Plants and Animals*, 317.
(1969b) Early cultivated plants in India and Pakistan, in UCKO, P.J. and DIMBLEBY, G.W. (eds.), *The Domestication and Exploitation of Plants and Animals*, 323.
ALLEN, J. (1972) The first decade in New Guinea archaeology, *Antiquity*, 46, 180.
ANATI, E. (1962) Prehistoric trade and the puzzle of Jericho, *Bulletin of the American Schools of Oriental Research*, 167, 25.
(1966) *Palestine Before the Hebrews.*
(1968) Anatolia's earliest art, *Archaeology*, 21, 22.
ANDEL, T.H. van and VEEVERS, J.J. (1967) *Morphology and Sediments of the Timor Sea.*
ANDERSON, J.E. (1967) The human skeletons, in BYERS, D.S. (ed.), *The Prehistory of the Tehuacán Valley*, vol. I, 91.
BAYARD, D.T. (?) *Non Nok Tha: the 1968 Excavation* (University of Otago: Studies in Prehistoric Anthropology, Vol. 4).
BELYAEV, D.K. (1969) Domestication of animals, *Science Journal*, 5, 47.
BENNETT, W.C. (1963) The Andean highlands: an introduction, in STEWARD, J.H. (ed.), *Handbook of South American Indians*, vol. 2, 1.
and BIRD, J.B. (1965) *Andean Culture History.*
BERRY, R.J. (1969) The genetical implications of domestication, in UCKO, P.J. and DIMBLEBY, G.W. (eds.), *The Domestication and Exploitation of Plants and Animals*, 207.
BEUG, H.J. (1967) Contributions to the post-glacial vegetational history of northern Turkey, in CUSHING, E.J. and WRIGHT, H.E. (eds.), *Quaternary Paleoecology*, 349.
BINFORD, L.R. (1968a) Archaeological perspectives, in BINFORD, S.R. and BINFORD, L.R. (eds.), *New Perspectives in Archaeology*, 5.
(1968b) Post-pleistocene adaptations, in BINFORD, S.R. and BINFORD, L.R. (eds.), *New Perspectives in Archaeology*, 313.
(1968c) Hunting vs. gathering as factors in subsistence, in LEE, R.B. and DEVORE, I. (eds.), *Man the Hunter*, 92.
(1968d) Methodological considerations of the archaeological use of ethnographic data, in LEE, R.B. and DEVORE, I. (eds.), *Man the Hunter*, 268.
(1972) Contemporary model building: paradigms and the current state of Palaeolithic research, in CLARKE, D.L. (ed.), *Models in Archaeology*, 109.
BINFORD, S.R. (1968a) Variability and change in the Near Eastern Mousterian of Levallois facies, in BINFORD, S.R. and BINFORD, L.R. (eds.), *New Perspectives in Archaeology*, 49.
(1968b) Ethnographic data and the understanding of the Pleistocene, in LEE, R.B. and DEVORE, I. (eds.), *Man the Hunter*, 274.

Bird, J.B. (1948) Preceramic cultures in Chicama and Virú, in Bennett, W.C. (ed.), *A Reappraisal of Peruvian Archaeology*, 21.

(1963) Pre-ceramic art from Huaca Prieta, Chicama valley, *Ñawpa Pacha*, 1, 29.

Birdsell, J.B. (1968) Some predictions for the Pleistocene based on equilibrium systems among recent hunter-gatherers, in Lee, R.B. and Devore, I. (eds.), *Man the Hunter*, 229.

Blake, I. (1969) Climate, survival and the second-class societies in Palestine before 3000 B.C., *Advancement of Science*, 409.

Boessneck, J. (1969) Osteological differences between sheep (*Ovis aries Linné*) and goat (*Capra hircus binné*), in Brothwell, D. and Higgs, E. (eds.), *Science in Archaeology*, 331.

Bökönyi, S. (1969) Archaeological problems and methods of recognizing animal domestication, in Ucko, P.J. and Dimbleby, G.W. (eds.), *The Domestication and Exploitation of Plants and Animals*, 219.

(1971a) The development and history of domestic animals in Hungary: the Neolithic through the Middle Ages, *American Anthropologist*, 73, 640.

(1971b) Zoological evidence for seasonal or permanent occupation of prehistoric settlements, in Ucko, P.J., Tringham, R. and Dimbleby, G.W. (eds.), *Man, Settlement and Urbanism*, 121.

Bonatti, E. (1966) North Mediterranean climate during the last Würm glaciation, *Nature*, 209, 984.

Boserup, E. (1965) *Conditions for Agricultural Growth*.

Bottema, S. (1967) A late Quaternary pollen diagram from Ioannina, north-western Greece, *Proceedings of the Prehistoric Society*, 33, 26.

Braidwood, R.J. (1951) From cave to village in prehistoric Iraq, *Bulletin of the American Schools of Oriental Research*, 124, 12.

(1957) Jericho and its setting in Near Eastern prehistory, *Antiquity*, 31, 73.

(1958) Near Eastern prehistory, *Science*, 127, 1419.

(1960) Levels in prehistory: a model for the consideration of the evidence, in Tax, S. (ed.), *The Evolution of Man*, 143.

(1960) The agricultural revolution, *Scientific American*, 203, 130.

(1962) The earliest village communities of Southwestern Asia reconsidered, *Atti del VI Congresso Internazionale delle Scienze Preistoriche e Protostoriche*, I, 115.

(1966) The paleo-environments of southwestern Asia and the appearance of food production; unpublished report to the National Science Foundation on termination of Grant GS-50.

Çambel, H., Redman, C.L. and Watson, P.J. (1971) Beginnings of village-farming communities in southeastern Turkey, *Proceedings of the National Academy of Science, U.S.A.*, 68, 6, 1236.

Çambel, H. and Watson, P.J. (1969) Prehistoric investigations in southeastern Turkey, *Science*, 164, 1275.

and Howe, B. (1960) *Prehistoric Investigations in Iraqi Kurdistan* (Studies in Ancient Oriental Civilisation, No. 31).

and Howe, B. (1962) Southwestern Asia beyond the lands of the Mediterranean littoral, in Braidwood, R.J. and Willey, G. (eds.), *Courses Toward Urban Life*, 132.

Howe, B. and Reed, C.A. (1961) The Iranian prehistoric project, *Science*, 133, 2008.

and Reed, C.A. (1957) The achievement and early consequences of food-production: a consideration of the archaeological and natural historical evidence, *Cold Spring Harbor Symposia of Quantative Biology*, 22, 19.

and Willey, G. (eds.) (1962) *Courses Toward Urban Life*.

Brandolini, A. (1970) Maize, in Frankel, O.H. and Bennet, E. (eds.), *Genetic Resources in Plants – their Exploration and Conservation*, 273.

Bronson, B. (1972) Farm labor and the evolution of food production, in Spooner, B. (ed.), *Population Growth: Anthropological Implications*, 190.

Brookfield, H.C. and White, J.P. (1968) Revolution or evolution in the prehistory of New Guinea highlands: a seminar report, *Ethnology*, 7, 43.

Brothwell, D.R. and Higgs, E.S. (eds.) (1969) *Science in Archaeology*.

Molleson, T., Gray, P. and Harcourt, R. (1969) The application of X-rays to the study of archaeological material, in Brothwell, D.R. and Higgs, E.S. (eds.), *Science in Archaeology*, 513.

Butzer, K.W. (1964) *Environment and Archaeology*.

(1970) Physical conditions in eastern Europe, western Asia and Egypt before the period of agricultural and urban settlement, in Edwards, I.E.S., Gadd, C.J. and Hammond, N.G.L. (eds.) *Cambridge Ancient History*, vol. I, pt. I, 35.

(1971) *Environment and Archaeology*.

and Freeman, L.G. (1968) Pollen analysis at the Cueva del Toll, Catalonia: a critical re-appraisal, *Geologie en Mijnbouw*, 47, 116.

Byers, D.S. (ed.) (1967a) *The Prehistory of the Tehuacán Valley*. Volume I. *Environment and Subsistence*.

(ed.) (1967b) *The Prehistory of the Tehuacán Valley*. Volume II. *The Non-Ceramic Artifacts*.

(1967c) The region and its people, in Byers, D.S. (ed.), *The Prehistory of the Tehuacán Valley*, vol. I, 35.

(1967d) Climate and hydrology, in Byers, D.S. (ed.), *The Prehistory of the Tehuacán Valley*, vol. I, 48.

(ed.) (1970) *The Prehistory of the Tehuacán Valley*. Vol. III. *Ceramics*.

Caldwell, J.R. (ed.) (1966) *New Roads to Yesterday*.

Callen, E.O. (1967a) The first New World cereal, *American Antiquity*, 32, 535.

(1967b) Analysis of the Tehuacán coprolites, in Byers, D.S. (ed.), *The Prehistory of the Tehuacán Valley*, vol. I, 261.

(1969) Diet as revealed by coprolites, in Brothwell, D.R. and Higgs, E.S. (eds.), *Science in Archaeology*, 235.

Çambel, H. and Braidwood, R.J. (1970) An early farming village in Turkey, *Scientific American*, 222, 51.

Cann, J.R. and Renfrew, C. (1964) The characterization of obsidian and its application to the Mediterranean region, *Proceedings of the Prehistoric Society*, 30, 111.

Carneiro, R.C. (1970) A theory of the origin of the state, *Science*, 169, 733.

(1972) From autonomous village to the state, a numerical estimate, in Spooner, B. (ed.), *Population Growth: Anthropological Implications*, 64.

Carr, E.H. (1961) *What is History?*

Cauvin, M.C. (1966) L'industrie natoufienne de Mallaha (Eynan), *L'Anthropologie*, 70, 485.

Chaney, R.P. (1972) Scientific inquiry and models of socio-cultural data patterning: an epilogue, in Clarke, D.L. (ed.), *Models in Archaeology*, 991.

Chang, K.C. (1968) *The Archaeology of Ancient China*.

(1970a) Prehistoric archaeology of Taiwan, *Asian Perspectives*, 13, 59.

(1970b) The beginnings of agriculture in the Far East, *Antiquity*, 44, 175.

Chaplin, R.E. (1969) The use of non-morphological criteria in the study of animal domestication from bones found on archaeological sites, in Ucko, P.J. and Dimbleby, G.W. (eds.), *The Domestication and Exploitation of Plants and Animals*, 231.

(1971) *The Study of Animal Bones from Archaeological Sites*.

Chard, C.S. (1972) Prehistoric Japan: a survey of cultural development down to the Late Jomon stage (approx. 2000 B.C.), in Barnard, N. (ed.), *Early Chinese Art and its Possible Influence in the Pacific Basin*. Volume 2. *Asia*, 373.

Charles, J.A. (1972) Physical science and archaeology, *Antiquity*, 44, 134.

Childe, V.G. (1952) *New Light on the Most Ancient East*.

(1954) *What Happened in History*.

(1956) *A Short Introduction to Archaeology*.

(1957a) *The Dawn of European Civilization*.

(1957b) Civilization, cities and towns, *Antiquity*, 31, 36.

Clark, J.D. (1971) A re-examination of the evidence for agricultural origins in the Nile valley, *Proceedings of the Prehistoric Society*, 37, 34.

Clarke, D.L. (1968) *Analytical Archaeology*.

(1972a) Models and paradigms in contemporary archaeology, in Clarke, D.L. (ed.), *Models in Archaeology*, 1.

(1972b) Review of Patty Jo Watson, Steven A. LeBlanc and Charles L. Redman: Explanations in Archaeology, *Antiquity*, 46, 237.

CLISBY, K.H. and SEARS, P.B. (1955a) Palynology in southern North America. Part III: microfossil profiles under Mexico City correlated with the sedimentary profiles, *Bulletin of the Geological Society of America*, 66.

(1955b) Palynology in southern North America. Part IV: Pleistocene climate in Mexico, *Bulletin of the Geological Society of America*, 66, 521.

CLUTTON-BROCK, J. (1969a) The origins of the dog, in BROTHWELL, D.R. and HIGGS, E.S. (eds.), *Science in Archaeology*, 303.

(1969b) Carnivore remains from the excavations of the Jericho tell, in UCKO, P.J. and DIMBLEBY, G.W. (eds.), *The Domestication and Exploitation of Plants and Animals*, 337.

COE, M.D. (1961a) *La Victoria, an Early Site on the Pacific Coast of Guatemala* (Papers of the Peabody Museum of Archeology and Ethnology, vol. 53).

(1961b) Social typology and the tropical forest civilizations, *Comparative Studies in Society and History*, 4, 65.

(1963) Cultural development in southeastern Mesoamerica, in MEGGERS, B.J. and EVANS, C. (eds.), *Aboriginal Cultural Development in Latin America: an Interpretative Review*, 27.

(1968) *America's First Civilization. Discovering the Olmec*.

(1969) Photogrammetry and the ecology of Olmec civilization. Paper read at Working Conference on Aerial Photography and Anthropology, Cambridge, Mass.

COE, M.D. and FLANNERY, K.V. (1964a) Microenvironments and Mesoamerican prehistory, *Science*, 143, 650.

(1964b) The pre-Columbian obsidian industry of El Chayal, Guatemala, *American Antiquity*, 30, 43.

(1967) *Early Cultures and Human Ecology in South Coastal Guatemala* (Smithsonian Contributions to Anthropology, 3).

COHEN, H.R. (1969) Environment of the early Neolithic settlements in south-central Anatolia. Paper read at Research Seminar on Archaeology and Related Subjects.

(1970) The paleoecology of South Central Anatolia at the end of the Pleistocene and the beginning of the Holocene, *Anatolian Studies*, 20, 119.

COLE, S. (1972) Animals of the New Stone Age, in BRODRICK, A.H. (ed.), *Animals in Archaeology*, 15.

COLLIER, D. (1962) The Central Andes, in BRAIDWOOD, R.J. and WILLEY, G.R. (eds.), *Courses Toward Urban Life*, 165.

CONTENSON, H. DE (1964) A further note on the chronology of basal Ras Shamra, *Bulletin of the American Schools of Oriental Research*, 175, 47.

(1966) Découvertes récentes dans le domaine du Néolithique en Syrie, *L'Anthropologie*, 70, 388.

(1971) Tell Ramad, a village of Syria of the 7th and 6th millennia B.C., *Archaeology*, 24, 278.

and LIERE, W.J. van (1966a) Premier sondage à Bouqras en 1965. Rapport préliminaire, *Annales Archéologiques Arabes Syriennes*, 16, 181.

and LIERE, W.J. van (1966b) Seconde campagne à Tell Ramad. Rapport préliminaire, *Annales Archéologiques Arabes Syriennes*, 16, 167.

CURTAIN, C.C. (1971) On the origin of domesticated sheep, *Antiquity*, 45, 303.

CUTLER, H.C. and WHITAKER, T.W. (1961) History and distribution of the cultivated cucurbits in the Americas, *American Antiquity*, 26, 469.

and WHITAKER, T.W. (1967) Cucurbits from the Tehuacán caves, in BYERS, D.S. (ed.), *The Prehistory of the Tehuacán Valley*, vol. I, 212.

DAGAN, J. and ZOHARY, D. (1970) Wild tetraploid wheats from West Iran cytogenetically identical with Israeli *T. dicoccoides*, *Wheat Information Service*, 31, 15.

DAKARIS, S.I., HIGGS, E.S. and HEY, R.W. (1964) The climate, environment and industries of Stone Age Greece: part I, *Proceedings of the Prehistoric Society*, 30, 199.

DALY, P. (1961) Approaches to faunal analysis in archaeology, *American Antiquity*, 34, 146.

DARLINGTON, C.D. (1963) *Chromosome Botany and the Origins of Cultivated Plants*.

(1969) The silent millennia in the origin of agriculture, in Ucko, P.J. and Dimbleby, G.W. (eds.), *The Domestication and Exploitation of Plants and Animals*, 67.

Davenport, W.A. (1970) Progress report on the domestication of *Capsicum* (chili peppers), *AAG proceedings*.

Davies, O. (1968) The origins of agriculture in West Africa, *Current Anthropology*, 9, 479.

Deevey, E. (1968) Measuring resources and subsistence strategy, in Lee, R.B. and Devore, I. (eds.), *Man the Hunter*, 94.

Dennell, R.W. (1972) The interpretation of plant remains: Bulgaria, in Higgs, E.S. (ed.), *Papers in Economic Prehistory*, 149.

Dimbleby, G.W. (1967) *Plants and Archaeology*.

(1969) Pollen analysis, in Brothwell, D. and Higgs, E. (eds.), *Science in Archaeology*, 167.

Dixon, J. E., Cann, J. R. and Renfrew, C. (1968) Obsidian and the origins of trade, *Scientific American*, 218, 38.

Donnan, C.B. (1964) An early house from Chilca, Peru, *American Antiquity*, 30, 2, 137.

Dornemann, R.H. (1969) An early village, *Archaeology*, 22, 69.

Drew, I.M., Perkins, D. and Daly, P. (1971) Prehistoric domestication of animals: effects on bone structure, *Science*, 171, 280.

Ducos, P. (1968) *L'Origine des Animaux Domestiques en Palestine*. (Publications de l'Institut de Préhistoire de l'Université de Bordeaux, 6.)

(1969) Methodology and results of the study of the earliest animals in the Near East (Palestine), in Ucko, P.J. and Dimbleby, G.W. (eds.), *The Domestication and Exploitation of Plants and Animals*, 265.

Dumond, D.E. (1972) Population growth and political centralization, in Spooner, B. (ed.), *Population Growth: Anthropological Implications*, 286.

Dyson, R.H. (1953) Archaeology and the domestication of animals in the Old World, *American Anthropology*, 55, 661.

Emiliani, C. (1970) Pleistocene paleotemperatures, *Science*, 169, 822.

Engel, F. (1963) *A Preceramic Settlement on the Central Coast of Peru: Asia, unit I* (Transactions of the American Philosophical Society, 53).

(1966a) Le complexe précéramique d'El Paraiso (Perou), *Journal de la Société des Américanistes*, 60, 43.

(1966b) *Geografa Humana Prehistorica y Agricultural Precolombina de la Quebrada de Chilca*.

(1967) Sites et établissements sans céramique de la côte Péruvienne, *Journal de la Société des Américanistes*, 46, 67.

(1972) *Le Monde Précolombien des Andes*.

Estrada, E. and Evans, C. (1963) Cultural development in Ecuador, in Meggers, B.J. and Evans, C. (eds.) *Aboriginal Cultural Development in Latin America: an Interpretative Review*, 77.

Evans, J.D. (1971) Neolithic Knossos: the growth of a settlement, *Proceedings of the Prehistoric Society*, 37, 81.

Farrand, W.R. (1971) Late Quaternary paleoclimates of the Eastern Mediterranean area, in Turekian, K.K. (ed.), *The Late Cenozoic Glacial Ages*, 529.

Flannery, K.V. (1965) The ecology of early food production in Mesopotamia, *Science*, 147, 1247.

(1966) The post-glacial 'readaptation' as viewed from Mesoamerica, *American Antiquity*, 31, 800.

(1967a) Vertebrate fauna and hunting patterns, in Byers, D.S. (ed.), *The Prehistory of the Tehuacán Valley*, vol. I, 132.

(1967b) Culture history v. culture process: a debate in American archaeology, *Scientific American*, 217, 119.

(1968) Archaeological systems theory and early Mesoamerica, in Meggers, B. (ed.), *Anthropological Archaeology in the Americas*, 67.

(1969) Origins and ecological effects of early domestication in Iran and the Near East, in Ucko, P.J. and Dimbleby, G.W. (eds.), *The Domestication and Exploitation of Plants and Animals*, 73.

Preliminary archaeological investigations in the valley of Oaxaca, Mexico 1966–1969.

Unpublished Report to the National Science Foundation and the Instituto Nacional de Antropología e Historia.

(1972) The origins of the village as a settlement type in Meso-America and the Near East: a comparative study, in UCKO, P.J., TRINGHAM, R. and DIMBLEBY, G.W. (eds.), *Man, Settlement and Urbanism*, 23.

(1973) The origins of agriculture, *Biennial Review of Anthropology*, 271.

and COE, M.D. (1968) Social and economic systems in Formative Mesoamerica in BINFORD, S.R. and BINFORD, L.R. (eds.), *New Perspectives in Archaeology*, 267.

FLANNERY, K.V., KIRKBY, A.V., KIRKBY, M.J. and WILLIAMS, A.W. (1967) Farming systems and political growth in ancient Oaxaca, *Science*, 158, 445.

(1970) Climate and man in Formative Oaxaca, *Archaeology*, 23, 144.

FONTON, E. DE (1966) Origine et développement des civilisations néolithiques méditerranéennes en Europe occidentale, *Palaeohistoria*, 12, 209.

FOWLER, M.L. (1971) The origin of plant cultivation in the central Mississippi valley: a hypothesis, in STRUEVER, S. (ed.), *Prehistoric Agriculture*, 122.

FREEMAN, L.G. (1968) A theoretical framework for interpreting archeological material, in LEE, R.B. and DEVORE, I. (eds.), *Man the Hunter*, 262.

FRENCH, D. (1972) Excavations at Can Hasan III 1969–1970, in HIGGS, E.S. (ed.), *Papers in Economic Prehistory*, 181.

GABEL, C. (1967) *Analysis of Prehistoric Economic Patterns*.

GALINAT, W.C. (1965) The evolution of corn and culture in North America, *Economic Botany*, 19, 350.

GARROD, D. and BATE, D. (1937) *The Stone Age of Mount Carmel*. Vol. I. *Excavations at the Wady el-Mughara*.

and CLARK, J.G.D. (1965) Primitive man in Egypt, Western Asia and Europe, in EDWARDS, I.E.S., GADD, C.J. and HAMMOND, N.G.L. (eds.), *Cambridge Ancient History*, vol. I, pt. I, 70.

GENTRY, H.S. (1969) Origin of the common bean, *Phaseolus vulgaris*, *Economic Botany*, 23, 55.

GILOT, E. and CAUVIN, J. (1973) Datation par le carbone-14 du village natoufien et précéramique de Mureybet sur l'Euphrate (Syria), *Bulletin de la Société Préhistorique Française*, 70, 37.

GLOVER, I. (1972) Settlements and mobility among the hunter-gatherers of Southeast Asia, in UCKO, P.J., TRINGHAM, R. and DIMBLEBY, G.W. (eds.), *Man, Settlement and Urbanism*, 157.

GOLSON, J. (1972) Both sides of the Wallace line: New Guinea, Australia, Island Melanesia and Asian Prehistory, in BARNARD, N. (ed.), *Early Chinese Art and its Possible Influence in the Pacific Basin*. Vol. 3. *Oceania and the Americas*, 533.

GORMAN, C.F. (1969) Hoabinhian: a pebble-tool complex with early plant associations in South-East Asia, *Proceedings of the Prehistoric Society*, 35, 355.

(1970) Excavations at Spirit Cave, North Thailand: some interim interpretations, *Asian Perspectives*, 13, 79.

(1971) The Hoabinhian and after: subsistence patterns in South-east Asia during the Late Pleistocene and early Recent periods, *World Archaeology*, 2, 300.

GREEN, D.F. and LOWE, G.W. (1967) *Altamira and Padre Piedra, Early Pre-Classic Sites in Chiapas, Mexico*. New World Archaeological Foundation, 20.

GRIGSON, C. (1969) The uses and limitations of differences in absolute size in the distinction between the bones of aurochs (*Bos primigenius*) and domestic cattle (*Bos taurus*), in UCKO, P.J. and DIMBLEBY, G.W. (eds.), *The Domestication and Exploitation of Plants and Animals*, 277.

HAMMEN, T. VAN DER, WIJMSTRA, T.A. and MOLEN, W.H. VAN DER (1965) Palynological study of a very thick peat section in Greece, and the Würm-glacial vegetation in the Mediterranean region, *Geologie en Mijnbouw*, 44, 37.

HARLAN, J.R. (1961) Geographic origin of plants useful to agriculture, in HODGSON, R.E. (ed.), *Germ Plasm Resources*, 3.

(1967) A wild wheat harvest in Turkey, *Archaeology*, 20, 197.

(1970) Evolution of cultivated plants, in FRANKEL, O.H. and BENNET, E. (eds.),

Genetic Resources in Plants – their Exploration and Conservation, 19.

(1972) Agricultural origins: centers and non-centers, *Science*, 174, 468.

and WET, J.M.J. DE (1965) Some thoughts on weeds, *Economic Botany*, 19, 16.

and WET, J.M.J. DE (1973) On the quality of evidence for origin and dispersal of cultivated plants, *Current Anthropology*, 14, 51.

and ZOHARY, D. (1966) Distribution of wild wheats and barley, *Science*, 153, 1074.

HARRIS, A. (1972) Some aspects of agriculture in Taita, in SPOONER, B. (ed.), *Population Growth: Anthropological Implications*, 80.

HARRIS, D.R. (1967) New light on plant domestication and the origins of agriculture: a review, *The Geographical Review*, 57, 90.

(1969) Agricultural systems, ecosystems and the origins of agriculture, in UCKO, P.J. and DIMBLEBY, G.W. (eds.), *The Domestication and Exploitation of Plants and Animals*, 3.

(1971) The ecology of swidden cultivation in the Upper Orinoco rain forest, Venezuela, *The Geographical Review*, 61, 475.

(1972) Swidden systems and settlement, in UCKO, P.J., TRINGHAM, R. and DIMBLEBY, G.W. (eds.), *Man, Settlement and Urbanism*, 245.

(1973) The prehistory of tropical agriculture: an ethnoecological model, in RENFREW, C. (ed.), *The Explanation of Culture Change: Models in Prehistory*, 391.

(in press) Traditional systems of plant food production and the origins of agriculture in West Africa, in HARLAN, J.R. (ed.) *The Origins of African Plant Domestication*.

HARRIS, M. (1969) *The Rise of Anthropological Theory: a History of Theories of Culture*.

HARRISS, J.C. (1971) Explanation in prehistory, *Proceedings of the Prehistoric Society*, 38.

HARRISSON, T. (1963) 100,000 years of Stone Age culture in Borneo, *Journal of the Royal Society of Arts*, 112, 174.

HAURY, E.W. (1962) The greater American Southwest, in BRAIDWOOD, R.J. and WILLEY, G.R. (eds.), *Courses Toward Urban Life*, 106.

HAWKES, J.G. (1967) The domestication of certain New World plants, *Information Bulletin, Society for Latin American Studies*, 7, 9.

(1969) The ecological background of plant domestication, in UCKO, P.J. and DIMBLEBY, G.W. (eds.), *The Domestication and Exploitation of Plants and Animals*, 17.

HAYDEN, B. (1972) Population control among hunter/gatherers, *World Archaeology*, 4, 205.

HEISER, C.B. (1965) Cultivated plants and cultural diffusion in Nuclear America, *American Anthropologist*, 67, 930.

HELBAEK, H. (1959a) How farming began in the Old World, *Archaeology*, 12, 183.

(1959b) Domestication of food plants in the Old World, *Science*, 130, 365.

(1960) The paleoethnobotany of the Near East and Europe, in BRAIDWOOD, R.J. and HOWE, B., *Prehistoric Investigation in Iraqi Kurdistan* (Studies in Ancient Oriental Civilisation No. 31), 99.

(1964) First impressions of the Çatal Hüyük plant husbandry, *Anatolian Studies*, 14, 121.

(1966a) Commentary on the phylogenesis of *Triticum* and *Hordeum*, *Economic Botany*, 20, 350.

(1966b) Pre-pottery Neolithic farming at Beidha, *Palestine Exploration Quarterly*, 98, 61.

(1969a) Plant-collecting, dry-farming, and irrigation agriculture in prehistoric Deh Luran, in HOLE, F., FLANNERY, K.V. and NEELY, J.A., *Prehistory and Human Ecology of the Deh Luran Plain*, 383.

(1969b) Palaeo-ethnobotany, in BROTHWELL, D. and HIGGS, E. (eds.), *Science in Archaeology*, 206.

(1970) The plant husbandry of Hacilar, in MELLAART, J., *Excavations at Hacilar*, vol. 1, 189.

HERRE, W. (1969) The science and history of domesticated animals, in BROTHWELL, D. and HIGGS, E. (eds.), *Science in Archaeology*, 256.

HESTER, J.J. (1966) Late Pleistocene environments and early man in South America, *The American Naturalist*, 100, 377.

(1967) The agency of man in animal extinctions, in MARTIN, P.S. and WRIGHT, H.E. (eds.), *Pleistocene Extinctions. The Search for a Cause*, 169.

HEY, R.W. (1963) Pleistocene screes in Cyrenaica (Libya), *Eiszeitalter und Gegenwart*, 14, 77.

HIGGS, E.S. (1961) Some Pleistocene faunas of the Mediterranean coastal areas, *Proceedings of the Prehistoric Society*, 27, 144.

(1962) The fauna of the early Neolithic site at Nea Nikomedeia, Greek Macedonia, *Proceedings of the Prehistoric Society*, 28, 271.

(ed.) (1972) *Papers in Economic Prehistory*.

and JARMAN, M.R. (1969) The origins of agriculture: a reconsideration, *Antiquity*, 43, 31.

and JARMAN, M.R. (1972) The origins of animal and plant husbandry, in HIGGS, E.S. (ed.), *Papers in Economic Prehistory*, 3.

and VITA-FINZI, C. (1966) The climate, environment and industries of Stone Age Greece: pt. 11, *Proceedings of the Prehistoric Society*, 32, 1.

and VITA-FINZI, C. (1972) Prehistoric economies: a territorial approach, in HIGGS, E.S. (ed.), *Papers in Economic Prehistory*, 27.

VITA-FINZI, C., HARRIS, D.R. and FAGG, A.E. (1967) The climate, environment and industries of Stone Age Greece: pt. 111, *Proceedings of the Prehistoric Society*, 33, 1.

and WEBLEY, D. (1971) Further information concerning the environment of Palaeolithic man in Epirus, *Proceedings of the Prehistoric Society*, 37, 367.

HIGHAM, C.F.W. (1967) Stock rearing as a cultural factor in prehistoric Europe, *Proceedings of the Prehistoric Society*, 33, 84.

(1968) Faunal sampling and economic prehistory, *Zeitschrift für Säugetierkunde*, 33, 297.

(1972) Initial model formulation in *terra incognita*, in CLARKE, D.L. (ed.), *Models in Archaeology*, 453.

HILL, J.N. (1972) The methodological debate in contemporary archaeology: a model, in CLARKE, D.L. (ed.), *Models in Archaeology*, 61.

HOLE, F. (1968) Evidence of social organization from western Iran, 8000–4000 b.c., in BINFORD, S.R. and BINFORD, L.R. (eds.), *New Perspectives in Archeology*, 245.

(1971) Answer to G. Wright's article, *Current Anthropology*, 12, 472.

(1973) Questions of theory in the explanation of culture change in prehistory, in RENFREW, C. (ed.), *The Explanation of Culture Change: Models in Prehistory*, 19.

and FLANNERY, K.V. (1967) The prehistory of Southwest Iran: a preliminary report, *Proceedings of the Prehistoric Society*, 32, 147.

FLANNERY, K.V. and NEELY, J.A. (1969) *Prehistory and Human Ecology of the Deh Luran Plain* (Memoirs of the Museum of Anthropology, University of Michigan, no. 1).

HOLMBERG, A.R. (1950) *Nomads of the Long Bow. The Siriono of eastern Bolivia* (Smithsonian Institution, Institute of Social Anthropology, no. 10).

HOOIJER,D.A. (1961) The fossil vertebrates of Ksar Akil, a Palaeolithic rock shelter in the Lebanon, *Zoologische Verhandelingen*, 49.

HOPF, M. (1969) Plant remains and early farming in Jericho, in UCKO, P.J. and DIMBLEBY, G.W. (eds.), *Domestication and Exploitation of Plants and Animals*, 355.

HOROWITZ, A. (1971) Climatic and vegetational developments in northeastern Israel during Upper Pleistocene-Holocene times, *Pollen et Spores*, 13, 255.

HUTCHINSON, G.E. and COWGILL, U.M. (1963) Chemical examination of a core from lake Zeribar, Iran, *Science*, 140, 67.

HUTCHINSON, J.B. (ed.) (1965) *Essays on Crop Plant Evolution*.

(1972) Conclusion: the biology of domestication, in HIGGS, E.S. (ed.), *Papers in Economic Prehistory*, 195.

ISAAC, E. (1962) On the domestication of cattle, *Science*, 137, 195.

(1970) *Geography of Domestication*.

ISSAR, A. (1968) Geology of the central coastal plain of Israel, *Israel Journal of Earth Sciences*, 17, 16.

IZUMI, S. and SONO, T. (1963) *Excavations at Kotosh, Peru 1960*.

JACOBS, J. (1969) *The Economy of Cities*.

JARMAN, H.N. (1971) Prehistoric economy and cereal evolution, *Acta Museorum Agriculturae*, 6, 11.

(1972) The origins of wheat and barley cultivation, in HIGGS, E.S. (ed.), *Papers in Economic Prehistory*, 15.

246

LEGGE, A.J. and CHARLES, J.A. (1972) Retrieval of plant remains from archaeological sites by froth flotation, in HIGGS, E.S. (ed.), *Papers in Economic Prehistory*, 39.

JARMAN, M.R. (1969) The prehistory of Upper Pleistocene and Recent cattle. Part I: East Mediterranean with reference to North-west Europe, *Proceedings of the Prehistoric Society*, 35, 236.

(1971) Review of P.J. Ucko and G.W. Dimbleby (eds.): The Domestication and Exploitation of Plants and Animals, *Proceedings of the Prehistoric Society*, 37, 237.

(1972a) A territorial model for archaeology: a behavioural and geographical approach, in CLARKE, D.L. (ed.), *Models in Archaeology*, 705.

(1972b) European deer economies and the advent of the Neolithic, in HIGGS, E.S. (ed.), *Papers in Economic Prehistory*, 125.

and JARMAN, H.N. (1968) The fauna and economy of early Neolithic Knossos, *Annual of the British School of Archaeology at Athens*, 63, 241.

and WILKINSON, P.F. (1972) Criteria of animal domestication, in HIGGS, E.S. (ed.), *Papers in Economic Prehistory*, 83.

JOLLY, C.F. (1970) The origins of agriculture, *Antiquity*, 44, 59.

JONES, V.H. (1953) Review of 'The grain amaranths: a survey of their history and classification' by Jonathan Deininger Sauer, *American Antiquity*, 19, 90.

KAPLAN, L. (1965) Archaeology and domestication in American *Phaseolus* (beans), *Economic Botany*, 19, 358.

(1967) Archaeological *Phaseolus* from Tehuacán, in BYERS, D.S. (ed.), *The Prehistory of the Tehuacán Valley*, vol. I, 201.

LYNCH, T.F. and SMITH, C.E. Jr. (1973) Early cultivated beans (*Phaseolus vulgaris*) from an intermontane Peruvian valley, *Science*, 179, 76.

KELLEY, D.H. and BONAVÍA, D. (1963) New evidence for pre-ceramic maize on the coast of Peru, *Ñawpa Pacha*, 1, 39.

KENYON, K.M. (1967) Jericho, *Archaeology*, 20, 268.

(1969) The origins of the Neolithic, *The Advancement of Science*, 26, 144.

KIRKBRIDE, D. (1966) Five seasons at the pre-pottery Neolithic village of Beidha in Jordan, *Palestine Exploration Quarterly*, 98, 8.

(1968) Beidha: early Neolithic village life south of the Dead Sea, *Antiquity*, 42, 263.

LANNING, E.P. (1965) Early man in Peru, *Scientific American*, 213, 68.

(1966) Early man in the Andean area; unpublished project proposal submitted to the National Science Foundation.

(1967a) *Peru Before the Incas*.

(1967b) Preceramic archaeology of the Ancón-Chillón region, central coast of Peru; unpublished report to the National Science Foundation.

LATHRAP, D.W. (1970) *The Upper Amazon*.

LEE, R.B. (1968) What hunters do for a living, or, how to make out on scarce resources, in LEE, R.B. and DEVORE, I. (eds.), *Man the Hunter*, 30.

(1972a) Work effort, group structure and land use in contemporary hunter-gatherers, in UCKO, P.J., TRINGHAM, R. and DIMBLEBY, G.W. (eds.), *Man, Settlement and Urbanism*, 177.

(1972b) Population growth and the beginnings of sedentary life among the !Kung bushmen, in SPOONER, B. (ed.), *Population Growth: Anthropological Implications*, 329.

LEGGE, A.J. (1972a) Cave climates, in HIGGS, E.S. (ed.), *Papers in Economic Prehistory*, 97.

(1972b) Prehistoric exploitation of the gazelle in Palestine, in HIGGS, E.S. (ed.), *Papers in Economic Prehistory*, 119.

LEOPOLD, L.B. (1951) Pleistocene climate in New Mexico, *The American Journal of Science*, 249, 152.

LEROI-GOURHAN, A. (1969) Pollen grains of Gramineae and Cerealia from Shanidar and Zawi Chemi, in UCKO, P.J. and DIMBLEBY, G.W. (eds.), *The Domestication and Exploitation of Plants and Animals*, 143.

LI, H.L. (1970) The origin of cultivated plants in Southeast Asia, *Economic Botany*, 24, 3.

LINARES DE SAPIR, O. and RANERE, A.J. (1971) Human adaptation to the tropical forests of western Panama, *Archaeology*, 24, 346.

Loon, M. van (1966a) Mureybat: an early village in inland Syria, *Archaeology*, 19, 215.
(1966b) First results of the 1965 excavations at Tell Mureybat near Meskene, *Annales Archéologiques Arabes Syriennes*, 16, 211.

Lorenzo, J.L. (1967) *La etapa lítica en Mexico* (Instituto Nacional de Antropologia e Historia Mexico).

Lynch, T.F. (1967) *The Nature of the Central Andean Preceramic* (Occasional Papers of the Museum, Idaho State University, no. 21).
and Kennedy, K.A.R. (1970) Early human cultural and skeletal remains from Guitarrero cave, northern Peru, *Science*, 169, 1307.

MacNeish, R.S. (1956) Prehistoric settlement patterns on the northeastern periphery of Meso-America, in Willey, G.R. (ed.), *Prehistoric Settlement Patterns in the New World*, 140.
(1958) *Preliminary Archaeological Investigations in the Sierra de Tamaulipas, Mexico* (Transactions of the American Philosophical Society, vol. 48).
(1964a) The Origins of New World civilization, *Scientific American*, 211, 5, 29.
(1964b) Ancient Mesoamerican civilization, *Science*, 143, 531.
(1964c) The food-gathering and incipient agricultural stage of prehistoric Middle America, in West, R.C. (ed.), *Handbook of Middle American Indians*, vol. I, 413.
(1965) The origins of American agriculture, *Antiquity*, 39, 87.
(1967a) A summary of the subsistence, in Byers, D.S. (ed.), *The Prehistory of the Tehuacán Valley*, vol. I, 290.
(1967b) Introduction, in Byers, D.S. (ed.), *The Prehistory of the Tehuacán Valley*, vol. I, 3.
(1967c) Conclusion, in Byers, D.S. (ed.), *The Prehistory of the Tehuacán Valley*, vol. I, 227.
(1967d) Conclusion, in Byers, D.S. (ed.), *The Prehistory of the Tehuacán Valley*, vol. II, 227.
(1969) *First Annual Report of the Ayacucho Archaeological-Botanical Project*. Robert S. Peabody Foundation in Archaeology.
(1970) Megafauna and man from Ayacucho, highland Peru, *Science*, 168, 975.
(1971a) Speculation about how and why food production and village life developed in the Tehuacán valley, Mexico, *Archaeology*, 24, 307.
(1971b) Early man in the Andes, *Scientific American*, 224, 36.
(1972) The evolution of community patterns in the Tehuacán valley of Mexico and speculations about cultural origins, in Ucko, P.R., Tringham, R. and Dimbleby, G.W. (eds.), *Man, Settlement and Urbanisation*, 67.
Nelken-Terner, A. and Cook, A.G. (1970) *Second Annual Report of the Ayacucho Archaeological-Botanical Project*.

Mangelsdorf, P.C. (1950) The mystery of corn, *Scientific American*, July.
(1953) Review of Agricultural origins and dispersals by Carl O. Sauer, *American Antiquity*, 19, 87.
(1965) The evolution of maize, in Hutchinson, J. (ed.), *Essays on Crop Plant Evolution*, 23.
MacNeish, R.S. and Galinat, W.C. (1964) Domestication of corn, *Science*, 143, 538.
MacNeish, R.S. and Galinat, W.C. (1967) Prehistoric wild and cultivated maize, in Byers, D.S. (ed.), *The Prehistory of the Tehuacán Valley*, vol. I, 178.
MacNeish, R.S. and Willey, G.R. (1964) Origins of agriculture in Middle America, in West, R.C. (ed.), *Handbook of Middle American Indians*, vol. I, 427.
and Reeves, R.G. (1959a) The origin of corn. *Botanical Museum Leaflets, Harvard University*, 18, 329; 389; 413.

Martin, P.S. (1967) Prehistoric overkill, in Martin, R.S. and Wright, H.E. (eds.), *Pleistocene Extinctions. The Search for a Cause*, 75.

Masson, V. (1961) The first farmers in Turkmenia, *Antiquity*, 35, 203.
(1965) The Neolithic farmers of Central Asia, *Acts VI International Congress of Pre- and Protohistoric Sciences*, vol. 2, 205.
and Sarianidi, V.I. (1972) *Central Asia. Turkmenia before the Achaemenids*.

Megard, R.O. (1967) Late quaternary cladocera of lake Zeribar, Western Iran, *Ecology*, 48, 179.

MEGGERS, G. (1966) *Ecuador.*

MELDGAARD, J., MORTENSEN, P. and THRANE, H. (1963) Excavations at Tepe Guran, Luristan, *Acta Archaeologia*, 34, 97.

MELLAART, J. (1965) *Earliest Civilizations of the Near East.*

(1967) *Çatal Hüyük. A Neolithic Town in Anatolia.*

(1970a) The earliest settlements in western Asia from the ninth to the end of the fifth millennium b.c. (b) Anatolia before 4000 b.c., in EDWARDS, I.E.S., GADD, C.J. and HAMMOND, N.G.L. (eds.), *Cambridge Ancient History*, vol. I, pt. I, 248.

(1970) *Excavations at Hacilar.*

(1971) Anatolia *c.* 4000 b.c.–*c.* 2300 b.c., in EDWARDS, I.E.S., GADD, C.J. and HAMMOND, N.G.L. (eds.), *Cambridge Ancient History*, vol. I, pt. 2, 363.

(1972) Anatolian Neolithic settlement patterns, in UCKO, P.J., TRINGHAM, R. and DIMBLEBY, C.W. (eds.), *Man, Settlement and Urbanism*, 279.

MEYERS, J.T. (1971) The origins of agriculture: an evaluation of three hypotheses, in STRUEVER, S. (ed.), *Prehistoric Agriculture*, 101.

MILLIMAN, J.D. and EMERY, K.O. (1968) Sea levels during the past 35,000 years, *Science*, 162, 1121.

MORTENSEN, P. (1963) Excavations at Tepe Guran, Luristan, *Acta Archeologica*, 34, 110.

(1964) Additional remarks on the chronology of early village-farming communities in the Zagros area, *Sumer*, 20, 28.

MURRAY, J. (1971) *The First European Agriculture: a Study of the Osteological and Botanical Evidence until 2000 B.C.*

NIEDERLANDER. A., LACAM, R. and ARNAL, J. (1966) *Le Gisement Néolithique de Roucadour* (*Thémines-Lot*).

NIKLEWSKI, J. and ZEIST, W. VAN (1970) A late quaternary pollen diagram from north-western Syria, *Acta Botanica Neerlandica*, 19, 737.

OATES, J.L. (1966) First preliminary survey in the region of Mandali and Badra, *Sumer*, 22, 51.

(1968) Prehistoric investigations near Mandali, Iraq, *Iraq*, 30, 1.

(1972) Prehistoric settlement patterns in Mesopotamia, in UCKO, P.J., TRINGHAM, R. and DIMBLEBY, G.W. (eds.), *Man, Settlement and Urbanism*, 299.

PADDAYYA, K. (1971) Radiocarbon dates and the south Indian Neolithic culture, *Antiquity*, 45, 134.

PARSONS, M.H. (1970) Preceramic subsistence on the Peruvian coast, *American Antiquity*, 35, 292.

PATTERSON, T.C. (1971a) Central Peru: its population and economy, *Archaeology*, 24, 316.

(1971b) The emergence of food production in central Peru, in STRUEVER, S. (ed.), *Prehistoric Agriculture*, 181.

and LANNING, E.P. (1964) Changing settlement patterns on the central Peruvian coast, *Ñawpa Pacha*, 2, 113.

and MOSELEY, M.E. (1968) Late preceramic and early ceramic cultures of the central coast of Peru, *Ñawpa Pacha*, 6, 115.

PAYNE, S. (1968) The origins of domestic sheep and goats: a reconsideration in the light of fossil evidence, *Proceedings of the Prehistoric Society*, 34, 368.

(1969) A metrical distinction between sheep and goat metacarpals, in UCKO, P.J. and DIMBLEBY, G.W. (eds.), *The Domestication and Exploitation of Plants and Animals*, 295.

(1972a) On the interpretation of bone samples from archaeological sites, in HIGGS, E.S. (ed.), *Papers in Economic Prehistory*, 65.

(1972b) Can Hasan III, the Anatolian Aceramic and the Greek Neolithic, in HIGGS, E.S. (ed.), *Papers in Economic Prehistory*, 191.

PEARSON, H.W. (1957) The economy has no surplus: critique of a theory of development, in POLANYI, K., ARENSBERG, C.M. and PEARSON, H.W. (eds.), *Trade and Market in the Early Empires*, 320.

PERKINS, D. (1964) Prehistoric fauna from Shanidar, Iraq, *Science*, 144, 1565.

(1966) The fauna from Madamagh and Beidha, *Palestine Exploration Quarterly*, 98, 66.

(1969) Fauna of Çatal Hüyük: evidence for early cattle domestication in Anatolia, *Science*, 164, 177.

and DALY, P. (1968) A hunter's village in Neolithic Turkey, *Scientific American*, 219, 5, 97.

PERROT, J. (1952) Le Néolithique d'Abou Ghosh, *Syria*, 29, 119.

(1962a) Eynan (Aïn Mallaha), *Revue Biblique*, 69, 384.

(1962b) Palestine–Syria–Cilicia, in BRAIDWOOD, R.J. and WILLEY, G. (eds.), *Courses Toward Urban Life*, 147.

(1966) Le gisement Natoufien de Mallaha (Eynan), Israël, *L'Anthropologie*, 70, 437.

(1967) Munhata, *Bible et Terre Sainte*, 93, 4.

(1968) La préhistoire Palestinienne, *Supplément au Dictionnaire de la Bible*, 8, 286.

PESO, C. DI (1963) Cultural development in northern Mexico, in MEGGERS, B.J. and EVANS, C. (eds.), *Aboriginal Cultural Development in Latin America: an Interpretative Review*, 1.

PICKERSGILL, G. (1969a) The domestication of chili peppers, in UCKO, P.J. and DIMBLEBY, G.W. (eds.), *The Domestication and Exploitation of Plants and Animals*, 443.

(1969b) The archaeological record of chili peppers (*Capsicum* spp.) and the sequence of plant domestication in Peru, *American Antiquity*, 34, 54.

PIGGOTT, S. (1965) *Ancient Europe*.

PRAUSNITZ, M.W. (1960) Tell 'El(Kh. esh-Sheikh 'Ali), *Israel Exploration Journal*, 10, 119.

(1965) From the Pre-pottery to the Pottery Neolithic in Galilee. Excavations at Tell Ely (Kh. es-Sheikh 'Ali), *Acts of the VI International Congress of Prehistoric and historic Sciences*, vol. 2, 216.

RAIKES, R.L. (1966) Beidha. Prehistoric climate and water supply, *Palestine Exploration Quarterly*, 98, 68.

(1967) *Water, Weather and Prehistory*.

REDMAN, C.L. (1973) Multivariate approach to understanding changes in an early farming community in south-east Anatolia, in RENFREW, C. (ed.), *The Explanation of Culture Change: Models in Prehistory*, 717.

REED, C.A. (1959) Animal domestication in the prehistoric Near East, *Science*, 130, 1629.

(1960) A review of the archaeological evidence on animal domestication in the pre-historic Near East, in BRAIDWOOD, R.J. and HOWE, B. (eds.), *Prehistoric Investigations in Iraqi Kurdistan*, 119.

(1961) Osteological evidence for prehistoric domestication in southwestern Asia, *Zeitschrift für Tierzüchtung und Züchtungsbiologie*, 76, 31.

(1969) The pattern of animal domestication in the prehistoric Near East, in UCKO, P.J. and DIMBLEBY, G.W. (eds.), *The Domestication and Exploitation of Plants and Animals*, 361.

and BRAIDWOOD, R.J. (1960) Toward the reconstruction of the environmental sequence of north-eastern Iraq, in BRAIDWOOD, R.J. and HOWE, B. (eds.), *Prehistoric Investigations in Iraqi Kurdistan*, 163.

and SCHAFFER, W.M. (1972a) How to tell the sheep from the goats, *Field Museum of Natural History Bulletin*, 43, 2.

and SCHAFFER, W.M. (1972b) *The Co-evolution of Social Behaviour and Cranial Morphology in Sheep and Goats* (Field Museum of Natural History, 61).

REEVES, C.C. (1965) Pleistocene climate of the llano etacado, *Journal of Geology*, 73, 181.

REICHEL-DOLMATOFF, G. (1965) *Colombia*.

RENFREW, C. (1968) Models in prehistory, *Antiquity*, 42, 132.

(1972) *The Emergence of Civilisation: the Cyclades and the Aegean in the Third Millennium B.C.*

DIXON, J.E. and CANN, J.R. (1966) Obsidian and early cultural contact in the Near East, *Proceedings of the Prehistoric Society*, 32, 30.

RENFREW, J. (1966) A report on recent finds of carbonized cereal grains and seeds from prehistoric Thessally, *Thessalika*, 5, 21.

(1969) The archaeological evidence for the domestication of plants: methods and problems, in UCKO, P.J. and DIMBLEBY, G.W. (eds.), *The Domestication and Exploitation of Plants and Animals*, 149.

(1973) *Palaeoethnobotany*.

RILEY, C.L., KELLEY, J.C., PENNINGTON, C.W. and RANDS, R.L. (eds.) (1971) *Man Across the Sea.*

RILEY, R. (1969) Evidence from phylogenetic relationships of the types of bread wheat first cultivated, in UCKO, P.J. and DIMBLEBY, G.W. (eds.), *The Domestication and Exploitation of Plants and Animals*, 173.

ROSSIGNOL, M. (1962) Analyse pollinique de sédiments marins quaternaires en Israël. II – Sédiments Pleistocenes, *Pollen and Spores*, 4, 121.

(1963) Analyse pollinique de sédiments quaternaires dans la plaine de Haifa, Israël, *Israel Journal of Earth Sciences*, 12, 207.

ROTH, H. L. (1887) On the origin of agriculture, *The Journal of the Anthropological Institute of Great Britain and Ireland*, 16, 102.

ROUSE, I. (1962) The intermediate area, Amazonia and the Caribbean area, in BRAIDWOOD, R.J. and WILLEY, G.R. (eds.), *Courses Toward Urban Life*, 34.

ROWE, J.H. (1965) An interpretation of radiocarbon measurements of archaeological samples from Peru, *Proceedings, Sixth International Conference, Radiocarbon and Tritium Dating*, 187.

RYDER, M.L. (1969) Changes in the fleece of sheep following domestication, in UCKO, P.J. and DIMBLEBY, G.W. (eds.), *The Domestication and Exploitation of Plants and Animals*, 495.

SAHLINS, M.D. (1964) Culture and environment, in TAX, S. (ed.), *Horizons of Anthropology*, 132.

(1968) Notes on the original affluent society, in LEE, R. and DEVORE, I. (eds.), *Man the Hunter*, 85.

SANDERS, W.T. (1965) *The Cultural Ecology of the Teotihuacán Valley.*

(1972) Population, agricultural history, and societal evolution in Mesoamerica, in SPOONER, B. (ed.), *Population Growth: Anthropological Implications*, 101.

and MARINO, J. (1970) *New World Prehistory. Archaeology of the American Indian.*

and PRICE. B.J. (1968) *Meso-America. The Evolution of a Civilization.*

SANKALIA, H.D. (1962) India, in BRAIDWOOD, R.J. and WILLEY, G.R. (eds.), *Courses Toward Urban Life*, 60.

SANOJA, M. (1963) Cultural development in Venezuela, in MEGGERS, B.J. and EVANS, C. (eds.), *Aboriginal Cultural Development in Latin America: an Interpretative Review*, 67.

SAUER, C.O. (1952) *Agricultural Origins and Dispersals.*

(1963a) Cultivated plants of South and Central America, in STEWARD, J.H. (ed.), *Handbook of South American Indians*, vol. 6, 487.

(1963b) Geography of South America, in STEWARD, J.H. (ed.), *Handbook of South American Indians*, vol. 6, 319.

SAUER, J.D. (1969) Identity of archaeological grain amaranths from the valley of Tehuacán, Puebla, Mexico, *American Antiquity*, 34, 80.

and KAPLAN, L. (1969) Canavalia beans in American prehistory, *American Antiquity*, 34, 417.

SHAW, T. (in press) Early crops in Africa: a review of the evidence, in HARLAN, J.R. (ed.), *The Origins of African Plant Domestication.*

SHERRATT, A.G. (1972) Socio-economic and demographic models for the Neolithic and Bronze Ages of Europe, in CLARKE, D.L. (ed.), *Models in Archaeology*, 477.

SILVER, A. (1969) The ageing of domestic animals, in BROTHWELL, D. and HIGGS, E. (eds.), *Science in Archaeology*, 283.

SLATKINE, A. and ROHRLICH, V. (1964) Sur quelques niveaux marins quaternaires du Mont Carmel, *Israel Journal of Earth Sciences*, 13, 125.

(1966) Données nouvelles sur les niveaux marins quaternaires du Mont Carmel, *Israel Journal of Earth Sciences*, 15, 57.

SMALLEY, I.J. (1968) The loess deposits and Neolithic culture of northern China, *Man*, 3, 224.

SMARTT, J. (1969) Evolution of American *Phaseolus* beans under domestication in UCKO, P.J. and DIMBLEBY, G.W. (eds.), *The Domestication and Exploitation of Plants and Animals*, 451.

SMITH, C.E. (1965a) The archaeological record of cultivated crops of New World origin, *Economic Botany*, 19, 323.

(1965b) Flora, Tehuacán valley, *Fieldiana: Botany*, 31, 107.

(1967) Plant remains, in BYERS, D.S. (ed.), *The Prehistory of the Tehuacán Valley*, vol. I, 220.

(1969) From Vavilov to the present – a review, *Economic Botany*, 23, 2.

and STEPHENS, S.G. (1971) Critical identification of Mexican archaeological cotton remains, *Economic Botany*, 25, 160.

SMITH, H. (1969) Animal domestication and animal cult in dynastic Egypt, in UCKO, P.J. and DIMBLEBY, G.W. (eds.), *The Domestication and Exploitation of Plants and Animals*, 307.

SMITH, P.E.L. (1968) Ganj Dareh Tepe, *Iran*, 6, 158.

(1970a) Ganj Dareh Tepe, *Iran*, 8, 178.

(1970b) Ecological Archaeology in Iran, a review of Prehistory and Human Ecology of the Deh Luran plain by Frank Hole, Kent V. Flannery and James A. Neely, *Science*, 168, 707.

(1972) Changes in population pressure in archaeological explanation, *World Archaeology*, 4, 5.

and CUYLER YOUNG, T. (1972) The evolution of early agriculture and culture in greater Mesopotamia: a trial model, in SPOONER, B. (ed.), *Population Growth: Anthropological Implications*, 1.

SOLECKI, R.L. (1964) Zawi Chemi Shanidar, a post-Pleistocene village site in northern Iraq, *Report of the VI International Congress on Quaternary*, 405.

SOLECKI, R.S. (1963) Prehistory in Shanidar valley, northern Iraq, *Science*, 139, 179.

(1969) A copper mineral pendant from northern Iraq, *Antiquity*, 43, 311.

and LEROI-GOURHAN, A. (1961) Paleoclimatology and archaeology in the Near East, *Annals of the New York Academy of Science*, 95, 729.

and RUBIN, M. (1958) Dating of Zawi Chemi, an early village site at Shanidar, northern Iraq, *Science*, 127, 1446.

SOLHEIM, W.G. (1969) Reworking southeast Asia prehistory, *Paideuma*, 15, 125.

SØRENSEN, P. (1972) The Neolithic cultures of Thailand (and north Malaysia) and their Lungshanoid relationship, in BARNARD, N. (ed.), *Early Chinese Art and its Possible Influence in the Pacific Basin*. Vol. 2. *Asia*, 459.

STEARN, W.T. (1965) The origin and later development of cultivated plants, *Journal of the Royal Horticultural Society*, 90, 279.

STEKELIS, M. and YIZRAELY, T. (1963) Excavations at Nahal Oren – preliminary report, *Israel Exploration Journal*, 13, 1.

STEPHENS, S.G. (1967) A cotton boll segment from Coxcotlan cave, in BYERS, D.S. (ed.), *The Prehistory of the Tehuacán Valley*, vol. I, 256.

STEWARD, J.H. (1933) Ethnography of the Owens Valley Paiute, *University of California, Publications in American Archaeology and Ethnology*, 33, 233.

STURDY, D.A. (1972) The exploitation patterns of a modern reindeer economy in west Greenland, in HIGGS, E.S. (ed.), *Papers in Economic Prehistory*, 161.

TCHERNOV, E. (1968) *Succession of Rodent Faunas During the Upper Pleistocene of Israel*.

TOWLE, M. (1961) *The Ethnobotany of Pre-Columbian Peru* (Viking Fund Publications in Anthropology, No. 30).

TRINGHAM, R. (1969) Animal domestication in the Neolithic cultures of the south-west part of European U.S.S.R., in UCKO, P.R. and DIMBLEBY, G.W. (eds.), *The Domestication and Exploitation of Plants and Animals*, 381.

(1971) *Hunters, Fishers and Farmers of Eastern Europe 6000–3000 B.C.*

UCKO, P.R. and DIMBLEBY, G.W. (eds.) (1969) *The Domestication and Exploitation of Plants and Animals*.

UCKO, P.R., TRINGHAM, R. and DIMBLEBY, G.W. (eds.) (1972) *Man, Settlement and Urbanism*.

UERPMANN, H.P. (1973) Animal bone finds and economic archaeology: a critical study of 'osteo-archaeological' method, *World Archaeology*, 4, 307.

VAUX, R. DE (1970) Palestine during the Neolithic and Chalcolithic periods, in EDWARDS, I.E.S., GADD, C.J. and HAMMOND, N.G.L. (eds.), *Cambridge Ancient History*, vol. I, pt. I, 499.

VAVILOV, N.I. (1926) *Studies on the Origin of Cultivated Plants.*

(1951) *The Origins, Variation, Immunity and Breeding of Cultivated Plants* (translated Starr Chester, K.).

VITA-FINZI, C. (1964) Observations on the late Quaternary of Jordan, *Palestine Exploration Quarterly*, 19.

(1969a) Geological opportunism, in UCKO, P.J. and DIMBLEBY, G.W. (eds.), *The Domestication and Exploitation of Plants and Animals*, 31.

(1969b) Late quaternary alluvial chronology of Iran, *Geologische Rundschau*, 58, 951.

(1969c) Mediterranean monoglacialism? *Nature*, 224, 173.

and HIGGS, E.S. (1970) Prehistoric economy in the Mount Carmel area of Palestine: site catchment analysis, *Proceedings of the Prehistoric Society*, 36, 1.

WASYLIKOWA, K. (1967) Late quaternary plant macrofossils from lake Zeribar, western Iran, *Revue of Palaeobotany and Palynology*, 2, 313.

WATSON, P.J. (1973) Explanations and models: the prehistorian as philosopher of science and the prehistorian as excavator of the past, in RENFREW, C. (ed.), *The Explanation of Culture Change: Models in Prehistory*, 47.

LEBLANC, S.A. and REDMAN, C.L. (1971) *Explanation in Archaeology. An Explicitly Scientific Approach.*

WATSON, R.A. and WATSON, P.J. (1961) *Man and Nature. An Anthropological Essay in Human Ecology.*

WATSON, W. (1969a) Early animal domestication in China, in UCKO, P.J. and DIMBLEBY, G.W. (eds.), *The Domestication and Exploitation of Plants and Animals*, 393.

(1969b) Early cereal cultivation in China, in UCKO, P.J. and DIMBLEBY, G.W. (eds.), *The Domestication and Exploitation of Plants and Animals*, 397.

WEBLEY, D. (1972) Soils and site location in prehistoric Palestine, in HIGGS, E.S. (ed.), *Papers in Economic Prehistory*, 168.

WELLHAUSEN, E.J., ROBERTS, L.M. and HERNANDEZ, X.E. (1952) *Races of Maize in Mexico* (Bussey Institute, Harvard University, Cambridge: Massachusetts).

WEST, R.G. (1968) *Pleistocene Geology and Biology.*

WET, J.M.J. DE and HARLAN, J.R. (1971) The origin and domestication of *Sorghum bicolor, Economic Botany*, 25, 128.

WHEELER, M. (1956) The first towns? *Antiquity*, 30, 132.

WHITAKER, T.W. and BIRD, J.B. (1949) *Identification and Significance of the Cucurbit Materials from Huaca Prieta, Peru* (American Museum Novitates, no. 1426).

and CUTLER, H.C. (1965) Cucurbits and cultures in the Americas, *Economic Botany*, 19, 344.

and CUTLER, H.C. (1971) Prehistoric cucurbits from the valley of Oaxaca, *Economic Botany*, 25, 123.

CUTLER, H.C. and MacNEISH, R.C. (1968) Cucurbit materials from three caves near Ocampo, Tamaulipas, *American Antiquity*, 22, 352.

and DAVIS, G.N. (1962) *Cucurbits. Botany, Cultivation and Utilisation.*

WIJMSTRA, T.A. (1969) Palynology of the first 30 metres of a 120 m. deep section in northern Greece, *Acta Botanica Neerlandica*, 18, 511.

WILKE, P.J., BETTINGER, R., KING, T.F. and O'CONNELL, J.F. (1972) Harvest selection and domestication in seed plants, *Antiquity*, 46, 203.

WILKINSON, P.F. (1971) Neolithic post-script, *Antiquity*, 45, 193.

(1972) Current experimental domestication and its relevance to prehistory, in HIGGS, E.S. (ed.), *Papers in Economic Prehistory*, 107.

WILLEY, G. (1971) *An Introduction to American Archaeology.* Vol. 2. *South America.*

WOLF, E.R. (1966) *Peasants.*

WRIGHT, G.A. (1971) Origins of food-production in southwestern Asia: a survey of ideas, *Current Anthropology*, 12, 447.

and GORDUS, A. (1969) Distribution and utilization of obsidian from Lake Van sources between 7500 and 3500 B.C., *American Journal of Archaeology*, 73, 75.

WRIGHT, H.E. (1960) Climate and prehistoric man in the Eastern Mediterranean, in BRAIDWOOD, R.J. and HOWE, B. (eds.), *Prehistoric Investigations in Iraqi Kurdistan*, 71.

(1961a) Late Quaternary climates and early man in the mountains of Kurdistan, *Report of the VI International Congress on Quaternary, Warsaw*, 341.

(1961b) Late Pleistocene soil development, glaciation, and cultural change in the Eastern Mediterranean region, *Annals of the New York Academy of Sciences*, 95, 718.

(1963) Pleistocene glaciation in Kurdistan, *Eiszeitalter und Gegenwart*, 14, 131.

(1968) Natural environment of early food production north of Mesopotamia, *Science*, 161, 334.

McANDREWS, J.H. and ZEIST, W. VAN (1967) Modern pollen rain in western Iran, and its relation to plant geography and Quaternary vegetational history, *Journal of Ecology*, 55, 415.

YOUNG, T. CUYLER and SMITH, P.E.L. (1966) Research in the prehistory of central western Iran, *Science*, 153, 386.

ZEIST, W. VAN (1967) Late Quaternary vegetation history of western Iran, *Review of Palaeobotany and Palynology*, 2, 301.

(1969) Reflections on prehistoric environments in the Near East, in UCKO, P.J. and DIMBLEBY, G.W. (eds.), *The Domestication and Exploitation of Plants and Animals*, 35.

(1970) The Oriental Institute excavations at Mureybit, Syria: preliminary report on the 1965 campaign. Part III. The palaeobotany, *Journal of Near Eastern Studies*, 29, 167.

(1971) Plant cultivation in the Near East: prelude and beginning, *Acta Museorum Agriculturae Pragae*, VI/1–2, 1.

(1972) Palaeobotanical results of the 1970 season at Çayönü, Turkey, *Helenium*, 12, 3.

and BOTTEMA, S. (1966) Palaeobotanical investigations at Ramad, *Annales Archéologiques Arabes Syriennes*, 16, 179.

and BOTTEMA, S. (1971) Plant husbandry in early Neolithic Nea Nikomedeia, Greece, *Acta Botanica Neerlandica*, 20, 524.

and CASPARIE, W.A. (1968) Wild einkorn wheat and barley from tell Mureybit in northern Syria, *Acta Botanica Neerlandica*, 17, 44.

TIMMERS, R.W. and BOTTEMA, S. (1968) Studies of modern and Holocene pollen precipitation in southeastern Turkey, *Palaeohistoria*, 14, 19.

and WRIGHT, H.E. (1963) Preliminary pollen studies at lake Zeribar, Zagros mountains, southwestern Iran, *Science*, 140, 65.

ZEUNER, F.E. (1955) The goats of early Jericho, *Palestine Exploration Quarterly*, 70.

(1963) *A History of Domesticated Animals*.

ZOHARY, D. (1960) Studies on the origin of cultivated barley, *Bulletin of the Research Council of Israel, Section D, Botany*, 9, 21.

(1969) The progenitors of wheat and barley in relation to domestication and agricultural dispersal in the Old World, in UCKO, P.J. and DIMBLEBY, G.W. (eds.), *The Domestication and Exploitation of Plants and Animals*, 47.

(1970a) Centers of diversity and centers of origin, in FRANKEL, O.H. and BENNET, E. (eds.), *Genetic Resources in Plants – their Exploration and Conservation*, 33.

(1970b) Wild wheats, in FRANKEL, O.H. and BENNET, E. (eds.), *Genetic Resources in Plants – their Exploration and Conservation*, 239.

(1971) Origin of south-west Asiatic cereals: wheats, barley, oats and rye, in DAVIS, P.H., HARPER, P.C. and HEDGE, I.C. (eds.), *Plant Life of South-west Asia*, 235.

HARLAN, J.R. and VARDI, A. (1969) The wild diploid progenitors of wheat and their breeding value, *Euphytica*, 18, 58.

General Index

Geographical Index

Author Index